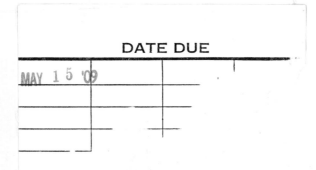

ELECTRICAL

DRAFTING AND DESIGN

ELECTRICAL DRAFTING AND DESIGN

CALVIN C. BISHOP

THIRD EDITION

McGRAW-HILL BOOK COMPANY, INC.

NEW YORK   TORONTO   LONDON   1952

THE MAPLE PRESS COMPANY, YORK, PA.

PREFACE

A need for a book on electrical drafting was felt several years ago when the author was engaged as an electrical engineer on the design and construction of a large power station and several substations. It was found that while the schools taught excellent courses in mechanical drafting and while their graduates could turn out good drawings of parts of machinery and many had a good understanding of electrical apparatus and circuits, practically none had training in properly showing how drawings should be made to convey to the contractor just how electrical work is to be carried out. It was felt that if a book could be furnished to those planning to enter the field of electrical design, a great amount of time would be saved in offices and that a person beginning his career as a draftsman and planning to advance to designer would not have to spend so much of his time in the office learning office procedure but could quickly become valuable and advance. The first edition of the book found that there was a need for such a book and it met with considerable success. With the great advances made in lighting, the almost universal adoption of unit substations, metal cubicles for switch gear, automatic control, the trend toward 440-volt 3-phase power for motors in industrial plants, the use of modern apparatus and equipment for use in hazardous locations and a revision of the National Electrical Code in 1951, a complete revision of the book was found necessary.

In this revision some of the old material that is still useful has been retained but much new material has been added. A change in the method of presentation has been made so that the important things to be learned in each chapter are summarized at the end of the chapter with suitable problems that illustrate principles and methods but do not require a needless amount of actual drafting.

The author wishes to express his thanks to the many manufacturers, publishers, and technical organizations for the valuable photographs and technical data that they have furnished.

CALVIN C. BISHOP

CONTENTS

tables, switches, fuses, circuit breakers, magnetic starters, auto-transformer starters, panelboards, electrical
clearances, data on motors, drop tables, lighting intensities, lamp data, Illuminating Engineering Society's
illumination tables.

ASA symbols for electric power and control, telephone,
telegraph and radio symbols for architectural plans,
explosion-proof fittings, line voltage starter connections,
d-c drop charts, a-c drop charts.

LIST OF TABLES AND CHARTS

Tables

Charts

INTRODUCTION

The purpose of this book is to acquaint a person with the methods used in preparing drawings for use in the electrical industry. The principal fields for electrical drafting are in the offices of engineers, architects, contractors, power companies, and the manufacturers of electrical apparatus and equipment. In entering the field of electrical drafting, a person should have a fair working knowledge of mechanical drafting and sketching as taught in technical high schools and institutes and should be familiar with electrical apparatus and circuits.

The work in an engineer's office often includes the obtaining of information in the form of notes and sketches and the preparation of plans and the listing of materials for various jobs. The exact nature of these plans will depend on the type of work carried on by the engineer.

In an architect's office, a knowledge of the construction of buildings and of the electrical circuits and apparatus used in them is necessary. A knowledge of the characteristics of electrical apparatus and equipment such as pumps, fans, elevators, etc., that use electric motors is desirable. A knowledge of the National Electrical Code of the National Fire Protection Association is absolutely essential. Much of the work of the architect has to do with lighting, so a knowledge of the various methods of modern illumination and of the proper intensities of illumination for various kinds of work is very important.

The work in the office of a power company is extensive and varied. It includes laying out circuits, designing power and substations, remodeling old installations, designing switchboards, and preparing bills of material and cost estimates.

The manufacturer of apparatus or equipment involving electrical circuits may call on the electrical draftsman to do the designing of some of the mechanical parts of the apparatus closely related to its electrical or magnetic circuits. In this field, besides a good working knowledge of electrical apparatus and circuits, the draftsman should have a knowledge of materials and shop methods. The knowledge of materials and methods should cover steel, brass, copper, aluminum, and plastics and the method of casting, rolling, forming, and fabricating these materials.

In all the above fields of work, a draftsman may be called upon to make sketches giving accurate and complete information obtained either in the field or in the office. From these sketches and notes either he or another person may make up finished electrical drawings. In whatever field of drafting one enters, it must always be remembered that the purpose of a drawing is to give complete and accurate information so that something can be made or done. In order that the job can be done with the least trouble and expense, certain methods of making drawings have been developed through a long period of years. These methods, which are practically standardized, show what is to be done clearly and by procedures known to all persons working in that particular industry. The purpose of this book is to outline some of the methods that are in use in the electrical field.

In general, the method of handling the various topics is as follows: First there is a discussion of the topic, and then a typical example is given and analyzed. The principal rules of the National Electrical Code are stated and the relevant sections of the 1951 edition of the Code are given by number. Usually a few practical hints from experience are also given. Following the discussion and the example, a typical problem is given for solution. A problem has been selected that will bring in as many principles as possible but that will not call for too much detail drafting.

It is urged that the person who uses this book and expects to follow the field of electrical drafting gradually acquire a library of catalogues and data sheets in his own particular field. All large engineering offices have a rather complete file of such catalogues, as well as their own standard data sheets. A few carefully selected tables and dimension sheets, furnished through courtesy of manufacturers of high-grade equipment, as well as tables and charts from nationally known organizations, are included in this book; there are enough to make it possible to handle all the problems in the book and many others that one will meet in practice. The student should begin at once to supplement these data sheets with sheets that he may obtain from technical magazines, catalogues, and handbooks as he finds further need for information in his own particular line of work.

CHAPTER 1

GENERAL INSTRUCTIONS FOR MECHANICAL AND ELECTRICAL DRAFTING

Sketching. The subject of sketching is very important to the draftsman, because many mechanical drawings are made either from sketches by a designer who is planning a new machine, or from sketches by the draftsman himself, who is often called upon to go out and make sketches of machinery where parts have been broken or where changes are to be made in existing machinery or installations.

A sketch may be thought of as the manuscript of a book; the mechanical drawing, in the form of a blueprint, as the printed page. The manuscript must be complete and accurate; the printed page is simply the means of getting the information to the many people who need it.

Before starting a sketch, study the piece to be sketched and decide upon what views will be necessary and how they will be arranged. Select the views that will best give the information for the particular job in hand. Where convenient, use an arrangement of views that will show the piece in the position in which it will be used. Often, in the case of machine details, this cannot be done, because it may happen that the part can be more clearly shown in some other position. It is possible that in some cases it may even be necessary to show it *upside down*, in order to make clear some interior detail. Show all views necessary, but no more.

Having decided upon the views that will be used and the arrangement, form an idea of the general proportions of the object, such as length equals twice the width, etc.; then sketch the object in, using a clear, firm line. Next decide upon what dimensions are necessary, and provide places for them. Put in dimension lines, reference lines, and arrows, leaving a break in the dimension lines for the dimensions themselves.   Do not take any dimensions thus far, but study carefully the scheme of dimensioning until satisfied that it is practical for the man who is to make the piece—that he can pick out the dimensions readily as he needs them and that, so far as possible, the dimensions are grouped according to the sequence in which they are needed. Be especially careful not to take dimensions from impractical places, such as the edge of a rough casting, but dimension from finished surfaces, centers of holes or center lines, which can be accurately located and used as a starting point for all the dimensions.   Where two pieces are to go together with bolts, screws, or dowels, take dimensions from the same end of both pieces so that holes will register properly.

Having put on all dimension lines, arrows, and reference lines, take the steel scale and calipers and measure up the piece, putting the dimensions in the places provided for them.   Use judgment in measuring.   Some dimensions must be held to extreme accuracy, others only to a reasonable accuracy.   Do not use sixty-fourths where thirty-seconds or even sixteenths will do.   Where several dimensions are to be "strung," see that they total up properly to the over-all dimension.   Add them and put the total on as a dimension.   Do not leave any dimensions to be added up by the man who is to make the piece.

Where two persons work together, it is a good plan for one to take the measurements and the other to put them down; then to change jobs, and have the one who took the measurements check the sketch while the other takes the measurements.

A sketch should be so complete that either the draftsman who made the sketch or another can make up a finished drawing without ever having to see the object after the sketch has once been made.   Often it is necessary to go great distances to make sketches, and the expense of doing the work is heavy; therefore, the sketch must be complete and accurate so that another trip will not be necessary.   When the draftsman is satisfied that the sketch is complete and accurate, he should give it a title and put on his name and the date on which it was completed.

Pictorial Sketching.   It is a good plan for the draftsman to practice making pictorial sketches as well as standard "three-view" or orthographic sketches.   The two methods commonly used for pictorial sketches are known as *isometric* and *oblique* projection.

Isometric Drawing or Projection.   An *isometric drawing* is a modified perspective drawing that is easily made and often gives a better idea of the relative position of the parts of an object than the regular plan-and-elevation method.   An isometric drawing is particularly useful in estimating material such as wire and cable because the lengths can be put on the vertical, horizontal, and slanting runs and accurately totaled.   To make an isometric drawing, take three axes, one vertical and two at

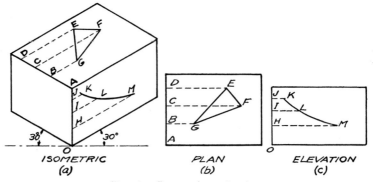

Fig. 1.   Isometric projection.

30 deg with the horizontal, as shown in Fig. 1.   On these axes lay off to scale the length, breadth, and thickness of any rectangular object.   If there are parts that are not rectangular, or are at an angle with the rectangular figures that will enclose the object, locate these parts by means of offsets measured parallel to the rectangular axes, as shown in (*b*).   If the object is curved, take several offsets, as shown in (*c*).

Figure 1 shows an isometric drawing of a block with a triangular hole through it from top to bottom and a curved line drawn on the face of the block.   On isometric drawing (*a*) the distances *AB*, *AC*, and *AD* are equal to the distances *AB*, *AC*, and *AD* on the plan in (*b*); also the distances *BG*, *CF*, and *DE* on the isometric drawing are equal to the distances *BG*, *CF*, and *DE* on the plan.   On the face of the block, the distances *OH*, *OI*, and *OJ* on the isometric drawing are equal to the distances *OH*, *OI*, and *OJ* on the elevation shown in (*c*).   Similarly, the distances *HM*, *IL*, and *JK* on the isometric drawing are equal to the distances *HM*, *IL*, and *JK* on the elevation.

Oblique Projection. A type of representation known as *oblique projection* often shows an object very clearly and can be used instead of isometric projection. In oblique projection, as in isometric projection, three axes are used, a vertical, a horizontal, and a third axis at an angle with the horizontal: 30 deg, 60 deg, or any other angle that the draftsman decides will best show the object he is to sketch. The method of laying off irregular or curved parts is similar to that used in isometric projection. Figure 2 shows the block of Fig. 1 drawn in oblique projection. Figures 3, 61, 65, 71, 86, and 128 show isometric and oblique projection applied to electrical jobs.

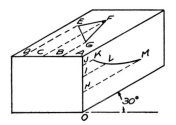

FIG. 2. Oblique projection.

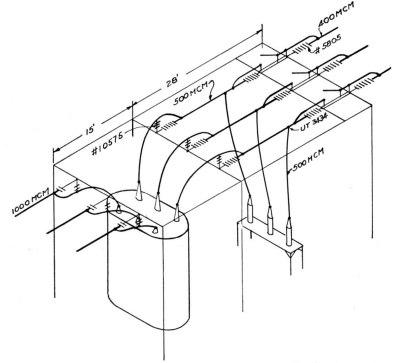

FIG. 3. Isometric sketch of the transformer bay of a distribution station.

Original Calculations. Engineering offices require that original calculations be kept for reference. In some offices each man is provided with a bound notebook; in others, printed letter-size forms are used, which are often punched for a loose-leaf binder. All calculations and notes relating to every job are kept on file. It is essential, therefore, that anyone planning to do engineering work should form the habit of putting his calculations in such shape that they can be readily followed through step by step in case reference to them later is necessary. Practice in making calculations systematically will soon enable one to arrange one's work so that the principal parts will stand out sharply on the sheet, and the calculations by which these parts or results are obtained will appear as subheadings near at hand. It is particularly essential that main results stand out clearly, so that the work may be checked through quickly by another person, or by the one making the calculations, who may find it necessary to change parts of his work as the design proceeds. In making original calculations, think the whole problem through first and divide it up into main headings and subheadings. As each heading is computed, the formulas and quantities worked with should be put down in such shape that they will stand out clearly. Then make the substitutions and finally show the result. To explain in more detail: Set down the formula, if one is to be used, near the left of the sheet and the values of the different symbols either at the right of the formula or directly below it. Usually it is best to transpose the formula so that the quantity to be obtained stands at the left of the equality sign and all others at the right before making substitutions. Then substitute quantities for the letters and show them clearly with proper signs of multiplication, etc., as indicated in the formula. Perform the multiplications, etc., either by slide rule or by working out. If they are worked out without using a slide rule, show all the work at the right of the paper and carry the answer over to the left and put it down, marking the name of the unit, as 110 volts, or 26 ft, 6 in., etc.   If the slide rule is used, make substitutions in the formula as before, but show only the answer.

As in sketching, use judgment in the degree of accuracy to which the computations are carried.   For instance, do not take values that are measured with an ordinary foot rule, and carry out the multiplication and division of these quantities to four decimal places.

It is easy to make a mistake in placing the decimal point, particularly if a slide rule is used.   Form the habit of checking results by a "common-sense method." That is, rough off quantities to the nearest whole numbers that are convenient to work with, and then make the computations mentally, to see if the answer is reasonable. Usually mistakes can be caught in this way. Another method is to make the computations in a different order the second time from the one used the first time. It is not a very good plan to depend on working a problem through twice the same way to check, because the same mistake may be made again, whereas, if the quantities are taken in different order the second time, the error will be caught.

In an office a set of calculations is usually checked by another person before the work is carried further. In the case of two working together, each should make the calculations and one act as a check on the other.

In computations the essential things are accuracy and clearness in showing principal parts of work and the manner of arriving at results. Computations, like sketches, should have title, name of person making them, and date.

Equipment for Mechanical and Electrical Drafting Work. This should consist of:

Drawing board 18 by 24 in.
24-in. T square
45-deg triangle
60-deg triangle
Irregular curve
Architects' scale
2H, 4H, and 6H pencils
Penholder with pen for lettering—Gillott No. 303 or Esterbrook No. 333 or equivalent
Black waterproof drawing ink
Pencil eraser
Artgum
Erasing shield
Six thumb tacks and Scotch drafting tape
Sharp pocket knife
Sandpaper block
Blotter
Chalk or tracing-cloth powder
Cloth for wiping pens
Cloth for wiping instruments and dusting off drawing
Set of instruments
Protractor
Template for drawing electrical symbols

The above equipment is the least that one can have and do good work on the usual kind of mechanical and electrical drawing. The drawing board must be straight on the left or working end, and the square must be straight in the blade and head and have the blade tightly fastened to the head.   The square should always be used against the left or working end of the board and never against the sides or opposite end.

The set of instruments should include at least the following pieces: compasses with lengthening bar, pencil and pen, hairspring dividers, bow dividers, bow pencil and bow pen, and two ruling pens.   The instruments should be heavy enough to be stiff and yet not so heavy as to be clumsy.   The compasses and dividers should be provided with a suitable means of adjusting in the hinge, so that they can be kept tight enough to stay in position with ordinary use when once set.   Usually screws are provided for this purpose.   The screws should be of good size and have good threads.   All other screws used for clamping and adjusting should be of good quality and have enough bearing in the pieces they fit, so as not to strip easily.   The points of all instruments must be kept sharp.   Care should be used that they are not dropped and bent or broken.   The drawing pens should have their points the same length and ground to an elliptical point.   One pen should be used for fine lines and the other for medium and heavy lines.   The pen should be cleaned before each refilling, and when it is put away for the day, it should be wiped out thoroughly.   Never use sandpaper on the pen.   Keep the ink bottle tightly closed, except when actually filling the pen.

DRAFTING ROOM STANDARDS

1. Supplies.   No pencil softer than 4H should be used for layout work, and no pencil harder than 4H for detailing.   Either a cone or a wedge point may be used, depending on the nature of the work.   Pencils must be kept sharp.

Paper comes in three basic sizes:

L: 8½ by 11 in.
A: 11 by 17 in.
B: 17 by 22 in.

Larger sheets are multiples of size *B*.

2. Name Plate. The size of name plate to be used varies with the dimensions of the paper:

A and B: $3\frac{1}{2}$ by $1\frac{5}{16}$ in.
   L: $\frac{1}{2}$ by $7\frac{1}{4}$ in. (at top of paper)

3. Lines. The styles and weights of lines shown in Fig. 4 represent good practice and should be used. Reference lines

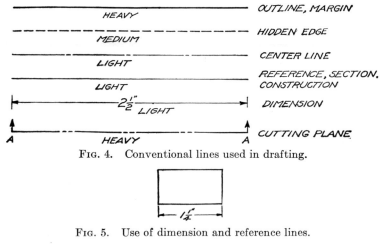

Fig. 4. Conventional lines used in drafting.

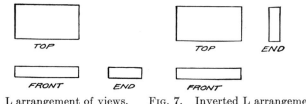

Fig. 5. Use of dimension and reference lines.

Fig. 6. L arrangement of views.   Fig. 7. Inverted L arrangement of views.

should not quite touch the piece that is to be dimensioned and extend not further than $\frac{1}{8}$ in. beyond the dimension line, as shown in Fig. 5.

4. Arrangement of Views. Third-angle projection is to be used for all drawings. The views may be arranged like either Figs. 6 or 7. Views are to be known as top, front, and end views; the arrangement shown in Fig. 6 is preferred.

5. Lettering. Plain capital letters with a 60-deg slope are to be used. The formation of letters is shown by the chart (Fig. 8). Sizes as follows: Titles, $\frac{3}{16}$ in.; subtitles, $\frac{1}{8}$ in.; dimensions,

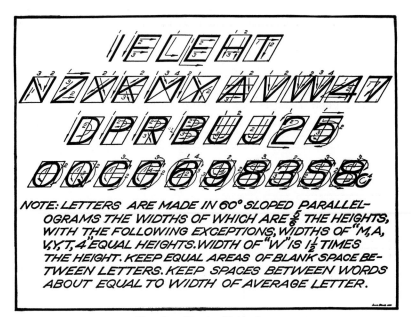

Fig. 8. Chart of lettering.

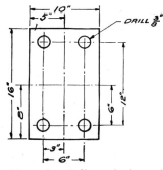

Fig. 9. Example of dimensioning rough work.

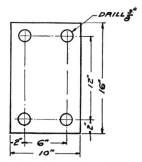

Fig. 10. Example of dimensioning finished work.

notes, etc., $\frac{3}{32}$ in. Guide lines are to be drawn with 4H or 6H pencil and lettering with 2H pencil.

 6. Dimensioning. Dimensions are to read from bottom and right of drawing. On machine parts, give all dimensions in inches; on electrical, structural, and architectural drawings, give dimensions in feet and inches (in inches up to 12). Thus, $11^{63}\!/_{64}$ in.; 1 ft 0 in.; 1 ft $0\frac{1}{2}$ in.

In case an object such as a pier is to be drawn, and it is necessary to place it on the paper in some unusual position, dimension the object so that the dimensions read from the bottom and right as the workman faces the object as it is to stand.

Dimension rough work from center lines (see Fig. 9).   Dimension finished work from edges (see Fig. 10).

FIG. 11.   Dimensioning radii.

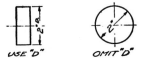

FIG. 12.   Dimensioning diameters.

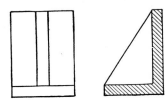

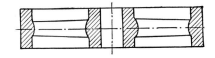

FIG. 13.   Section of an angle plate with a web.

FIG. 14.   Section of a wheel.

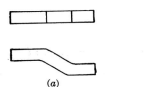

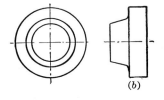

(a)

(b)

FIG. 15.   Drawing showing lines of intersection.

7. Radii.   Use R after a radius, as in Fig. 11.

8. Diameters.   Use D after diameters, as in Fig. 12.

9. Sectioning.   Sectioning should usually be 45 deg with center line of section.   On assemblies, section same parts on separate views in same direction.   Section a web as in Fig. 13 and arms of a wheel as in Fig. 14, regardless of whether there is an even or odd number of arms.

Break section lines for figures, but not for dimension lines or arrows.

10. Lines of Intersection. On details like Figs. 15a and b, show line of intersection only when clearness demands.

11. Structural Conventions. The electrical draftsman is often called upon to draw simple structural details and to specify structural materials. Some of the more common structural conventions are given for the guidance of the electrical draftsman in the problems of this type that he will most likely meet.

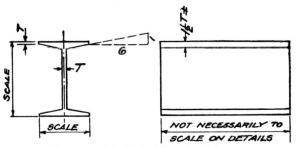

FIG. 16.   Method of drawing I beams.

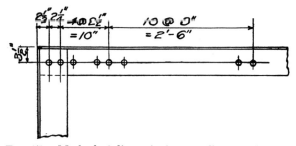

FIG. 17.   Method of dimensioning equally spaced holes.

The tables given in the Appendix give the structural shapes most used in electrical drafting work. In making drawings of I beams the method of Fig. 16 may be used. The depth of the beam, width of flange, and thickness of web and flange are drawn to scale. The sloping part of the flange may be drawn with a slope of 6 to 1, and only two lines instead of three need be shown on the projected view of the flange. In details the length of the beam need not be to scale.

In structural drafting where the center distances of several equally spaced holes are to be dimensioned, the method of Fig. 17

should be used.   The same method may be used by the electrical draftsman in dimensioning several equally spaced conduits.

Rivets that are driven in the shop are called *shop rivets;* rivets that are driven on the job are known as *field rivets.*   The method of drawing shop and field rivets is shown in Fig. 18.

Angles when punched or drilled should be done according to certain standard distances measured from the back of the angle to the center of the hole.   This distance is called the *gauge distance.*

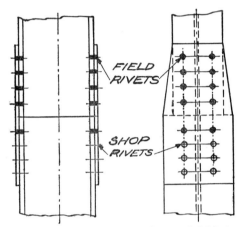

FIG. 18.   Method of showing shop and field rivets.

Table 9 gives the gauge distances for the angles commonly used.

In specifying materials, the following is good practice:

Bars and Plates.   Up to 6 in. wide, flat material is called a *bar;* above 6 in. in width the material is called a *plate.*   Give number of pieces, width, and thickness thus:

$$\text{1 Bar—6''} \times \tfrac{1}{2}'' \times 0'\text{-6''}$$
$$\text{2 Pcs—12''} \times \tfrac{1}{2}'' \times 1'\text{-8}\tfrac{1}{4}''$$

Angles.   Give number, width of legs and thickness, and length thus:

$$\text{1∠—6''} \times 4'' \times \tfrac{1}{2}'' \times 0'\text{-7}\tfrac{1}{2}''$$
$$\text{4∠—3''} \times 3'' \times \tfrac{3}{8}'' \times 5'\text{-10}\tfrac{1}{2}''$$

Beams and Columns.   Give number, size, shape, weight per foot, and length thus:

$$\text{1—12'' I—31.8}\# \times 19'\text{-6}\tfrac{3}{4}''$$
$$\text{1—14'' Beth. H—161}\# \times 25'\text{-7}\tfrac{1}{2}''$$

Channels   Give number, weight per foot, and length thus:

$$1—12'' \, [−20.7\# \times 12'–10''$$
$$7—8'' \, [\text{s}—11.5\# \times 15'–11\tfrac{1}{2}''$$

T Bars.   Give number, flange width first, then stem, weight per foot, and length thus:

$$1—T—3'' \times 3\tfrac{1}{2}'' \times 8.6\# \times 12'–11''$$

Rods.   Give number, size, kind (round or square) and length thus:

$$2 \text{ Rods } \tfrac{3}{4}'' \, \phi \times 2'–11''$$
$$2 \text{ Rods } \tfrac{3}{4}'' \, \square \times 2'–8''$$

Rivets.   Give number, diameter, and length thus:

$$450 \text{ Rivets } \tfrac{3}{4}'' \times 1\tfrac{1}{2}'' \text{ long}$$

(Round head rivets are always understood unless otherwise specified.)

$$450 \text{ Rivets csk. hd. } \tfrac{3}{4}'' \times 1\tfrac{1}{2}'' \text{ long}$$

Bolts.   Give number, diameter, and length thus:

$$2 \text{ Bolts } \tfrac{1}{2}'' \times 2''$$

(Square head machine bolts are always understood unless otherwise specified.)

$$2 \text{ Fin. bolts hex. hd. \& nut } \tfrac{1}{2}'' \times 2''$$

Washers.   Give number and diameter of bolt thus:

$$4—\tfrac{3}{4}'' \text{ washers}$$

(Where it is necessary to detail a washer, see Table 14.)

PROBLEMS

1. Using the dimensions of the U67 condulet given in Table 37, page 168, draw the two views shown and a front view looking into the openings for the two conduits.   Use a scale of 12 in. to the foot and dimension completely.

2. Make an isometric drawing of the box for a CR4061-A3C and CR4161-A3C shown in Fig. 6 of page 97.   The door of the box is to be closed.   Use a scale of 3 in. to the foot and dimension completely.

3. Using the box of Problem 2, make a drawing of the box in oblique projection with the door open 45 deg.   Use a scale of 3 in. to the foot and dimension completely.

CIRCUIT DIAGRAMS

General. Because a large part of the work of the electrical draftsman has to do with circuits, it is important that he should have a thorough understanding of the more common circuits and the methods of showing them before he attempts to do layout work. The method of showing circuits has become practically standard and is based on symbols that have been developed through the years as the result of much study by engineers and draftsmen and the various associations representing the engineering profession. A few of the more common symbols are shown in Charts 1 to 3. There are hundreds more, however, with which the reader should become familiar. These may be purchased in pamphlet form at a nominal price from the American Standards Association, which is now the accepted authority for the latest revision of symbols of all kinds. Those shown in tables in this book are reproduced by permission of the association and represent the latest revision.

The circuit diagrams that follow, taken from the first edition of this book, represent fairly well the symbols now in use. They are reproduced just as originally printed and are to be used as checking problems by the reader to gain practice in checking electric circuits and to become acquainted with the new symbols now in use which he will substitute in some cases for those shown.

Circuits are usually shown by one or all of the following methods: (1) complete circuit diagram, (2) one-line diagram, (3) schematic diagram. Each of these methods will be taken up in order and explained by means of examples. Problems will then be given which will bring out the important features of each circuit shown in the diagrams.

Complete Circuit Diagram. A complete circuit diagram, as its name indicates, gives every detail of connection and every wire in the circuit. Apparatus is represented by symbols, and every wire is shown either by itself or included in an assembly of several wires which appears as one line on the drawing. Separate wires are numbered where they go into such an assembly and are numbered again with the same numbers where they come out. This method is used on switchboard drawings and on drawings of control apparatus, for if the many wires were shown separately, there would be a needless amount of work and the drawing would be confusing.

Figures 19 to 47 show the more common complete circuit diagrams for bells, lighting, and power. These circuits are to

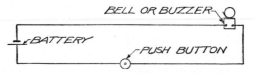

Fig. 19.   Bell or buzzer controlled from one station.

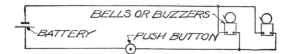

Fig. 20.   Two bells or buzzers controlled from one station.

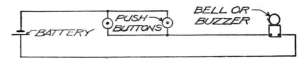

Fig. 21.   Bell or buzzer controlled from two or more stations.

be used as checking problems. They are to be studied for correctness of connections and for the proper use of symbols as explained in Problem 1 of this chapter.

One-line Diagram. In order to simplify drawings of circuits in power stations, substations, etc., it is customary to use what is known as a *one-line diagram* instead of the regular complete circuit diagram. A one-line diagram gives a picture of what apparatus is to be used and how the various pieces of apparatus are connected in relation to one another. It is as easily understood as the complete circuit diagram and requires much less time to draw. As an example, consider a three-phase alternator connected to buses, as in Fig. 37. As far as the circuits and

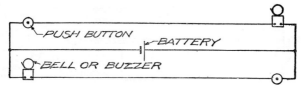

FIG. 22.   Return-call circuit.

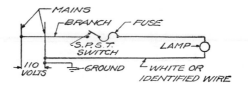
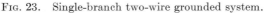

FIG. 23.   Single-branch two-wire grounded system.

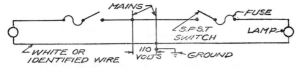

FIG. 24.   Double-branch two-wire grounded system.

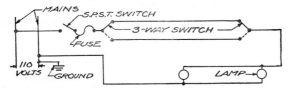

FIG. 25.   Branch circuit with lamps controlled from two stations.

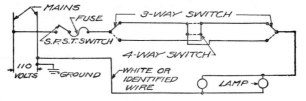

FIG. 26.   Branch circuit with lamps controlled from three stations.

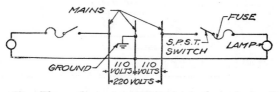

FIG. 27.   Three-wire mains with two-wire branch circuits.

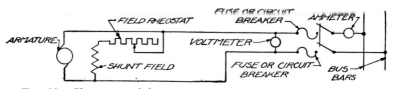

Fig. 28.   Shunt-wound d-c generator with connections to bus bars.

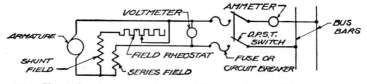

Fig. 29.   Series-wound d-c generator with connections to load.

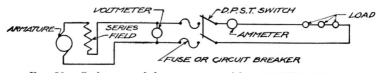

Fig. 30.   Short-shunt compound-wound d-c generator with connections to bus bars.

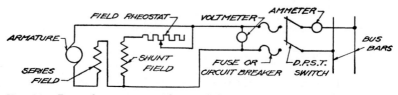

Fig. 31.   Long-shunt compound-wound d-c generator with connections to bus bars.

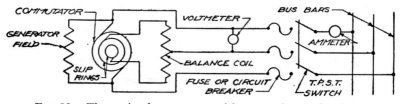

Fig. 32.   Three-wire d-c generator with connections to bus bars.

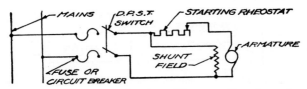

FIG. 33. Shunt-wound motor with connections to mains.

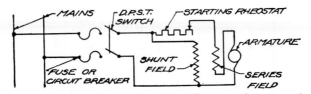

FIG. 34. Compound-wound motor with connections to mains.

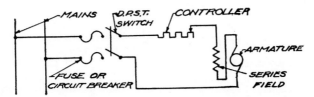

FIG. 35. Series-wound motor with connections to mains.

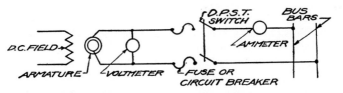

FIG. 36. Single-phase alternator with connections to bus bars.

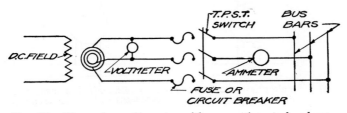

FIG. 37. Three-phase alternator with connections to bus bars.

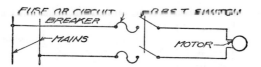

Fig. 38. Single-phase induction motor with connections to mains.

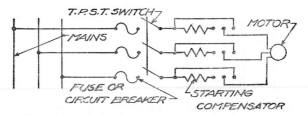

Fig. 39. Three-phase induction motor with connections to mains.

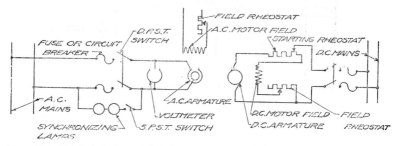

Fig. 40. Single-phase synchronous motor coupled to d-c motor with electrical connections to a-c and d-c mains.

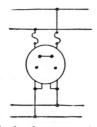 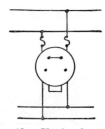

Fig. 41. Single-phase transformer connected with primaries in series and secondaries in parallel.

Fig. 42. Single-phase transformer connected with primaries in series and secondaries in series.

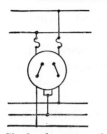

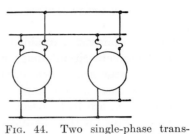

Fig. 43. Single-phase transformer connected with primaries in parallel and secondaries three-wire.

Fig. 44. Two single-phase transformers connected in parallel.

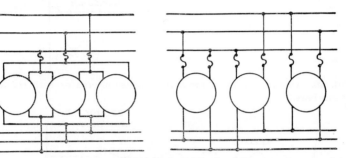

Fig. 45. Two methods of connecting three single-phase transformers delta to delta.

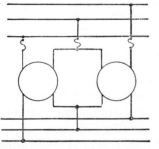

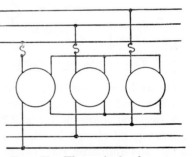

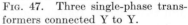

Fig. 46. Two single-phase transformers connected open delta or V.

Fig. 47. Three single-phase transformers connected Y to Y.

apparatus are concerned, the circuit can just as well be shown by one line, as in Fig. 48.

Starting at the left, the symbols indicate an a-c generator, a voltmeter, a fuse, a switch and ammeter, and finally a bus. If the symbols alone were used, it would not be clear whether the circuit is single-phase, two-phase, or three-phase, nor would it be clear how many meters are to be used. Notes supply this information.

Unless otherwise explained, it is understood that each line of the complete circuit diagram contains whatever instruments and apparatus are shown on the one-line diagram. When this is not the case, a note explains how many instruments, transformers, etc., are to be used. There are practically always one or more notes on the one-line diagram. The circuit of Fig. 48 is 220-volt, three-phase, three-wire, 60-cycle, and has one volt-

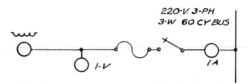

Fig. 48. One-line diagram for a three-phase alternator with connections to bus bars.

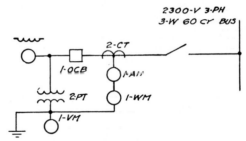

Fig. 49.   One-line diagram for a 2,300-volt switchboard.

meter and one ammeter. The meters are therefore noted 1-V and 1-A, and the circuit is marked 220-V, 3-ph, 3-W, 60-cy.

A one-line diagram for a 2,300-volt switchboard that has a generator, oil circuit breaker, disconnecting switches, one voltmeter, one ammeter, one wattmeter, two potential transformers, and two current transformers is shown in Fig. 49.

Schematic Diagram. A schematic diagram shows in the simplest possible manner the connections to the devices that constitute the switching and other control equipment. The two examples just given in Figs. 48 and 49 are so simple that the one-line diagram serves also as a schematic diagram. Where there are relays, remote-control switches, interlocking circuits, and signaling circuits, a separate drawing is required to make clear the operation of each piece of equipment and the sequence of the operations.

Relays. In order to understand the operation of a large switchboard where the switches are operated by remote control from a low-voltage control board, it is necessary to understand the operation of a relay and at least three circuits in which relays are used. These circuits are (1) the ordinary relay circuit in which a circuit of large capacity is opened by the relay that sends current through a trip coil, and closed by a relay that sends current through a closing coil; an auxiliary switch may be used with the relay; (2) a circuit known as a *sealing-in* circuit, where the circuit once closed by, for instance, a push button, remains closed even though the finger is taken off the push button; and

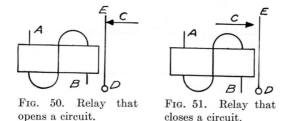

FIG. 50. Relay that opens a circuit.

FIG. 51. Relay that closes a circuit.

(3) an interlocking circuit where switching must follow a predetermined sequence for the circuit to operate.

A relay is a device that operates by a variation in the conditions of one electric circuit to affect the operation of other devices in the same or another electric circuit. While there are more than 60 types of relays used in power work alone, the principles involved in an ordinary motor-starting device and in the tripping of an oil circuit breaker will give a good understanding of the functioning of relays in general.

Using the symbol of Fig. 50, AB is one circuit and CD is an entirely separate circuit. An overload on AB will attract armature DE and open circuit CD. Similarly, an overload on the relay of Fig. 51 will close circuit CD. In power work, the relay is generally shown as in Fig. 52. A relay that is normally closed is shown at (a), and one that is normally open, at (b). Coil AB and contacts CD do not need to be shown near each other on the circuit diagram as long as they are definitely numbered or lettered so that it is clearly understood which circuits operate together.

Sealing-in Circuit. A circuit of the type shown in Fig. 53, known as a *sealing-in circuit*, is commonly used on push-button starters for motors.   Push button 1 is normally closed and push button 2 is normally open.   When 2 is closed, current flows to the motor through coil AB, but if button 2 were released, it would open the circuit, were it not for coil AB and contact CD.

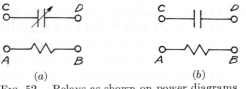

(a)   (b)

FIG. 52.   Relays as shown on power diagrams.

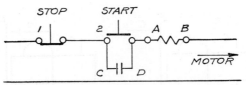

FIG. 53.   Diagram of a sealing-in circuit.

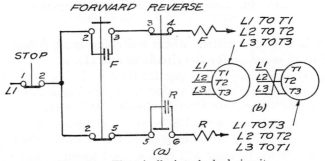

FIG. 54.   Electrically interlocked circuit.

When 2 closes, AB is energized and closes CD, so if 2 is opened, current continues to flow to the load until push button 1 is opened.

Interlocking Circuit.   Figure 54a shows diagrammatically an electrically interlocked circuit such as is used in starting, stopping, and reversing a three-phase induction motor.   Since in order to reverse a three-phase motor it is only necessary to reverse one phase, that is, two phase wires, the controller shown reverses wires L-1 and L-3, as shown in Fig. 54b.   Drawing (a) shows the control circuit and one contactor for FORWARD and one for REVERSE. Actually, there are three contactors F and three contactors R. There is but one operating coil F and one operating coil R. The FORWARD and REVERSE push buttons are mechanically connected as shown. When the FORWARD button is pushed, contacts 2 and 5 open before 2 and 3 close, so that it is impossible to throw current on both the forward and

FIG. 55. Typical modern metal-clad control switchboard. (*Westinghouse Electric Corporation.*)

reverse circuits at the same time. Similarly, on REVERSE, 3 and 4 open before 5 and 6 close.

In running forward, then, the FORWARD button is pushed and contact is made through L1-2, 2-3, 3-4 and coil F to phase 1 of the motor. While this is being done, the other two contactors allow current to flow from L-3 to T-3 and from L-2 to T-2.

When the motor is reversed, the REVERSE button is pushed; this first opens 3-4 and then closes 5-6. The reverse coil R closes the reverse contactors, and the current flows from L-1 to T-3, L-3 to T-1, and L-2 to T-2, as is shown by the diagrammatic sketch of Fig. 54b.

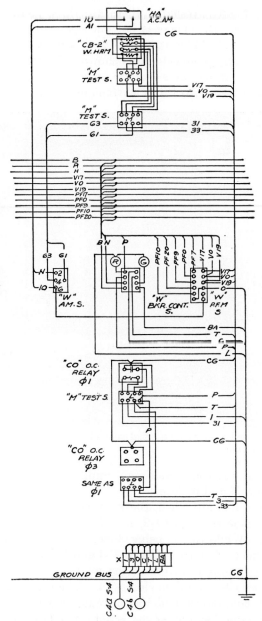

Fig. 56. Details of apparatus and wiring for feeder circuit 1 on rear of panel 4.

Practical Illustration of the Use of Circuit Diagrams. In order to illustrate the use of circuit diagrams, a complete diagram, a one-line diagram, a schematic diagram, and a structure diagram for a Westinghouse control switchboard for a 13,000-volt three-phase circuit will be analyzed. This board consists of two generator panels, one transformer panel, and two feeder panels, each with two feeder circuits. The board has only the control apparatus mounted on it. All the power apparatus such as generators,

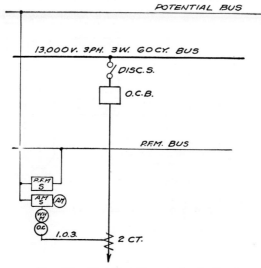

FIG. 57. One-line diagram for feeder 1.

transformers, and oil switches is located at a distance from the switchboard.

Control Switchboard and Circuits. The switchboard is made of metal and is of the type shown in Fig. 55. The front panels are hinged at the left to open like the cover of a book. The meters and control wiring are mounted on the back of this swinging panel so that when it is swung clear open and one stands facing it, the wiring will appear as shown in Fig. 56. Figure 56 shows only one of the feeder control circuits that are mounted on the panel. There are two just alike. The terminal board is mounted on the stationary part of the switchboard, and the control wiring is brought to it by flexible conductors. The circles shown at the lower part of Fig. 56 and lettered C4aS-4 and C4bS-4 represent conduits that carry the control wiring to the apparatus which is at a considerable distance from the control board. Figure 57 shows the one-line diagram for feeder 1. Figure 59 shows the schematic diagram giving connections for the switching equipment of feeder 1. The apparatus controlled from this panel

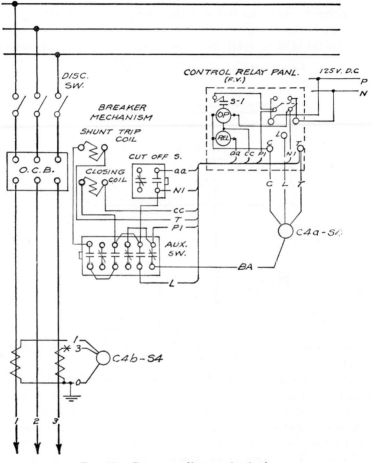

FIG. 58. Structure diagram for feeder 1.

is the relay panel for the circuit breaker shown on the structure diagram of Fig. 58. The current transformers that supply current for the meters are also shown on this drawing. Conduits S4aS-4 and C4bS-4 appear as circles near the apparatus to which their conductors connect.

In addition to the wiring shown in Figs. 56 to 59, there is often another drawing showing the ON and OFF positions of the voltmeter, ammeter, and power-factor meter switches. This is generally put on the drawing near the meters. When one panel is similar or nearly similar to another panel already drawn, a note is put on the panel saying, "Same as panel . . . " or "Same as panel . . . , except . . . ," and the wiring is not repeated.

Drawings Required for a Switchboard. The number of drawings required for a switchboard will depend on its size and on the

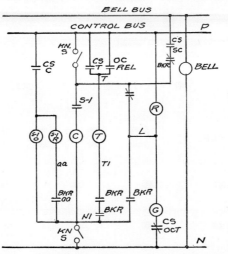

FIG. 59. Schematic diagram for showing connections for the switching equipment of feeder 1.

complexity of its circuits. A simple board such as that shown in Fig. 60 will require a plan, front and side views, and a circuit diagram. A large board like the Westinghouse control switchboard may require the following drawings:

Front assembly showing the location of the equipment.

Rear assembly showing equipment and wiring.

One-line diagram showing the main power circuits, the switching devices, and the metering equipment.

A drawing showing the connections of the apparatus separate or away from the switchboard, such as the connections for operating the oil circuit breakers that may be located at some distance from the control board. Such a drawing is sometimes called a *structure diagram.*

A schematic diagram showing the operation of the control equipment.

Details of Control Switchboard. The feeder panel of the Westinghouse control board of Fig. 55 will be explained by the use of the various diagrams already discussed.

FIG. 60.   Modern metal-enclosed d-c switchboard.   (*Westinghouse Electric Corporation.*)

We first refer to Fig. 56, which gives the details of the complete wiring of feeder circuit 1 on feeder panel 4. This circuit is located at the right-hand side of the panel as viewed from the rear of the panel. At the lower part of the drawing are two circles lettered C4a-S4 and C4b-S4. These circles represent conduits. The conduit marked C4a-S4 carries the control wires for the breaker mechanism to the breaker of circuit 1 and will be found again on the drawing of the breaker mechanism on the structure diagram of Fig. 58.

The conduit marked C4b-S4 carries the wires to the current transformers connected in the main power circuit. This conduit also shows on the structure diagram and is near the lower part of the drawing.

One-line Diagram. We next refer to the one-line diagram of Fig. 57 for feeder circuit 1 of panel 4. Here we find that in leaving the bus we go to the clip side of the disconnecting switch, then to the oil circuit breaker, then to the current transformers, and finally out to the line and to whatever apparatus is to be fed.

Each feeder requires an ammeter, a watthour meter, and a power-factor meter. It also requires an overcurrent relay to open the oil circuit breaker in case of an overload or short circuit. The voltmeter, power-factor meter, and watthour meter require potential to operate them. This is obtained by stepping down the 13,000 volts by potential transformers to a potential bus as shown at the upper part of the drawing.

Structure Diagram. In a large installation, the oil circuit breaker, current transformers, and potential transformers are very large and are located at a distance from the switchboard, which is only a control board and has none of the power circuits brought to it. The circuit breaker may have a panel of its own, on or near it, and the control circuits for it may be very complicated. For this reason, a drawing of the apparatus that is separate from the main switchboard is made up; it is known as a *structure diagram.* This drawing shows all the wires and where they go, and each wire is numbered or lettered. Where wires or cables go from one place to another, as from the control board to, say, the oil switch panel, circles are shown below the panels to represent the conduits that carry the wires. There may be a half dozen or more wires going into a conduit. Each of these wires is numbered where it goes into the conduit and numbered again with the same number where it comes out.

Schematic Diagram. The schematic diagram of Fig. 50 shows how the circuit breaker is operated. On this particular job, suppose that the control switch is turned to the CLOSE position. Current goes from control bus P through control switch contact CS—C, control relay operating coil S-1-0, one pole of switch KN—S to bus N. This current causes the control relay to operate and to complete the circuit through the circuit breaker closing coil. This closing coil circuit is from bus P through one pole of switch KN—S, contact S-1, breaker closing coil C, and to the other pole of KN—S to bus N. The breaker closes and latches in. Auxiliary contact $BKRaa$ in the circuit of relay coil S-1R closes when the breaker mechanism operates and resets the control relay, causing contact S-1 to open. When the circuit breaker closes, an auxiliary contact completes the circuit through indicating lamp R. This can be traced from bus P through lamp R, contact BKR, one pole of KN—S to bus N.

The circuit breaker is tripped manually by turning the control switch handle to TRIP. This completes the circuit from bus P through control switch contact CS—T, circuit breaker trip coil T, two auxiliary contacts BKR in series, one pole of KN—S to bus N. When the circuit breaker opens, this circuit is immediately interrupted by contacts BKR. Lamp G indicates the open position of the circuit breaker. Its circuit is from bus P through one pole of KN—S, contact BKR, lamp G, and control-switch contact CS—OCT to bus N.

If the type CO overcurrent relays operate, their contacts OC REL close and complete the tripping circuit in the manner described for manual tripping. Automatic tripping of the circuit breaker by means of the overcurrent relays starts the bell alarm. This bell circuit is from bus P through one pole of KN—S, contact BKR, contact CS—SC to bell bus B, and thence through the bell to bus N. Turning the control switch handle to TRIP opens contact CS and silences the bell alarm.

Bill of Material. On switchboards and other jobs a bill of material is required. Where there is room, the bill of material may be put directly on the drawing. A good way to make up bills of material is to have narrow printed forms with spaces for the various items lined off and numbered by a printer. These should be printed on vellum. As the job proceeds, the spaces are filled in by the draftsman, and the number of each item on the bill of material is put on the drawing in a circle near the part.

The thin vellum on which the bill of material has been prepared can then be fastened to the drawing and blueprinted with it, since the numbering and lettering will readily print through. If there is no room on the drawing, the bill of material may be lettered or typed on separate sheets, usually of letter size. Some offices use letter-size sheets for all bills of material. These are regular forms printed on vellum so that they can be blueprinted after being filled in by the draftsman.

In making out a bill of material it is a good plan to group similar equipment, so that in case one wants to find out about any one kind of equipment, as for instance meters, one will find all such information in one part of the bill of material.

Checking Circuits. In checking electric circuits, it is customary to make a print of the drawing which is marked *checking print,* and on this print to check each line and piece of apparatus. A common method of checking is to trace each line on the checking print with a colored "blueprint pencil" (usually a yellow pencil for work on a blueprint). Where an error is found, the error is marked with a red pencil and the correct method is shown on the print. With this system there is no opportunity to miss a line because, when the checking job is finished, each circuit that is correct will be in yellow and each circuit that has been drawn incorrectly will be marked in red, and the correction to be made shown. In other words, every line on the checking print will be marked in yellow or corrected in red.

Explanation of the Indexing of the 1951 Edition of the National Electrical Code. The Code is divided into ten chapters as follows:*

1. General
2. Wiring Design and Protection
3. Wiring Methods and Materials
4. Equipment for General Use
5. Special Occupances
6. Special Equipment
7. Special Conditions
8. Communication Systems
9. Construction Specifications
10. Tables, Diagrams, and Examples

* Volume V of the National Fire Codes, The Nationalal Electric Code, 1951 Edition, contains also an appendix giving the Rules of Procedure of the National Electrical Code Committee. It also contains a compilation of selected excerpts from other NFPA standards useful in the application of the National Electrical Code, but not a part of it.

Each chapter is divided into articles and sections by key numbers, thus,

Chapter 2 is on Wiring and Protection and has the key number 2
  200 is the first article of Chap. 2
    2001 is the first section of Article 200
  210 is the second article of Chap. 2
    2101 is the first section of Article 210

Using actual topics from the Code,
  Under Chap. 2, Wiring Design and Protection,

Article 200 is Polarity Identification of Systems and Circuits
  Section 2001 is General
  Section 2002 is Connection to Grounded System
Article 210 is Branch Circuits
  Section 2101 is Scope
  Section 2113 is Voltage
  Section 2114 is Heavy-duty Lamp Holders.

In Chap. 9, Section 92401 is read as follows:

The first figure 9 is the chapter;
The next three figures 240 indicate that the section refers to Article 240, Overcurrent Protection;
The last number 1 indicates that this is the first item of this series.

IMPORTANT 1951 NEC RULINGS THAT APPLY TO CIRCUITS
(Numbers refer to sections.)

Chapter 1
112 Working Space about Electrical Equipment

Chapter 2
2002 Connection to Grounded System
2005 Means of Identification of Conductors
2008 Identification of Terminals
2103 Classification of Branch Circuits
2115 Branch Circuits Required
2116 Calculation of Load
2121a Carrying Capacity of Conductors
2121c-1 Range Loads
2126 Permissible Loads
2201 Feeder Size
2203 Calculation of Load

2322 Clearance of Service Drop
2403 Overcurrent Protection of Conductors
2511, 2514, 2525, 2594 Grounding

Chapter 3
3005 Runs—Continuous
3011 Conductors of Different Systems
3102 Conductor Insulation
3462 Rigid Metal Conduit
3471 Bends—Number in One Run
3482 Electrical Metallic Tubing
3502 Flexible Metal Conduit
3702 Use of Round Boxes
3802 Wiring of Three-way and Four-way Switches
3806, 3807 Position of Knife Switches

PROBLEMS

1. Following the method described in the paragraph on checking circuits, check each circuit of Figs. 19 to 47 for correctness of electrical connections and for correctness in the use of the latest symbols. For example, Fig. 19 shows the symbol for a bell; so, with the latest symbol the word *buzzer* should be marked out if a bell is to be used. Also, the latest symbol for a push button is a square and not a circle.

2. Draw a one-line diagram for Fig. 36.

3. Draw a one-line diagram for Fig. 39.

4. Draw a one-line diagram for Fig. 40.

5. Draw a one-line diagram for a three-phase power circuit as follows: There are two incoming lines numbered 1 and 2, numbering from the left. Each incoming line has two disconnecting switches, an oil circuit breaker, two current transformers, and two potential transformers. The two incoming lines connect to a main bus so that, if one line goes out, the bus can be fed from the other incoming line. There are three present outgoing feeders, each with two disconnecting switches and one oil circuit breaker. These are at the left of incoming circuit 1. In addition to these three present feeders, there is to be a future feeder between feeder 3 and incoming line 1.

6. Following the method used for the three-phase motor of Chart 6, make a schematic diagram for the starter of Table 69.

7. Explain the operation of the autotransformer starter of Table 68 by making two diagrams: (a) connections for the fingers in the starting position and (b) fingers in the running position. Show all wiring and the paths of the current in both drawings. How are the transformers connected: parallel, series, delta, open delta, or Y?

8. Make a complete wiring diagram for three 150-kva transformers, each for 2,300 volts on the primaries and 230 volts on the secondaries connected delta to delta. What is the primary line voltage and current? Neglecting the efficiency, what is the secondary line voltage and current?

9. Make a complete wiring diagram for the three transformers of Problem 7 connected Y to Y. What is the primary line voltage and current? Neglecting efficiency, what is the secondary line voltage and current?

SWITCHBOARD FOR A DIRECT-CURRENT GENERATOR

Switchboards at the present time are of what is known as the "dead-front" type; that is, they have no live parts on the front that can give a person a shock or that will make it possible for a short circuit to occur. Usually the boards are of metal, and the wiring is all enclosed in a metal housing or cubicle that forms the rear part of the switchboard.

Figure 60 shows a modern switchboard of the dead-front type as made by the Westinghouse Electric Corporation. The two cuts at the right and left show the method of constructing the framework and the manner of supporting the circuit breaker and buses. On this type of board, the meters and small wiring are mounted on the inside of a door which is hinged at the left as one faces the board. As one opens the door, all control wiring is available for inspection or repairs. Flexible conductors connect the wiring on the door to the wiring inside the cubicle through a terminal board located in the cubicle. The rear of the switch structure is permanently fastened to the frame, but the ends are attached by screws so that they may be removed to enable one to work on the circuit breaker or heavy wiring of the board.

Figure 61 is an isometric drawing of a board that is to be designed and constructed in a manner similar to the board shown in Fig. 60. Westinghouse equipment is to be used. The details of the circuit breaker, meters, rheostat shunt, and ground-detector lamps are shown in Fig. 62. All other parts of the board are to be designed and the job drawn to the scale $1\frac{1}{2}$ in. to the foot.

The procedure is first to study the general method of constructing the board and the details of supporting the circuit breaker and buses, and of connecting the breaker to the buses; then to make a complete wiring diagram as shown at the right in Fig. 61.   The long dash lines enclosing the wiring diagram represent the edges of the board.   At the upper left the wiring is shown as it will appear as you face the board when the door on which the wiring is mounted is wide open.   The other wiring

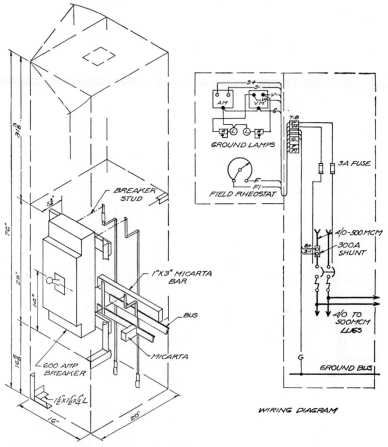

FIG. 61.   Details of construction and wiring for a d-c generator panel.

on the wiring diagram is the heavy wiring in the stationary part of the board; it is shown diagrammatically.   Figure 61 shows how the circuit breaker is supported and how the connections to the buses are to be made.   The buses are to be rigidly supported by micarta blocks, the details of which are to be worked out.   Figure 62 shows the dimensions of the apparatus to be used.

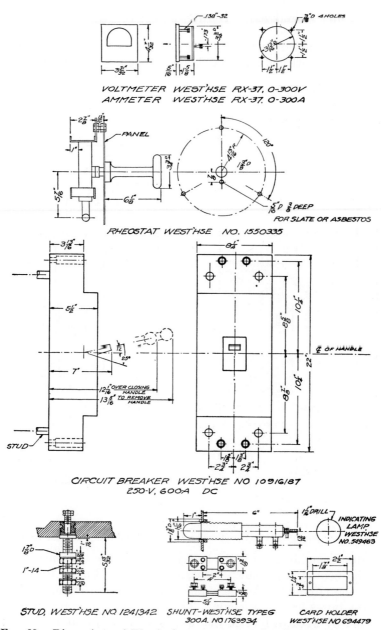

FIG. 62.   Dimensions of Westinghouse apparatus for d-c generator panel.

Suggestions for Making Layouts.

1. Use a good grade of paper, preferably tracing paper or vellum. When you are drawing on tracing paper or vellum, it is a good plan to put a piece of cross-section paper under the drawing. This will help you to keep things lined up and speed your work.

2. Use a 4H pencil for center lines and for blocking in, and a 2H pencil for improving lines or "heavying in." If the job is to be blueprinted directly from the pencil drawing, a pencil softer than a 2H may be used. Keep your pencils sharp.

3. Visualize how the job is to go together, and do not put anything on the drawing until you are sure of it. Make a few sketches first if necessary.

4. Work from center lines and see that they are not erased.

5. Block in large apparatus first. If several identical small parts have to be drawn, it is a good plan to draw one very carefully and then to trace it as many times as needed.

6. If the drawing is to be inked or traced, ink in the center lines first, then small circles, large circles, and curves. Next ink horizontal, vertical, and slanting lines. Use both the T square and triangles in inking or tracing. In electrical drafting there are many small circles to be inked which, if out of line, spoil the appearance of a drawing. In order to keep them in line in inking, it is a good plan to go over the drawing after the center lines have been inked, and prick the centers of all small circles with the point of a pair of dividers, using a magnifying glass if necessary. With this method, the point of your bow compass will go where you want it to go and your circles will all be properly centered.

7. Be careful with your lettering and with the leaders from the lettering to the parts they refer to. In general, slanting leaders give the job a better appearance than horizontal leaders or leaders made freehand.

8. Check your drawing carefully. The method of checking circuits has been explained on page 35. While there are many things to watch for in checking mechanical details, the following rough-and-ready rule will generally catch most of the mistakes and omissions. Look for

NAME, MATERIAL, QUANTITY, SCALE, LENGTH, BREADTH, THICKNESS, SIZE AND SPACING OF HOLES.

IMPORTANT 1951 NEC RULINGS THAT APPLY TO SWITCHBOARDS

(Numbers refer to sections)

Chapter 1	3812 Grounding of Enclosures
1112 Working Space	3813 Large Knife Switches
Chapter 2	3841 Where Rules Apply
2403 Overcurrent Protection of Equipment	3843 Rigid Support for Bus Bars and Conductors
Chapter 3	3851 Location of Switchboards
3102 Conductor Insulation	3854–3855 Clearances
3462 Use of Rigid Metal Conduit	3856 Conductor Covering
3502 Use of Flexible Metallic Conduit	**Chapter 5**
	5001 Hazardous Locations
3701 Installation of Boxes and Fittings	**Chapter 7**
	7161 Live Parts to Be Grounded
3801 Switches in Grounded Conductors	7162 Isolation by Elevation
	7163 Working Space
3803 Enclosures for Switches	**Chapter 9**
3800–3807 Position of Knife Switches	93847 Spacing of Bare Metal Parts

PROBLEM

Make a finished drawing of the switchboard shown in Fig. 61, as follows: Paper size: approximately 17 by 22 in.; scale: $1\frac{1}{2}$ in. = 1 ft.

At the left: Show plan, front, and right-hand end view of the switchboard. The end view is to be drawn with the cover removed to show clearly the details of the method of supporting the circuit breaker, buses, and bus connections.

Near the center: Draw a wiring diagram similar to that shown in Fig. 61. Outline the panel with long dash lines directly opposite the end view of the switchboard. Draw the meters, etc., and the electrical circuits in approximately the position they occupy on the switchboard, as viewed from the front with the swinging front panel or door wide open.

At the right: Lay out a form for a bill of material, giving in the following order: item number, name of part, size, make, catalogue number, number required. Fill in this form as the job proceeds. Circle the item numbers given in the bill of material on the drawing of the switchboard, and place them as near to the parts they refer to as possible. Put the circles where they will show the parts best, but do not repeat them. Using $\frac{1}{8}$-in. letters, letter carefully all notes necessary. Check the drawing, following the suggestions given on page 41 and from the standpoint that you have to write the order for the materials and equipment, and build the board.

CHAPTER 4

SWITCHBOARD FOR 2300-VOLT SERVICE

Modern switchboards for alternating currents are of the metal-clad type described in Chap. 3. In the higher voltage types of a-c boards the circuit breakers and the potential transformers with their fuses are of the *drawout type;* that is, they are so constructed that is is not necessary to loosen connections or take

Fig. 63. Typical modern switchboard enclosing drawout metal-clad air circuit breakers. (*General Electric Company.*)

off nuts to remove the apparatus from the circuit. Some of the relays and meters on this type of board are also of the drawout type.

A modern metal-clad switchboard is shown in Fig. 63. Note that the depth of the board is greater than the width of a panel. This depth is necessary, for each cubicle has to accommodate the breaker, buses, current, and potential transformers and the potheads through which the power cables are brought to the

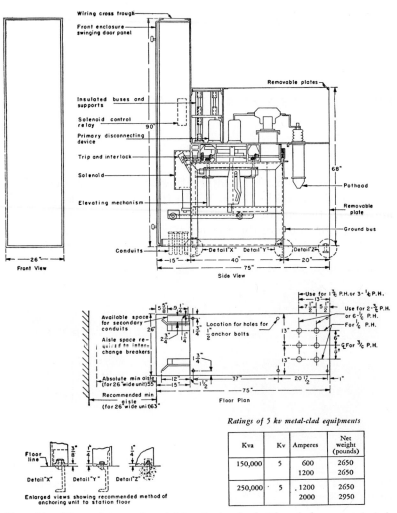

FIG. 64. Dimensions and weights of standard 5-kv. indoor metal-clad switchgear. (*General Electric Company.*)

switchboard. Figure 64 shows a section of a cubicle similar to those of Fig. 63. In order to show how the apparatus is arranged and how the taps are taken off from the buses, the isometric sketch of Fig. 65 has been made. The circuit breaker, which is of the air-break type, is located at the front and bottom of the cubicle. It has six studs that project upward; when the breaker is raised, these studs engage the disconnecting devices shown as cylinders in the sketch.

Figure 66 shows a cubicle for a generator and exciter, and Fig. 67 shows a cubicle for a feeder.   The breaker, which is provided

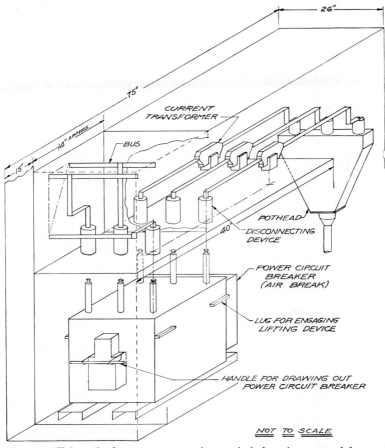

FIG. 65.   Triangular bus arrangement in metal-clad equipment and drawout air circuit breaker lowered and ready for drawing out. (*General Electric Company.*)

with wheels, is wheeled into place directly under the disconnecting devices and then raised by a mechanism built into the structure that engages the lugs shown at the side of the breaker.   When it is desired to remove the breaker for inspection or adjustment, it is simply lowered and wheeled out.   There is a special safety

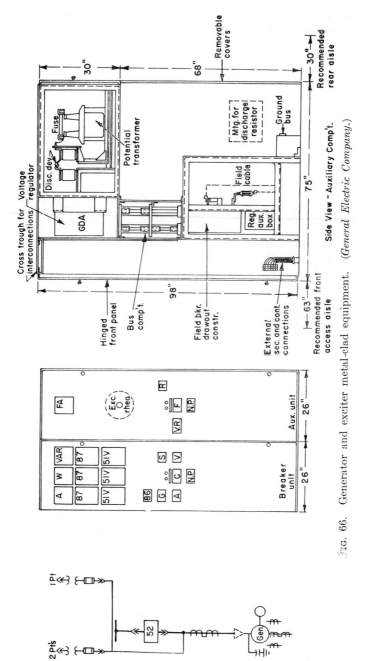

FIG. 66. Generator and exciter metal-clad equipment. (*General Electric Company.*)

1—GENERATOR AND EXCITER METAL-CLAD EQUIPMENT(S)

Rated 4160 volts, 2500 KVA

Each equipment consisting of:

1 Metal-clad stationary unit
1 Auxiliary compartment
2 Compartments, superstructure type
1 Ammeter, a-c indicating
1 Wattmeter, 3-phase indicating
1 Varmeter, 3-phase indicating
1 Field indicating ammeter, with shunt
1 3-phase ammeter transfer switch
1 3-phase voltmeter transfer switch
1 Synchronizing switch
1 Governor motor control switch (if required)
1 Circuit breaker control switch with lamps
1 Control power cutout
1 Electrically operated field breaker
1 Field breaker control switch, with lamps
1 Field rheostat control switch (if required)
  Provision for mounting exciter field rheostat
  Provision for mounting field discharge resistor

3 Time-overcurrent voltage restraint relays
1 Power circuit breaker, removable element
    type AM-5-150, 1,200 amp
    with d-c solenoid closing mechanism
1 Circuit breaker closing relay
1 Lock-out relay
3 Generator differential relays
1 Voltage regulator and accessories
1 Current transformer for voltage regulator
3 Potential transformers, connected line-to-line
    (one for voltage regulator)
3 Double secondary current transformers
3 Current transformers to be mounted in the external wye-
    connection of the generator leads by the purchaser
1 3-phase surge capacitor to be mounted at the generator
    terminals by the purchaser
1 Three-conductor pothead

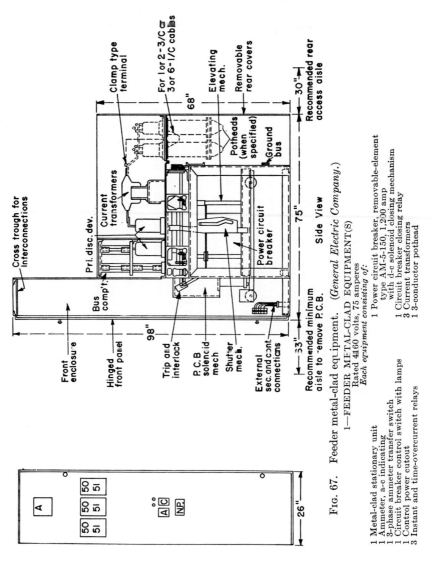

FIG. 67.   Feeder metal-clad equipment.   (*General Electric Company.*)

1—FEEDER METAL-CLAD EQUIPMENT(S)
Rated 4160 volts, 75 amperes
Each equipment consisting of:

1 Metal-clad stationary unit
1 Ammeter, a-c indicating
1 3-phase ammeter transfer switch
1 Circuit breaker control switch with lamps
1 Control power cutout
3 Instant and time-overcurrent relays

1 Power circuit breaker, removable-element
type AM-5-150, 1,200 amp
with d-c solenoid closing mechanism
1 Circuit breaker closing relay
3 Current transformers
1 3-conductor pothead

device, not shown on the isometric sketch, that slides a shutter over the holes through which the breaker studs have to go to enter the disconnecting devices. This shutter closes as soon as the breaker studs leave the disconnecting devices, and thus prevents contact of any kind with the live conductors of a panel while the circuit breaker is not in place.

Figure 68 shows a typical breaker and the details of the disconnecting device. The power cables are brought up through the floor at the rear part of each cubicle, and the control cables are brought up at the front. The control cables are accessible when the front panel is swung open. The power cables terminate in potheads. These devices have means for clamping or soldering the lead sheath of the cable to the outside of the pothead. The cable itself is carried to the inside of the pothead and to the terminals shown in detail in Fig. 69. After connections have been made inside the pothead, the pothead is filled with an insulating compound that effectively seals the cable against moisture.

Where this type of equipment is to be installed, the job for an electrical draftsman consists of making a one-line diagram for the plant, laying out the circuits, calculating the proper size of power cables, determining the size of conduits for the power and control cables, and then making a floor plan that shows the method of fastening the switchboard to the floor.

IMPORTANT 1951 NEC RULINGS THAT APPLY TO SWITCHBOARDS
(Numbers refer to sections)

	Chapter 1	3812	Grounding of Enclosures
1112	Working Space	3813	Large Knife Switches
	Chapter 2	3841	Where Rules Apply
2403	Overcurrent Protection of Equipment	3843	Rigid Support for Bus-bars and Conductors
	Chapter 3	3851	Location of Switchboards
3102	Conductor Insulation	3854–3855	Clearances
3462	Use of Rigid Metal Conduit	3856	Conductor Covering
3502	Use of Flexible Metallic Conduit		Chapter 5
		5001	Hazardous Locations
3701	Installation of Boxes and Fittings		Chapter 7
		7161	Live Parts to Be Grounded
3801	Switches in Grounded Conductors	7162	Isolation by Elevation
		7163	Working Space
3803	Enclosures for Switches		Chapter 9
3806–3807	Position of Knife Switches	93847	Spacing of Bare Metal Parts

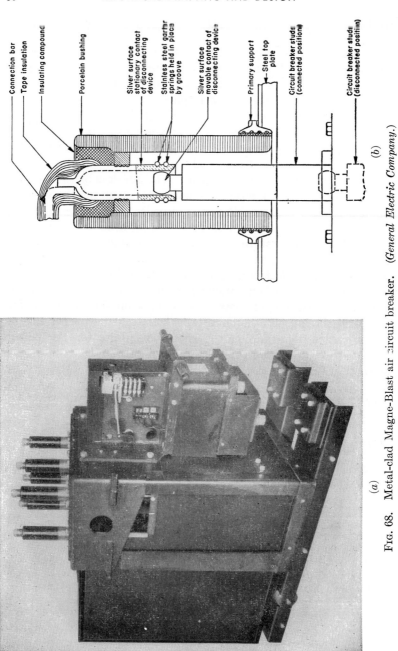

Connection bar
Tape insulation
Insulating compound
Porcelain bushing
Silver surface stationary contact of disconnecting device
Stainless steel garter springs held in place by groove
Silver surface movable contact of disconnecting device
Primary support
Steel top plate
Circuit breaker studs (connected position)
Circuit breaker studs (disconnected position)

(b)

(a)

FIG. 68. Metal-clad Magne-Blast air circuit breaker. (*General Electric Company.*)

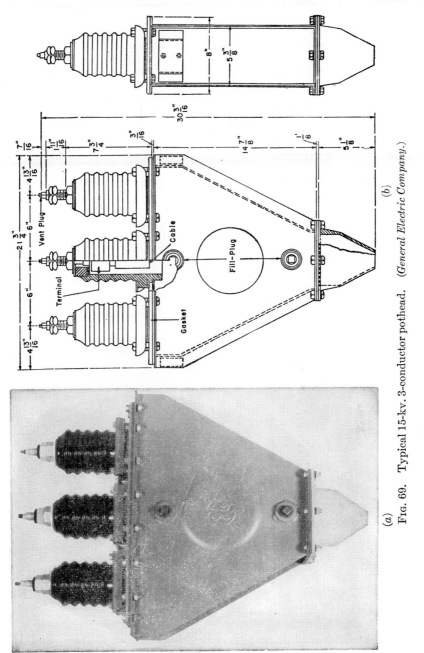

Fig. 69. Typical 15-kv. 3-conductor pothead. *(General Electric Company.)*

PROBLEMS

Equipment consisting of a generator and exciter panel similar to Fig. 66 is to be purchased and installed in a room that has a concrete floor. The generator is three-phase, 2,300-volt, 800-amp. Three feeder panels each of 75 amp capacity, similar to Fig. 67, are to be installed at present, and two more panels of larger capacity are to be installed later.

1. Make a one-line diagram for the job, including the two future panels.

2. Make a layout showing the switchboard in place, with provision for the two future panels. Allow suitable working space around the board.

3. Make a floor plan showing how you will fasten the switchboard to the floor. Show what size conduits you will use for the power and control cables and where you will locate them.

CHAPTER 5

OUTDOOR SUBSTATION

Purpose. The outdoor transformer substation shown in Fig. 70 is one of a very modern design, built of structural steel suitable

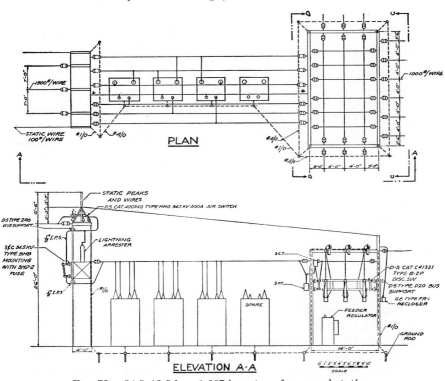

FIG. 70. 34.5–12.5 kv., 1,667-kva. transformer substation.

for supplying a village or large industrial plant. The isometric sketch of Fig. 71 shows clearly the wiring and the location of the various pieces of apparatus.

General Description. The incoming high-voltage lines go first to the air-break switches, then to the lightning arresters, then to the high-voltage fuses, then to the high-voltage buses, and finally to the primaries of the power transformers. The secondary or low-voltage leads from the transformers connect to the transformer buses. These buses go to two current transformers and then to two potential transformers. From the low-voltage buses four outgoing lines are taken off. Each line has disconnecting switches, a circuit recloser, and lightning arresters.

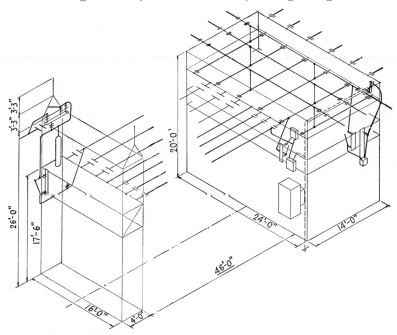

Fɪɢ. 71.   Isometric sketch of transformer substation.

High-voltage Side. The high-voltage insulators for the incoming lines are of the dead-end type similar to those shown in Table 42. The lightning arresters on the high-voltage side may be of any standard type, such as an oxide-film arrester. The power and metering transformers may also be of any standard type; the feeder regulator is automatic. All other apparatus is specified on the drawing.

The high-voltage air-break switch is Delta Star Type MK-40 shown in Fig. 72. This drawing also shows the Type ZRO bus

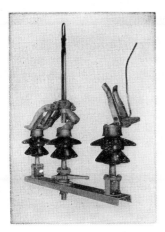

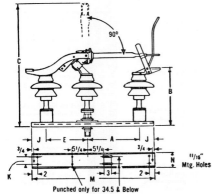

Type "MK-40" – Horn Gap – 69 Kv and Below
Upright Mounting

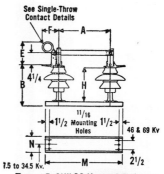

See Single-Throw
Contact Details

Type "B-2K" 69 Kv and Below

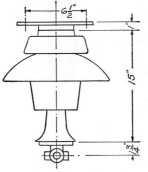

34.5KV. BUS SUPPORT
DELTA STAR TYPE ZRO

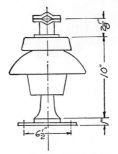

15 KV. BUS SUPPORT
DELTA STAR TYPE DZO

FIG. 72. Types MK-40 and B-2K switches and ZRO and DZO bus supports.
(*Delta Star Electric Company.*)

supports for supporting the wiring from the air-break switch to the high-voltage fuses and from the fuses to the buses. The high-voltage S & C Type BMD fuse mounting is shown with the details of a fuse in Fig. 73.

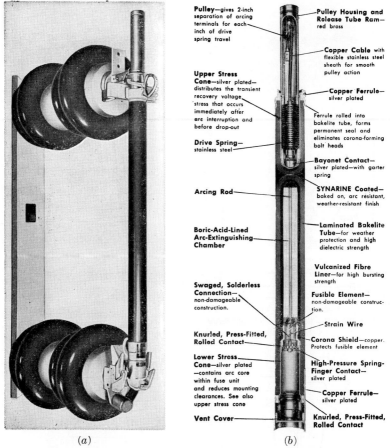

Pulley—gives 2-inch separation of arcing terminals for each inch of drive spring travel

Upper Stress Cone—silver plated—distributes the transient recovery voltage stress that occurs immediately after arc interruption and before drop-out

Drive Spring—stainless steel

Arcing Rod

Boric-Acid-Lined Arc-Extinguishing Chamber

Swaged, Solderless Connection—non-damageable construction.

Knurled, Press-Fitted, Rolled Contact

Lower Stress Cone—silver plated—contains arc core within fuse unit and reduces mounting clearances. See also upper stress cone

Vent Cover

Pulley Housing and Release Tube Ram—red brass

Copper Cable with flexible stainless steel sheath for smooth pulley action

Copper Ferrule—silver plated

Ferrule rolled into bakelite tube, forms permanent seal and eliminates corona-forming bolt heads

Bayonet Contact—silver plated—with garter spring

SYNARINE Coated—baked on, arc resistant, weather-resistant finish

Laminated Bakelite Tube—for weather protection and high dielectric strength

Vulcanized Fibre Liner—for high bursting strength

Fusible Element—non-damageable construction.

Strain Wire

Corona Shield—copper. Protects fusible element

High-Pressure Spring-Finger Contact—silver plated

Copper Ferrule—silver plated

Knurled, Press-Fitted, Rolled Contact

(a)   (b)

FIG. 73. Type BMD fuse mounting and fuse. (*S & C Electric Company.*)

Low-voltage Side. The low-voltage bus supports are of the dead-end type similar to those shown in Table 42. The post-type insulators used to carry the wiring to the circuit reclosers are Delta Star Type DZO and are shown in Fig. 72. The low-voltage lightning arresters, made by Hubbard and Company, are shown

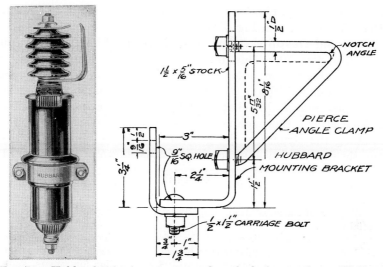

Fig. 74. Hubbard lightning arrester and method of mounting. (*Hubbard & Company.*)

Fig. 74a. Automatic Recloser Type FR-1, relayed. (*General Electric Company.*)

with mounting in Fig. 74. The circuit recloser, made by General Electric, is shown in Fig. 74a.

Plan and Elevation.   The general layout of the substation is shown in Fig. 70.   This drawing requires one elevation and a one-line diagram in order to make it complete.   The drawing of the one-line diagram and of the elevation constitutes the principal problem of this chapter.   These two drawings should be started after a thorough study has been made of the method of building the structure, the general arrangement of the wiring, and the details of each piece of apparatus shown in Figs. 72 to 74.

PROBLEMS

1. Using the standard symbols given in Chart 1, page 251, make a one-line diagram of the substation, properly lettering any symbols that require special notes.

2. Make a one-line diagram of the substation, showing the necessary switches if the feeder regulator is to be used.   The feeder regulator should have disconnecting switches to remove it from the line for repairs, and a short-circuiting switch to short-circuit it when not needed.

3. What type of connection is used on the primaries of the transformers?

4. What type of connection is used on the secondaries?

5. Refer to the plan and elevation A-A of Fig. 70, and make a drawing showing the elevation taken along line C-C.   The scale of this drawing is to be 3 ft 16 in. to the foot.   Check the distance of each conductor from the structural steel and also from any conductor of opposite polarity, to see that the spacing requirements called for in Table 71, page 216, are met.

6. Referring to your one-line diagram, draw an elevation D-D, showing how you would mount the switches if the feeder regulator were to be installed.   Check the conductors for spacing and also to see that they are rigidly supported to withstand a short circuit.

CHAPTER 6

RESIDENCE WIRING

In the wiring of a residence it is necessary to consider the arrangement of the lamps for convenience, utility, and decorative effect. Where the installation is very simple, the architect usually indicates the lamps, base plugs, heater plugs, switches, etc., by means of the standard symbols. A line is drawn from a lamp outlet to a switch, which indicates that the lamp is controlled from the switch to which the line is drawn.

The details of wiring, number of circuits, etc., are left to the electrician. Before installing the wiring, the electrician examines the plans and determines how many circuits he will use and which lamps he will put on the different circuits. The study can be done quickly and accurately by sketches showing all the lamps in their relative position and branch circuits running to the cut-out box, which is usually located in the basement.

If the installation is complicated by the use of special arrangements for switching, such as master switches and three- and four-way switches, the sketches should be worked out in considerable detail and each circuit studied carefully to see that the circuits are correct before the work of wiring is started.

Figures 75 to 80 show the electrical circuits of a small residence worked out in detail. There are four circuits, a fairly large number of wall and ceiling lamps, and a convenient and useful master-switching arrangement by which practically the whole house can be lighted from either the entrance to the living room or from the front or rear bedrooms upstairs. There is the usual three-way switch arrangement for controlling the stair lamps from either upstairs or downstairs.

The master switching is taken care of by installing three-way instead of two-way switches in each of the rooms where it is desired to have the lamps controlled by the master switches.

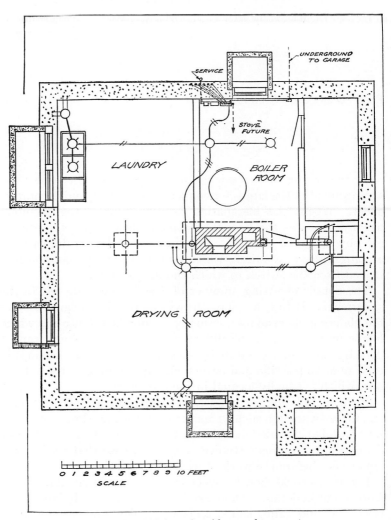

Fig. 75.   Wiring of residence—basement.

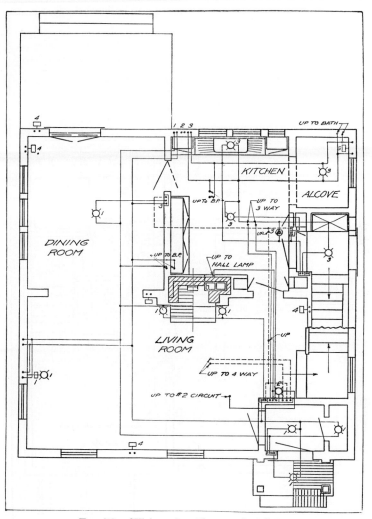

FIG. 76.   Wiring of residence—first floor.

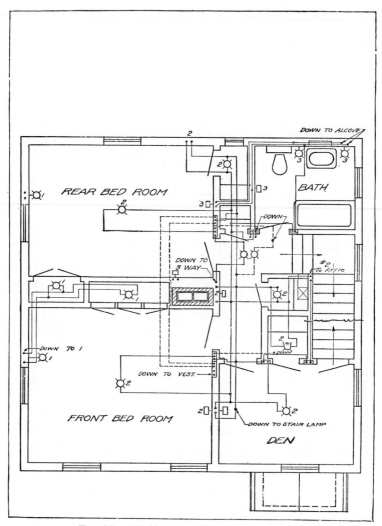

Fig. 77. Wiring of residence—second floor.

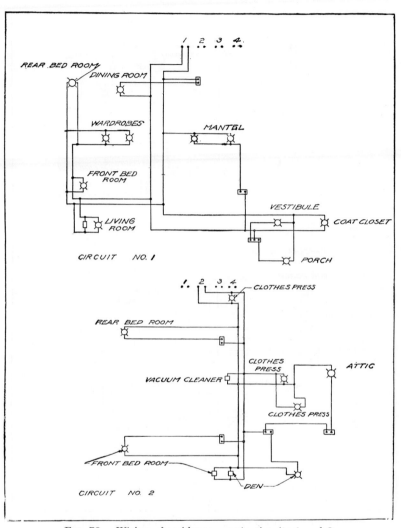

FIG. 78.   Wiring of residence—main circuits 1 and 2.

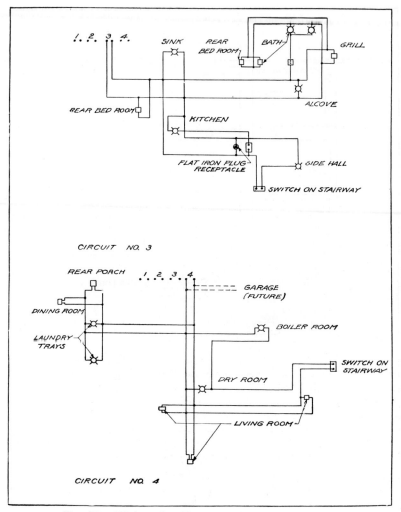

FIG. 79. Wiring of residence—main circuits 3 and 4.

The middle point of the three-way switch is connected in every case to the lamp itself. The left-hand points of each of the switches, as one faces them, are all connected together. The wire that connects them is shown by a dash line on the drawings. The right-hand point of each switch is connected to one wire of a branch circuit. In making this connection it is necessary that it be the same side of the line in every case. The master switches themselves are connected to the opposite side of the circuit and to

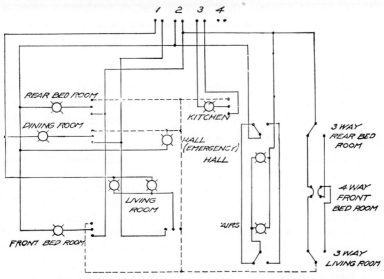

FIG. 80. Wiring of residence—emergency and hall light circuits.

the wire that connects all the switches together. The operation is as follows: Suppose all lamps are off. Each three-way switch contact is on the left-hand point of the switch and, therefore, in connection with the line joining all switches. If now a master switch is closed, current passes from one side of the line, through the lamps of all rooms mastered, to the other side of the line. If the lights are thrown on by a master switch, they must be thrown off by a master switch. It is not necessary, however, to throw them off by the same master switch. For instance, if lamps are thrown on downstairs, they may be thrown off upstairs. This is accomplished by using the ordinary three-point control, namely, a three-way switch at each of the end points and a four-way switch at the middle point. In this case the three-way switches are in the living room and rear bedroom and the four-way switch in the front bedroom.

In studying the drawings, it will be seen that the master-switch arrangement does not interfere with the switching of the lights in the separate rooms. For instance, starting as before with all lights out, suppose that the switch in the dining room is thrown. Connection is from the line to the right-hand point of the switch, to the lamp, and to the other side of the line.

If it should happen that another switch is thrown while a master switch is on, no harm will be done; a slight "wink" of the lamp will be noticed as the switch is thrown. The lamp will remain on after the master switch is again thrown to the OFF position.

Residence of W. M. Smith.[1] Figures 81 to 83 show the floor plans of a residence which has been circuited up in Figs. 84 and 85 in accordance with the specifications of the architect. The specifications are, briefly, as follows:

The service shall be three-wire, 120-volt, 120/240-volt, 60-cycle, single-phase. The service conductors shall terminate approximately 18 ft above ground level and are to be not smaller than No. 4 except that the neutral may be smaller if permitted by local regulations. The service switch shall be 100-amp and suitably fused. The panelboard shall be three-wire with terminals for two 35- to 60-amp fuses and receptacles for 14 fuse plugs. Approved circuit breakers may be substituted for switches and fuses.

At least six 15-amp circuits shall be provided for lights and convenience outlets in addition to those noted for appliance circuits in the dining room, breakfast nook, kitchen, and laundry. The total number of outlets shall be divided as equally as possible among these circuits. In the living room and all bedrooms the outlets shall be divided between two or more branch circuits.

Two appliance branch circuits shall be installed to supply all convenience outlets in the dining room, breakfast nook, kitchen, and laundry. These circuits shall not be smaller than No. 12 wire and shall not supply any other outlets.

A three-wire circuit not smaller than No. 6 shall be carried to the

[1] This residence wiring is described in the third edition of the "Handbook of Interior Wiring Design," by the Industry Committee on Interior Wiring Design, and is quoted by permission.

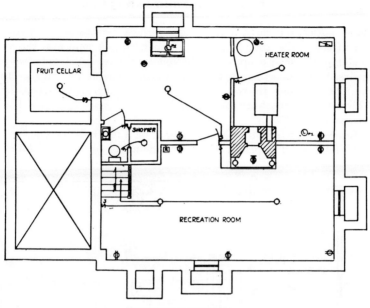

BASEMENT FLOOR PLAN

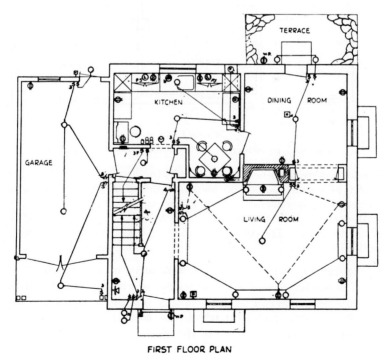

FIRST FLOOR PLAN

FIG. 81.   Residence of W. M. Smith—basement and first-floor plans.

range outlet and have a three-pole surface receptacle. A two-wire circuit not smaller than No. 12 shall be carried to a point near the water heater which shall operate on 240 volts and have a 250-volt two-pole enclosed disconnecting switch. A two-wire circuit not smaller than No. 12 shall supply the two bathroom heaters, which are to be 1500-watt, 120-volt, with two-heat control, and shall terminate in a steel box to enclose the heaters.

Bracket outlets in the bathroom shall be 5 ft above the floor and in the kitchen shall be placed 6 in. below the upper cupboards. All other

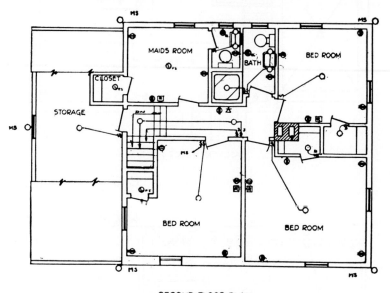

SECOND FLOOR PLAN

Fig. 82.   Residence of W. M. Smith—second-floor plan.

bracket outlets shall be 5 ft 6 in. above the floor. Wall switches shall be 4 ft above the floor. Convenience outlets shall be in the baseboard, except that convenience outlets in the kitchen, breakfast nook, and bathrooms shall be placed at suitable heights, in general, about 4 ft above the floor. The clock outlet shall be 7 ft above the floor, and the outlet for the washer near the laundry tubs shall be on the ceiling.

Figures 84 and 85 show the arrangement of the circuits as worked out for this job. The method of working out the circuits for this residence can be used for any building which has a large number of outlets and for which the architect has specified certain arrangements for some of the circuits.

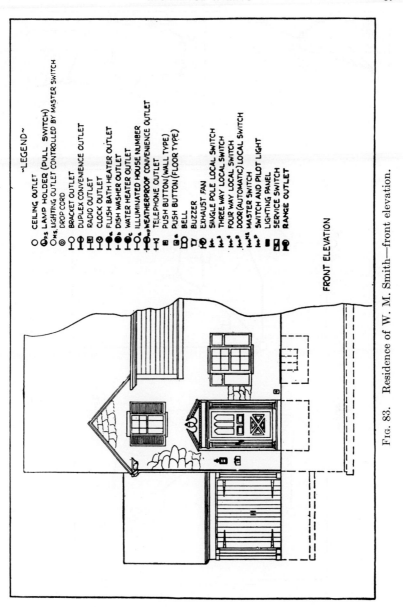

~LEGEND~

○ CEILING OUTLET
○PS LAMP HOLDER (PULL SWITCH)
○MS LIGHTING OUTLET CONTROLLED BY MASTER SWITCH
Ⓢ DROP CORD
○─ BRACKET OUTLET
⊖ DUPLEX CONVENIENCE OUTLET
⊙ RADIO OUTLET
⊡ CLOCK OUTLET
⊖ₕ FLUSH BATH HEATER OUTLET
⊖ₐ DISH WASHER OUTLET
⊖ᵥ WATER HEATER OUTLET
⊖ₑ ILLUMINATED HOUSE NUMBER
⊖ₙₚ WEATHERPROOF CONVENIENCE OUTLET
⊢⊣ TELEPHONE OUTLET
▣• PUSH BUTTON (WALL TYPE)
▣ PUSH BUTTON (FLOOR TYPE)
◖ BELL
◐ BUZZER
ↄ EXHAUST FAN
S SINGLE POLE LOCAL SWITCH
S³ THREE WAY LOCAL SWITCH
S⁴ FOUR WAY LOCAL SWITCH
Sᴅ DOOR (AUTOMATIC) LOCAL SWITCH
Sₘₛ MASTER SWITCH
Sₚ SWITCH AND PILOT LIGHT
▣ LIGHTING PANEL
▣ SERVICE SWITCH
◖ RANGE OUTLET

FRONT ELEVATION

FIG. 83. Residence of W. M. Smith—front elevation.

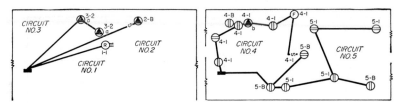

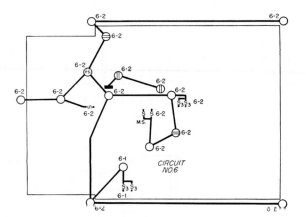

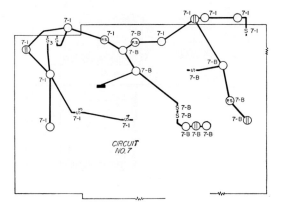

Fig. 84.   Residence of W. M. Smith—circuiting of outlets.

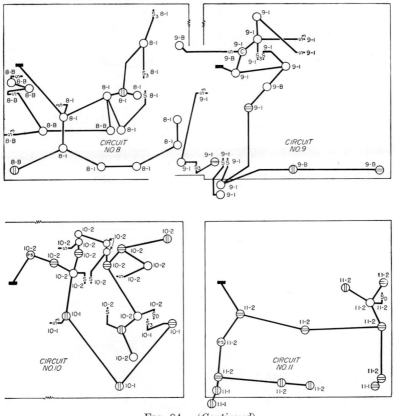

FIG. 84.—(*Continued*)

The procedure for circuiting is as follows: First, circuit up the outlets whose circuiting has been specified by the architect, giving an identification number to each circuit and outlet. On this job an outlet in the basement has a circuit number with a dash and the letter *B* following it; on the first floor, an outlet has the circuit number followed by a dash and 1. On the second floor an outlet has the circuit number followed by a dash and 2.

The circuits specified by the architect will be as follows:

Circuit 1: 1 range, 1st floor, 1-1
Circuit 2: 1 water heater, basement, 2-*B*
Circuit 3: 2 bathroom heaters, 2d floor, each 3-2
Circuit 4: 7 convenience outlets, basement and 1st floor, 4-1 and 4-*B*
Circuit 5: 7 convenience outlets, basement and 1st floor, 5-*B* and 5-1

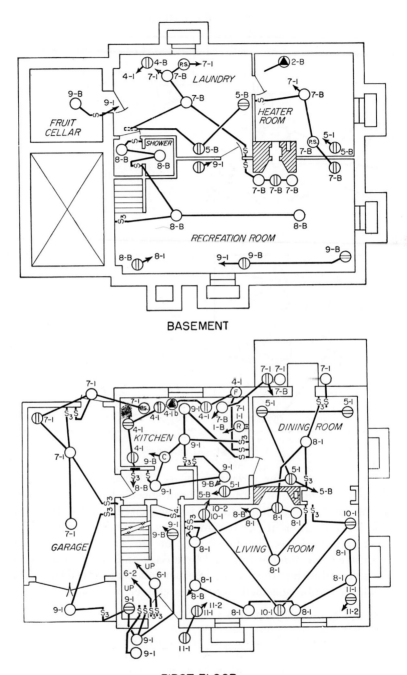

BASEMENT

FIRST FLOOR

Fig. 85. Residence of W. M. Smith—electrical plans and schedule of outlets.

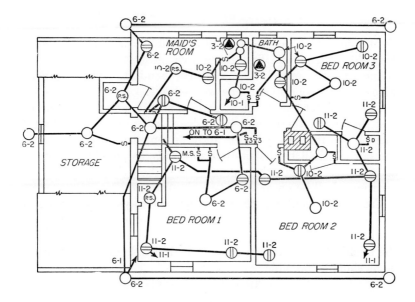

SECOND FLOOR

SCALE 0' 2' 4' 6' 8' 10' 12'

DESCRIPTION AND SYMBOL	RANGE	50A.3P. REC'P	HEATER	250V.30A. SW.	HEATER	2 BOXES	FAN	D.P. SWITCH	CONVENIENCE OUTLETS ○ ⓒ								LAMP OUTLETS ○							
CIRCUIT	1	1	2	2	3	3	4	4	4	5	6	7	8	9	10	11	4	5	6	7	8	9	10	11
BASEMENT	–	–	1	1	–	–	–	–	1	3	–	2	1	3	–	–	–	–	–	7	4	1	–	–
1st FLOOR	1	1	–	–	–	–	1	1	4	4	–	2	1	3	3	3	–	–	1	7	10	7	–	–
2nd FLOOR	–	–	–	–	2	2	–	–	–	–	4	–	–	–	9	6	–	–	10	–	–	–	9	2

DESCRIPTION AND SYMBOL	2 POLE SWITCHES								3 POLE SWITCHES								4 POLE SWITCHES							
CIRCUIT	4	5	6	7	8	9	10	11	4	5	6	7	8	9	10	11	4	5	6	7	8	9	10	11
BASEMENT	–	–	–	3	2	1	–	–	–	–	–	–	–	1	–	–	–	–	–	–	–	–	–	–
1st FLOOR	–	–	–	2	2	5	–	–	–	–	1	3	3	4	2	–	–	–	–	1	–	–	–
2nd FLOOR	–	–	3	–	–	–	6	1	–	–	1	1	–	–	–	–	–	–	–	–	–	–	–	–

SCHEDULE OF OUTLETS

FIG. 85.—(*Continued*)

73

Before circuiting up the remaining outlets, examine the plans of Figs. 81 and 82 and find the above outlets. The heavy lines connecting the outlets represent the conduit. The number of wires in each conduit is to be worked out.

The architect has specified that, in addition to the five circuits just described, there shall be at least six more circuits to take care of the remaining lamps and convenience outlets, and that the outlets shall be distributed as evenly as possible among the six circuits. It is further specified that the living room and each bedroom shall be on at least two circuits.

From this point on, there are several ways of circuiting the remaining outlets. Convenience and economy in the use of material should be considered in the final arrangement. From the standpoint of voltage drop, it is desirable also that the runs be as short as possible.

Switching. Examination of the floor plans shows 16 three-pole switches and 1 four-pole switch. These switches are for the control of lights from two places, with the exception of the first-and second-floor hall lights, where the lights are controlled from three places (see Chap. 2, Figs. 25 and 26). The plan of control for the garage is from the rear door and the side door leading into the house and from the front and side doors of the garage. The control for the lights in the halls on the first and second floors is from the front door and the rear end of the first-floor hall near the door leading into the garage, and from the second-floor hall.

The control for the basement stair lights is from the foot of the stairs in the basement and from the first-floor hall near the side door leading into the garage.

The switching of the basement and hall lights is clearly shown by the pictorial and diagrammatic sketch of Fig. 86. Simple sketches of the type shown in Fig. 86 will often clear up difficulties in understanding switching when only the symbols for the switches are shown on the plans.

Circuits to Be Specified by the Engineer. Having now met all the specifications of the architect as to the circuiting, the remaining outlets can be divided up as equally as possible among the circuits. In a job of this kind it is easy to forget an outlet or two and to find that, after the outlets are counted up by floors, they do not check with the outlets as counted up by circuits. The

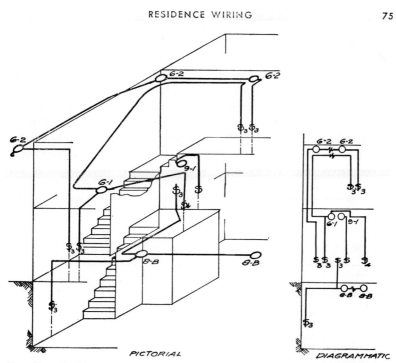

FIG. 86.   Residence of W. M. Smith—switching of basement and hall lights.

following method of counting the outlets is simple and will provide an accurate count for preparing the *Schedule of Outlets*
shown in Fig. 85.

Take each room by itself and total the outlets by room and by
circuit.   Taking the garage for example, we would have:

	Lamps	Convenience outlets	2-pole swiches	3-pole switches	4-pole switches
	4	1	1	4	0
Total................	4	1	1	4	0
Circuit 7-1...........	3	1	1	3	0
Circuit 9-1...........	1	0	0	1	0
Total..............	4	1	1	4	0

With the above method each room is checked as you proceed.
When the totals are tabulated on the schedule of outlets as in
Fig. 85, the totals by floors will equal the totals by circuits and
the outlets will all be properly listed.

Summary of Required Outlets for Residences. The drawings of Figs. 87 to 98 and the tabulated data accompanying the drawings give the number of outlets recommended, their location, and the location of the switches for the various rooms in residences. A complete discussion of residence lighting is covered in the "Handbook of Residential Wiring Design for Single Family Dwellings," prepared by the Industry Committee on Interior Wiring Design of the Edison Institute. The summary of required outlets is taken from the "Handbook" and quoted by permission of the Edison Institute.

Space	Lighting outlets	Type of circuit	Convenience outlets	Type of circuit	Special purpose outlets	Type of circuit
Living room, library, den, sun room	1 ceiling outlet, wall-switch-controlled, 2 outlets where room length exceeds width. Wall, cove, or valance outlets may be substituted.	Gen.	No point at wall line more than 6 ft from an outlet; wall spaces 3 ft or more to have outlet; outlet in mantle shelf. Two or more outlets switch-controlled.	Gen.		

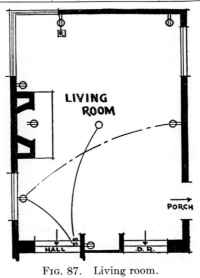

Fig. 87. Living room.

Space	Lighting outlets	Type of circuit	Convenience outlets	Type of circuit	Special purpose outlets	Type of circuit
Dining room, dinette, breakfast room	1 ceiling outlet, wall-switch-controlled.	Gen.	No point at wall line more than 10 ft from an outlet; wall spaces 3 ft or more to have outlet.	App.		

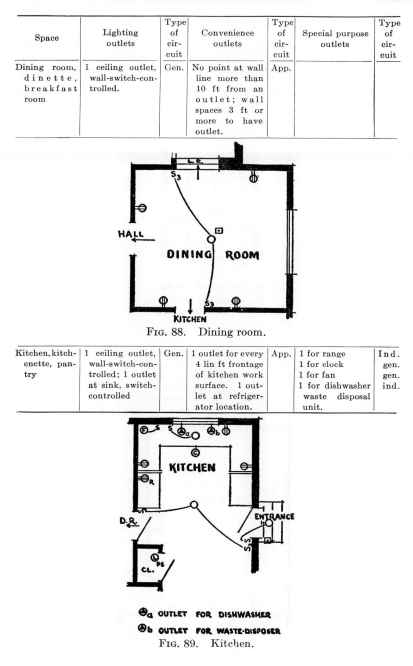

Fig. 88. Dining room.

| Kitchen, kitchenette, pantry | 1 ceiling outlet, wall-switch-controlled; 1 outlet at sink, switch-controlled | Gen. | 1 outlet for every 4 lin ft frontage of kitchen work surface. 1 outlet at refrigerator location. | App. | 1 for range
1 for clock
1 for fan
1 for dishwasher waste disposal unit. | Ind.
gen.
gen.
ind. |

ⓐₐ OUTLET FOR DISHWASHER

ⓐb OUTLET FOR WASTE-DISPOSER

Fig. 89. Kitchen.

Space	Lighting outlets	Type of circuit	Convenience outlets	Type of circuit	Special purpose outlets	Type of circuit
Laundry	1 ceiling outlet at washing center. 1 ceiling outlet at ironing center. Wall-switch control for one ceiling outlet	Gen.			1 for washer	App. or ind.
					1 for hand iron or ironer	app.

Ⓐc OUTLET FOR WASHER
Ⓐd OUTLET FOR HAND IRON
OR IRONER

FIG. 90.   Laundry.

Bedrooms	1 overhead outlet, wall-switch-controlled.	Gen.	No point at wall line more than 6 ft from an outlet. Wall spaces 3 ft or more to have outlet.	Gen.		

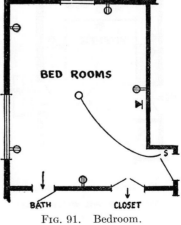

FIG. 91.   Bedroom.

Space	Lighting outlets	Type of circuit	Convenience outlets	Type of circuit	Special purpose outlets	Type of circuit
Bathrooms, lavatories	1 outlet each side mirror, wall-switch-controlled. 1 ceiling outlet in shower compartment, wall-switch-controlled 1 ceiling outlet in rooms 60 sq ft and over, wall-switch-controlled.	Gen.	1 near mirror.	Gen.		

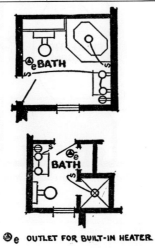

⊕e OUTLET FOR BUILT-IN HEATER

Fig. 92. Bath.

Space	Lighting outlets	Type of circuit	Convenience outlets	Type of circuit	Special purpose outlets	Type of circuit
Recreation room	1 ceiling outlet for each 150 sq ft of floor area, wall-switch-controlled. Wall, cove, or valance outlets may be substituted.	Gen.	No point at wall line more than 10 ft from an outlet; wall spaces 3 ft or more to have outlet; outlet in mantle shelf.	Gen.		

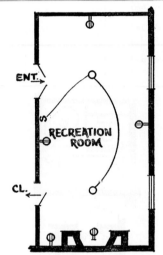

Fig. 93.   Recreation room.

Space	Lighting outlets	Type of circuit	Convenience outlets	Type of circuit	Special purpose outlets	Type of circuit
Closets	1 outlet in closets 3 ft or more deep or having a floor area of 10 sq ft or more.	Gen.				

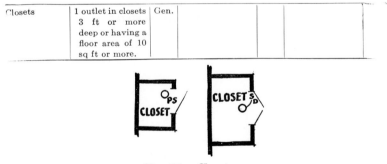

Fig. 94.   Closets.

Space	Lighting outlets	Type of cir- cuit	Convenience outlets	Type of cir- cuit	Special purpose outlets	Type of cir- cuit
Basement util- ity space	1 outlet for each enclosed space, 1 for work bench and 1 for fur- nace location. Sufficient addi- tional outlets to provide 1 for each 150 sq ft of open space.	Gen.	1 at work bench location, 1 at furnace location.	Gen.	1 for electrical equipment used in connection with furnace op- eration.	Ind.

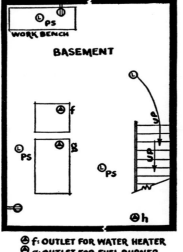

⊕ f: OUTLET FOR WATER HEATER
⊕ g: OUTLET FOR FUEL BURNER
⊕ h: OUTLET FOR HOME FREEZER

FIG. 95.   Basement.

Space	Lighting outlets	Type of circuit	Convenience outlets	Type of circuit	Special purpose outlets	Type of circuit
Covered porches	1 outlet for each 150 sq ft porch floor, wall-switch-controlled.	Gen.	1 for each 15 lin ft of house wall bordering porch.	Gen.		

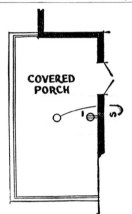

FIG. 96.   Covered porch.

Space	Lighting outlets	Type of circuit	Convenience outlets	Type of circuit	Special purpose outlets	Type of circuit
Halls	1 outlet for each 15 lin ft, wall-switch-controlled.	Gen.	1 for each 15 lin ft.	Gen.		
Stairways	1 outlet on each floor, illuminating head and foot of stairway. Each outlet to have separate switch control at the head and foot of stairway.	Gen.				
Reception hall	1 ceiling outlet, wall-switch-controlled. Wall, cove, or valance outlets may be substituted.	Gen.	No point at wall line more than 10 feet from an outlet; wall spaces 3 ft or more to have outlet.	Gen.		
Exterior entrances (front and trade)	1 or 2 outlets, wall-switch-controlled.	Gen.	1 at front entrance.	Gen.		

Space	Lighting outlets	Type of circuit	Convenience outlets	Type of circuit	Special purpose outlets	Type of circuit
Accessible attics	1 outlet, wall-switch-con-trolled. 1 outlet for each enclosed space.	Gen.	1 for general use.	Gen.		

Fig. 97.   Entrance.

| Garage | 1 interior wall switched outlet for one- or two-car garage, plus 1 for each additional two cars. 1 outlet for exterior lighting, multiple switch controlled if garage is detached from house. | Gen. | 1 for one- or two-car garage, plus 1 for each additional two cars. | Gen. | | |

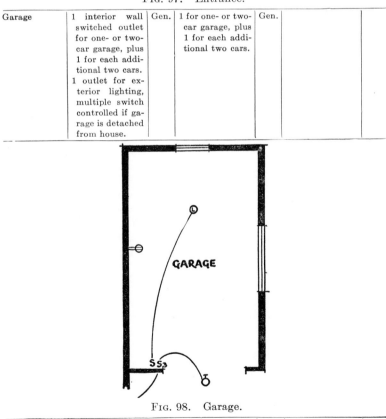

Fig. 98.   Garage.

| Terraces and patios | | | 1 for each 15 lin ft of house wall bordering porch. | Gen. | | |

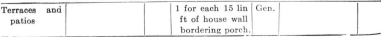

The master switching of this residence is different from that of the residence previously described and shown in Figs. 75 to 80. In the present residence the purpose of the master switch is to enable the owner to floodlight the grounds from a switch in the master bedroom. The master switching can easily be carried further by using the scheme shown in Fig. 80 to master swich one emergency light in each principal room.

PROBLEMS

The following problems refer to the plans of the bungalow shown in Figs. 99 and 100.

1. Make a layout of a board suitable for mounting the meter, switch, and fuse box, to conform to the requirements of your local ordinance.

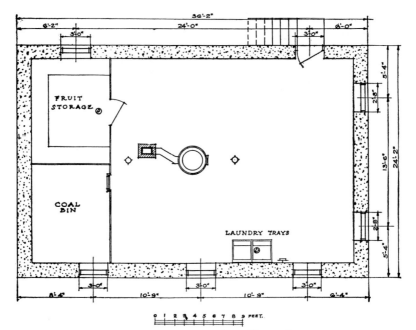

FIG. 99.   Basement plan of bungalow.

2. Following the general plan shown in Figs. 84 and 85, circuit up the lamps, switches, and convenience outlets for the bungalow, using four circuits. Arrange circuits so that at least one light in each room may be master-switched from the front entrance, or the side entrance, and both bedrooms.

3. Make an isometric or oblique projection sketch of each circuit by itself; and mark on each horizontal, vertical, or slanting run the number of feet of BX cable needed. Total the number of feet of cable for the job.

4. Total the number of lamp outlet boxes.

5. Total the number of boxes for switches and convenience outlets: single, double, triple, etc.

6. Total the number of switches: single-pole, three-pole, four-pole, etc.

7. Assuming that the lighting fixtures are to be selected by the owner and are to be on a separate contract, what other material such as bushings, switch plates, etc., will be necessary for the completion of this job, and how many of each?

8. Tabulate all material systematically in a bill of material so that everything needed can be ordered out for the job.

9. Referring to Fig. 84, show the actual wires needed to circuit up circuit 7. Follow the method shown in Fig. 118 in circuiting the lights of the office building.

10. Show the actual wiring for circuit 6.

11. Show the wiring and the switches to be added to enable the owner to light one emergency light in the first- and second-floor halls, living room, dining room, kitchen, and in each bedroom. These lights are to be turned on and off from either the front entrance or the master bedroom.

12. Referring to Figs. 81 and 82, lay out the telephone wiring for the residence.

13. Referring to Fig. 81, lay out the bell wiring for the residence.

IMPORTANT 1951 NEC RULINGS THAT APPLY TO THESE JOBS
(Numbers refer to sections)

Chapter 1
1117–1118 Connections to Terminals—Splices

Chapter 2
2002 Connection to Grounded System
2004 Connections to Screw Shells
2005 Means of Identification of Conductors
2115–2116 Branch Circuits Required—Calculation of Load
2121a, b Conductors: Carrying Capacity—Minimum size
2122 Overcurrent Protection
2124 Receptacle Outlets Required
2125 Maximum Load—Motor Operated Appliances
2126 Permissible Loads

2202 Voltage Drop—Feeders
2304 Size of Service Conductors
2357 Rating of Service Switch
2371 Overcurrent Protection—Where Required
2403 Overcurrent Protection of Conductors—Fuses
2512–2514 Grounding
2525 Conductor to Be Grounded

Chapter 3
3005–3008 Wiring Details
3011 Conductors of Different Systems
3462 Rigid Metal Conduit—Use
3482 Electrical Metallic Tubing—Use
3502 Flexible Metal Conduit—Use
3702–3706 Outlet Boxes

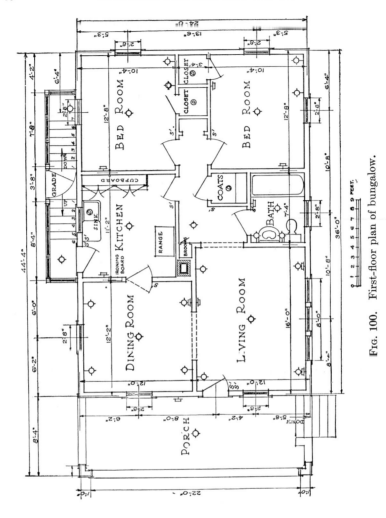

Fig. 100. First-floor plan of bungalow.

IMPORTANT 1951 NEC RULINGS THAT APPLY TO THESE JOBS—*(Continued)*

(Numbers refer to sections)

3708   Pull and Junction Boxes

3732–3733   Cabinets and Cutout
         Boxes—Damp Locations

3802   Switches—Wiring

Chapter 4

4003   Use of Flexible Cords

4241   Control and Protection of
         Appliances

CHAPTER 7

LAYING OUT WIRING

Motor Wiring for a Machine Shop with Individual Motor Drive. The purpose of this layout job is to show how the wiring is laid out in a machine shop where all the machines have individual motors and push-button starters similar to those shown in Table 67 mounted directly on the machines. The plan view of Fig. 101 shows the machine shop as originally laid out for 220 volts d-c. The job is to modernize the shop, using 208-volt three-phase 60-cycle current, but to use the old cabinet and conduits if possible.

Before proceeding with the redesign of the circuits, the following details of the original layout should be studied:

1. The location of the cabinet. The cabinet was placed near the northeast corner of the shop so that it would be as near as possible to the main switchboard. The plan and elevation of the cabinet show clearly how high it is mounted and just where the conduits are brought into the cabinet. It should be noted that the height of mounting of the cabinet and the height of the conduit stubs are given by elevations. This method of locating heights is often used, since it gives heights from some definite base line or grade and does not depend on measurements taken from the floor which, in this case, was not in until after the conduits and cabinet were installed.

2. The method of dimensioning the center lines of conduit stubs should also be noted. On this job it was found that the brick walls would be in at the time of installation of the conduit, so that the dimensions were taken from the walls. There is always a question as to whether to dimension the conduits individually from the wall or whether to dimension them as shown in Fig. 101. If the dimensions are taken each time from the wall, an error in locating one conduit does not throw off all the others.

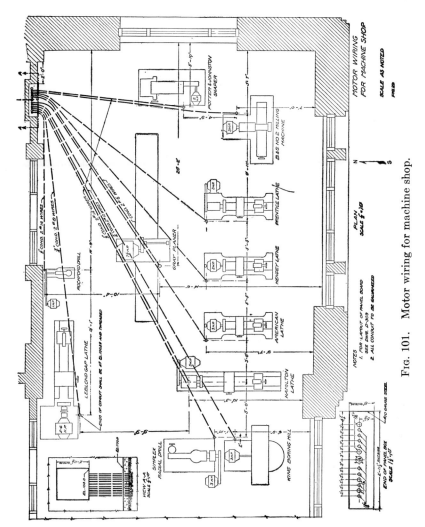

Fig. 101. Motor wiring for machine shop.

On this job, the dimensions from one machine to the next were considered the important ones; so they were "strung" lengthwise of the room, but crosswise each time from one wall for each group of machines, except for the Simplex radial drill and the King boring mill, for which the distance between conduit centers was the important dimension. Because it is desirable that the Rockford drill and the LeBlond lathe be rather accurately located in relation to the north wall, dimensions to the north wall would be more desirable than the method shown. If both methods of dimensioning are used, the 9 ft 9 in. dimension and the 10 ft 4 in. dimension should be marked ≠ to show that if there is a

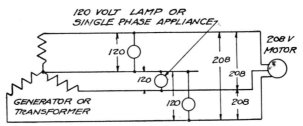

Fig. 102. Method of obtaining three-phase power and single-phase light from a three-phase circuit.

slight variation in the dimensions to the walls, those two dimensions are the ones to change.

Before figuring the size of wires to use, the reason for the 208-volt motors should be clearly understood. The plan of distribution that is becoming almost universal now is to use three-phase four-wire circuits and to take both power and balanced lighting from them. As lighting is standardized at 120 volts, this voltage is the starting point of the method, and the 208 volts is the natural result of using 120 volts for lights. The reason for the 208 volts is clearly shown by Fig. 102. The motors are taken off lines 1, 2, and 3; and the lighting circuits are balanced as nearly as possible across each line 1, 2, and 3 and the neutral or line 4. In this way the load on the transformers is practically balanced. The 208 volts comes from the fact that the voltage from line to line is the *geometrical* or *vector* difference between two phase voltages 120 deg apart. This can easily be seen by drawing two equal lines, say ten units long, at an angle of 120 deg with each other to represent phase voltages, and by reversing one. Then construct a parallelogram on these two lines as adjacent sides and draw the long diagonal which will be the resultant of the two voltages in magnitude and phase. This line will measure 1.73 times either of the original lines. If the original lines are 120 units long, the diagonal will be 120×1.73, or 208. The reason that the two voltages are subtracted by reversing one line or *vector* is easily seen by thinking of the two 120-volt phase voltages as two batteries with their plus sides connected together at the neutral. The voltage across the two lines will be the difference of the battery voltages and not their sum. In an a-c circuit the phase as well as the magnitude of the voltages has to be considered.

Data Sheet of Wires, Conduits, and Circuit Breakers. On this job it is proposed to use Westinghouse multibreakers and a Westinghouse panelboard and cabinet. The first step is to prepare a table of motor sizes and rated amperes and then a column of 125 per cent amperes, because the Code requires that the wiring of a single motor shall be designed for 125 per cent of the full-load current of the motor. Having found the proper current, look up the proper wire size in Table 54 and then the proper conduit size to carry three wires to each motor in Table 61. As small circuit breakers are made only in certain sizes, we select 15-, 25-, and 35-amp breakers for this job. Figure 103 is the complete data sheet. The next step is to check the conduit size in the data sheet just prepared against the conduit originally installed on the job; if the old conduit is large enough, it will be used. If some of it is not large enough, mark definitely the new size and its location on the floor plan, and the spot where it comes up into the cabinet.

The last step of the work is to select a panelboard from Table 70. The method of determining the size of the panelboard and cabinet is completely shown by a study of the table.

PROBLEMS

1. Make a drawing to show the dimensions of the panelboard you select from Table 70. Mark all dimensions according to the method given in the table.

2. If the panelboard will go in the old box, make a drawing to show how you will support it.

3. Make a complete drawing of the machine shop, showing all the conduits and the cabinet properly dimensioned as called for in your new layout of Problem 1.

4. What size feeder would you use to supply the panelboard, to meet the Code ruling as to a conductor that supplies several motors?

DATA ON WIRES, CONDUITS & BREAKERS FOR MACHINE SHOP

1	2	3	4	5	6	7	8
ITM	MACHINE	H.P.	RATED AMP	125% AMP	WIRE SIZE	COND. SIZE	BK'R. SIZE
1	ROCKFORD DRILL	1	4.2	5.25	14	$\frac{1''}{2}$	15
2	POTTER & JOHNSON SHAPER	2	7.8	9.25	14	$\frac{1''}{2}$	15
3	B. & S. MILLING MACHINE	3	9.54	11.9	14	$\frac{1''}{2}$	15
4	PRENTICE LATHE	3	9.54	11.9	14	$\frac{1''}{2}$	15
5	HENDEY LATHE	3	9.54	11.9	14	$\frac{1''}{2}$	15
6	AMERICAN LATHE	3	9.54	11.9	14	$\frac{1''}{2}$	15
7	KING BORING MILL	3	9.54	11.9	14	$\frac{1''}{2}$	15
8	SIMPLEX RADIAL DRILL	3	9.54	11.9	14	$\frac{1''}{2}$	15
9	HAMILTON LATHE	5	18	22.6	10	$\frac{3''}{4}$	25
10	LE BLOND GAP LATHE	5-6	26.4	33	8	$\frac{3''}{4}$	35
11	GRAY PLANER	7.5	26.4	33	8	$\frac{3''}{4}$	35
12	SPARE	10	32.4	40.5	8	$\frac{3}{4}$	50

COL. 4 AMPS – 1949 CODE – 208 VOLT, 3 PH MOTORS
COL. 6 RUBBER COVERED – TYPE R
COL. 7 1949 CODE
COL. 8 WESTINGHOUSE MULTI BREAKER

FIG. 103. Data on wires, conduits, and breakers for machine shop.

5. If the panelboard is 200 ft from the switchboard and loaded up to 70 per cent of the panelboard capacity with a load at 80 per cent power factor, what will be the drop in volts from the switchboard to the panelboard? What will be the per cent drop? Is the per cent drop within the allowable limit for a circuit that supplies only a power load?

Mill Room. Figure 104 shows the plan of a mill room where lumber is to be cut up to send to various woodworking shops. The motors of the planer and ripsaw are directly connected to

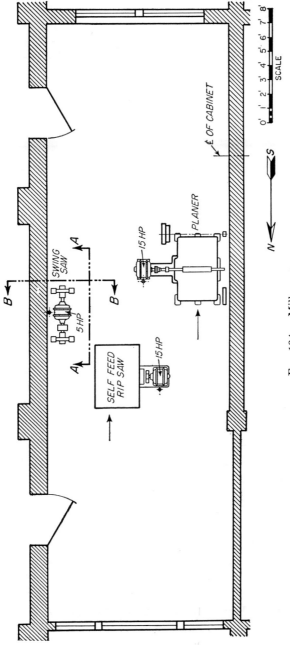

Fig. 104.   Mill room.

(a)   *(b)*

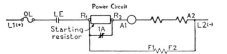

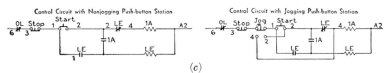

(c)

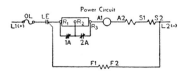

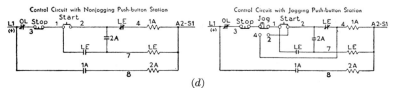

(d)

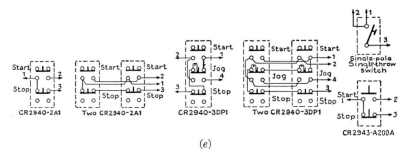

(e)

Fig. 105.   Type CR4061-A1A and CR4061-A1C reduced voltage d-c starter. *(General Electric Company)*

the machines. The motor of the swing saw is mounted 10 ft above the floor of the room. All machines have automatic starters of the type shown in Figs. 105 and 106. The voltage is 220 volts d-c.

The CR4061-A1C magnetic starter shown in Fig. 105 is made by the General Electric Company and is for constant-speed, nonreversing d-c motors without dynamic braking. Figures 105c and d show the schematic or elementary wiring diagrams for controllers with one and two resistances, respectively. Referring to (d), pressing the START button energizes the coil of the accelerating contactors 1A and 2A. A normally open interlock on the final accelerating contactor closes and energizes the coil of the line contactor LE which connects the motor to the line with all resistance in the armature circuit.

A normally closed interlock on the line contactor deenergizes the coil of 1A which drops out after a preset time delay, thus cutting out the first block of resistance, R1-R2. On the CR4061-A1C starter, an interlock on 1A deenergizes the coil of 2A, which drops out after a preset time delay and cuts out the remaining block of resistance. When all the resistance is cut out by 1A, or 1A and 2A, the motor is directly across the line. When the STOP button is pressed, the holding circuit is broken, thus dropping out LE and removing the motor from the line.

If the overload relay is tripped, interlock OL breaks the holding circuit of coil LE and removes the motor from the line.

If it is desired to "jog" or "inch" the motor, that is, to turn it slightly from rest to give a small movement to the driven machine, the JOG button is pressed. Contactor 1A picks up, causing 2A to pick up in turn. An interlock on 2A closes and picks up line contactor LE. LE cannot seal in, since the seal-in circuit is broken by the normally closed contacts of the JOG button.

PROBLEMS

1. Locate the cabinet near the southwest corner of the room at the point marked "CL of Cabinet."

2. Prepare a table of wires and conduit sizes.

3. Draw to scale an elevation of the swing saw looking east, as shown by A-A, and a section looking north, as shown by B-B. On these elevations, show clearly where you will mount the push-button station and what type of conduits, condulets, etc., you would use to make a first-class job of wiring.

DIMENSIONS (For Estimating Only)

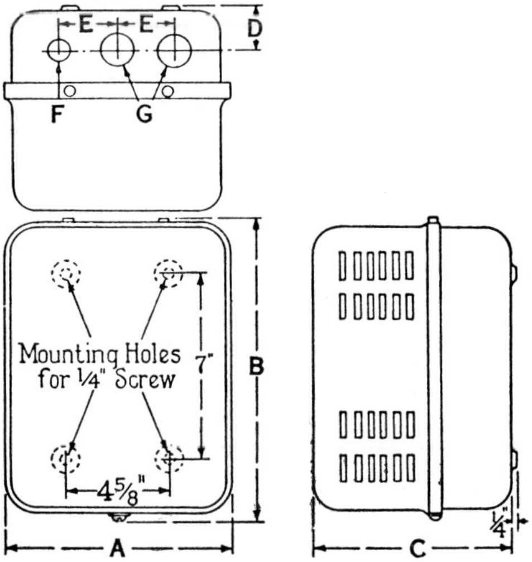

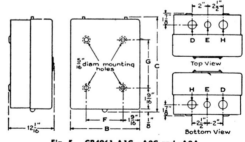

Fig. 3. CR4061-A1A

Rating	Part No.	Dimensions in Inches						
		A	B	C	D	E	F	G
½ through 3 Hp 115 or 230 volts	1	8 9/32	12	7 1/32	1 55/64	2 1/4	3/4	3/4
3 Hp 230 volts only	2	9 5/16	13 1/2	7 5/16	1 3/4	1 1/2	1/2	3/4

Fig. 5. CR4061-A1C, -A2C and -A3A
CR4161-A1C, -A2C and -A3A

Symbol	Part No.	Dimensions in Inches						
		B	C	D	E	F	G	H
CR4061-A1C	4	12 1/4	18 7/8	3/4 & 1 1/4	1/2 & 3/4	9 1/4	15 3/4	1 & 1 1/2
CR4061-A2C and -A3A CR4161-A1C -A2C and -A3A	5	14 1/4	23 7/8	3/4 and 1 1/4	1/2 and 3/4	11 1/2	20 3/4	1 and 1 1/2

FIG. 106. Dimensions of CR4061 reduced voltage d-c starters. *(General Electric Company.)*

Knockouts in top and bottom for 3/4" conduit 1 1/2" conduit
5/16" diam

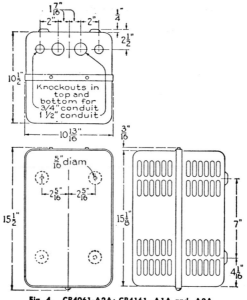

Fig. 4. CR4061-A2A; CR4161 -A1A and -A2A CR7505-W3A or -W4A and CR7507F101

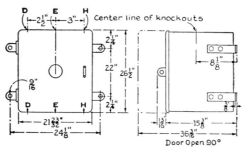

D
E
H
Center line of knockouts
Door Open 90°

Fig. 6. CR4061-A3C and CR4161-A3C

Symbol	Part No.	Dimensions in Inches		
		D	E	H
CR4061-A3C CR4161-A3C	6	1 and 1½	½ and ¾	2 and 2½

FIG. 106. *(Continued)*

4. Locate the conduits on the plan, giving their size and the number and size of the wires in each conduit.

5. Make a layout of the required cabinet and panelboard in sufficient detail to enable a contractor to compute the cost of the cabinet and panelboard.

6. Check your drawing carefully to see that every item necessary for an estimate on the whole wiring job is properly drawn or noted on the drawing.

Carpentry Shop. The carpentry shop shown in Fig. 107 was originally on direct current and had an old type of automatic

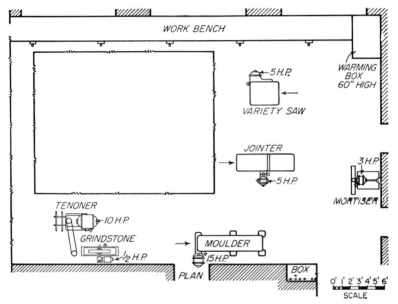

Fig. 107.   Carpentry shop.

starter on four of the machines and ordinary rheostats on the others. The old starters were mounted in a cabinet $56\frac{3}{4}$ in. wide, $56\frac{1}{4}$ in. high, and $21\frac{1}{8}$ in. deep, inside. This cabinet is shown near the lower right-hand corner of the plan. The conduits to the machines were of the following sizes:

Tenoner. . . . . 1 in.
Grindstone. . . . . $\frac{1}{2}$ in.
Moulder. . . . . $1\frac{1}{4}$ in.
Jointer. . . . . 1 in.
Variety saw. . . . . 1 in.
Mortiser. . . . . $\frac{1}{2}$ in.
Warming box. . . . . $\frac{3}{4}$ in.

The old feeder is No. 3/0 and the cabinet is 150 ft from the switchboard.

It is proposed to modernize the shop by putting it on 440 volts three-phase 60-cycle alternating current and to use push-button starters of the type shown in Table 67 on each machine. The cabinet will be used for the housing of the panelboard, and the old conduits will be used if they are large enough for the three wires of the new three-phase circuits.

PROBLEMS

1. Make a table of wire, conduit, and circuit-breaker sizes for each machine, similar to that of Fig. 103, and check with the old conduit sizes to be sure that the old conduits are large enough for the three wires of the new three-phase circuits. Explain how you would determine the size of the wire for the warming box which requires 5,500 watts.

2. Lay out a panelboard for all the present circuits and one spare. Obtain the size of circuit breakers from Table 70.

3. Show the angle-iron framing by which you will mount the panelboard in the cabinet that originally contained the starters.

Note: The final finished drawing of the panelboard and cabinet is to be drawn to the scale of 1 in. = 1 ft in the space just above the tenoner shown on the plan in Fig. 107.

Before making the final drawing, make a large-scale skeleton drawing of the panelboard on a separate sheet. Show the center lines of the buses, switches, and fuses; and check for allowable spacing of live parts, for convenience in operating the switches and for safety in replacing fuses. Then draw the cabinet, the panelboard, and the framing in the space above the tenoner to the scale of 1 in. = 1 ft. Show a front view, a side elevation just inside the cabinet, and a plan view of the bottom of the cabinet, giving the size and spacing of holes for the conduit. If some of the old conduits are not large enough for the wires of the three-phase circuits, show the size needed to carry the new wires.

4. Make a finished drawing of the whole job, including the conduits to the machines and the location of the stub-up at each machine.

5. Calculate the drop in the feeder from the switchboard to the panelboard, assuming that the current is 280 amp and the power factor 80 per cent. What is the allowable drop in a circuit that supplies a panelboard when the board is for power only?

Cabinet Shop with Lighting and Power on One Panelboard.

The cabinet shop shown in Fig. 108 is to have both power and light on the same panelboard. Figure 102 shows how three-phase 208-volt motors may be operated across lines 1, 2, and 3, and how 120-volt lamps, small single-phase motors, and small equipment may be operated across the neutral and one or all of

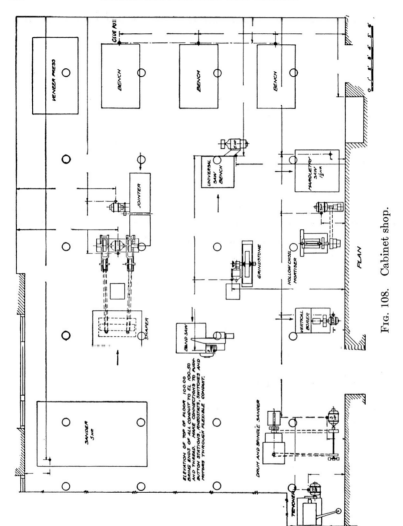

Fig. 108.   Cabinet shop.

lines 1, 2, and 3. In order to make this possible on a job, it is only necessary to carry the neutral to the panelboard in addition to the regular phase wires, 1, 2, and 3. On this job the wattage of the lamps has been computed by the methods of Chap. 8, on Illumination; the lamps should be circuited up so that there will not be more than 1,500 watts on any one circuit.

This job works out for three circuits, which can therefore be balanced across the phases: one circuit from 1 to N, one circuit from 2 to N and one from 3 to N. The panelboard must have a neutral bus.

The Code requires that the size of the wire to an individual motor shall be computed for 125 per cent full-load motor current. The motors are 208-volt and all are three-phase, 60-cycle. The starters are of the push-button type and are located directly on the machines, so there are only three wires to each motor. The lamps are 120-volt and each lamp circuit has but two wires. To simplify the job, the lamps are switched from the panelboard only. On this job breakers instead of fuses are to be used on each circuit. The size of the conduit is to be taken from Table 61, page 200.

PROBLEMS

In solving these problems, follow the general method used in the three preceding problems.

1. Compute the size of wires, conduits, and circuit breakers for the motors and gluepots.

2. Specify the proper size of push-button starters for each motor.

3. Allowing 200 watts per outlet, circuit up the lamps and compute the proper size of wire and conduit for each circuit.

4. Specify a suitable panelboard from Table 70, page 214.

5. Make a finished drawing of the cabinet shop, giving all conduit and wire sizes and locations, the location of each starter and its size, and complete information about the panelboard and cabinet so that, with the exception of the lighting fixtures, a contractor can estimate the job and install it from the information given on your drawing only.

IMPORTANT 1951 NEC RULINGS THAT APPLY TO THESE JOBS
(Numbers refer to sections)

	Chapter 1	2005	Means of Identification of
1112	Working Space about Electrical Equipment		Conductors
		2008	Identification of Terminals
	Chapter 2	2103	Rating of Branch Circuits
2001–2002	Connection to Grounded System	2121	Carrying Capacity of Conductors

MPORTANT 1951 NEC RULINGS THAT APPLY TO THESE JOBS—*(Continued)*
(Numbers refer to sections)

2201	Feeder Sizes	4343	Several Motors on One Branch
2203	Calculation of Load		
2403	Overcurrent Protection	4512	Overcurrent Protection
2511, 2514, 2525, 2594 Grounding			Chapter 5
	Chapter 3	5001, 5006 Hazardous Locations	
3005	Continuous Runs	5054	Wiring Methods
3011	Conductors of Different Systems	5076	Motors and Generators Chapter 6
3102	Conductor Insulation	6711	Wiring Methods for Machine Tools
3462	Rigid Metal Conduit		
3471	Number of Bends	6741	Branch Circuit Protection
3482	Electrical Metallic Tubing	6752	Grounding
3502	Flexible Metal Conduit		Chapter 7
3702	Use of Round Boxes Chapter 4	7161	Guarding Live Parts Chapter 9
4312	Branch Circuits for Motors	94304	Meaning of Code Letters on Motors
4326	Location of Fuses		

CHAPTER 8

ILLUMINATION

General. A previous chapter had to do with the placing of lamps in a residence for convenience and with the circuiting of the lamps to meet the requirements of the National Electrical Code. In the present chapter, methods are explained by which the proper type and size of lamp and reflector can be selected to give the correct illumination in a room where a given kind of work is to be done.

In order that the reader may have a variety of practical lighting problems in which he can see the application of the methods outlined, an office building that has a basement and three floors has been chosen as the principal problem of this chapter. The third floor has been completely worked out as a guide for the reader to follow in working out the other floors; the second floor has been partly worked out, while the basement and first floor have been left as problems for the reader to work out entirely by himself.

The tables from which the calculations have been made have been taken from the 1951 edition of the "Lighting Handbook of the Illuminating Engineering Society" and are reprinted by permission of the Illuminating Engineering Society.

Units of Measurement. To calculate the proper intensity of illumination for a room for a given kind of work, it is necessary to have units of measurement for illumination, just as it is necessary to have units of measurement for distance as, for instance, the inch, the foot, and the yard, and units for use in electrical measurement as the ampere, the volt, the ohm, and the watt.

In lighting work, the units most used are the *candlepower*, the *footcandle*, and the *lumen*.

Definitions. *Candlepower.* The light-giving intensity of a source of light is expressed in *candlepower.* By one candlepower is meant the light-giving power of a candle made to certain standard specifications.

Footcandle. The intensity of illumination on a surface is measured in *footcandles.* One footcandle is the intensity of illumination on a surface one foot away from a light source of one candlepower.

Lumen. The amount of light flux that falls on a surface is measured in *lumens.* A lumen is the amount of light flux that falls on one square foot of surface on which the intensity of illumination is one footcandle.

In considering the light falling on a surface, the lamp itself should be thought of as a point source of light at the center of a hollow sphere of 1 ft radius. The surface then on which the light falls is the inside surface of the sphere, every point of which is equidistant from the source of light. In practice, however, the surface to be lighted is usually a flat surface, and all points of it are therefore not at the same distance from the light source. The average illumination on one square foot of flat surface is used in ordinary lighting calculations.

Application of Units of Measurement. In order that a person may see clearly and work without too much fatigue due to eye strain, the work should be illuminated to the proper intensity. Suitable intensities in footcandles for different kinds of work have been found by experience and experiment and are given in Table 82, page 228. This chart gives the intensity of illumination on the plane where the work is to be done, or *work plane,* as it is called.

If values of footcandle intensities are taken from this table and if suitable consideration is given to the proper selection and placing of the lamps and reflectors, a satisfactory lighting job will result.

In order to select lamps to give a certain intensity of illumination on the work plane, it is first necessary to find the lumens required. This is done by multiplying the desired intensity in footcandles by the area to be lighted. Expressed as a formula,

$$\text{Lumens} = \text{footcandles} \times \text{area}$$

If no other considerations such as mounting height, type of reflector, color of walls, etc., entered the problem, we could simply refer to a table of lumens, given by type and size of lamps, and select the lamps needed. The problem is made more difficult than this because the mounting height, spacing, shape of the room, color of the walls and ceiling, and the type of reflector, as well as the kind of maintenance the job gets after the work is installed, have to be considered. The necessary modifications of the simple lumen formula are easily taken care of by the coefficients next explained.

Room Index. The room index is a ratio that involves the width of the room, its length, and the mounting height of the lamps. The ratio of these dimensions determines how effective the light rays from the lamp are in lighting the room. If the room is square and has dark walls and ceilings, so that reflection is negligible, and if the lamp is mounted in the center of the room, the floor will be quite evenly lighted. If the room length is increased by, say 50 per cent, the original floor space will still be lighted as before, but the added floor space will receive light at less intensity because of the greater slant of the light rays, and the average intensity of illumination over the whole room will be less than with the square room. If the lamp is lowered, the intensity directly under the lamp will increase, but the space near the walls will receive practically no light. From the above it will be seen that the proportions of width, length, and mounting height all affect the amount of useful light on the working plane which has been taken as the floor in the analysis given.

The room index, or ratio involving room length, room width, and mounting height, varies according to the formulas given on page 106. It can be found directly, without computation, from Table 89. In practice the room index varies from 0.6 (J) to 5.0 (A).

Coefficient of Utilization. The coefficient of utilization is a decimal fraction that expresses how effectively the light from a given source is used. It depends on several factors: the width and length of the room and the mounting height of the lamp, which are included in the room index; it also depends on the type of reflector used and on the color of the walls and ceiling. Examination of the tabulation of room indexes of Table 89 shows that, as the room index increases from 0.6 (J) to 5.0 (A), the coefficient of utilization, that is, the actual effective lumens from the lamp as a fraction or per cent of its total lumen output increases. For instance, with RLM dome reflector of Table 90-1, Item 1, and a room index J (0.6), page 242, the effective lumens are 0.37, or 37 per cent of the lumen output of the lamp; with a room index of A (5.0), the effective lumens are 0.72, or 72 per cent of the lumen output of the lamp used in this reflector.

Coefficients That Affect the Quality of Illumination. In planning a lighting installation there are three principal coefficients that have to be considered. First, the room index, which has to do with the relationship between room width, length, and ceiling height; second, the coefficient of utilization, which involves the type of luminaire, the spacing of units, color of walls and ceilings, and includes the room index just mentioned; third, the maintenance factor, which has to do with the conditions under which the lamps operate after the job is installed. Maintenance factor involves the replacement of lamps, the cleaning of lamps and reflectors, and the condition of the walls and ceilings after the lamps have been in use for a time.

Calculation of the Numerical Value of the Room Index. For indirect and semi-indirect luminaires (Table 89),

$$\text{Room index} = \frac{2 \times \text{room width} + \text{length (feet)}}{4 \times (\text{ceiling height in feet}) - 2.5}$$

For direct, semi-direct, general diffuse, and direct-indirect luminaires (Table 89),

$$\text{Room index} = \frac{2 \times \text{room width} + \text{length (feet)}}{6 \times (\text{mounting height in feet}) - 2.5}$$

Note that in the above formulas for indirect and semi-indirect luminaires the ceiling height is used; while for direct, semi-direct, general diffuse, and direct-indirect luminaires, mounting height is used.

While the above formulas give a numerical value for the room index, in actual practice a letter symbol is used. When expressed as letters, the numerical values of the room index as calculated by the above formulas are as follows:

Numerical value......	0.6	0.8	1.0	1.25	1.5	2.0	2.5	3.0	4.0	5.0
Letter symbol.........	J	I	H	G	F	E	D	C	B	A

Example. Semi-indirect type of luminaire similar to item 48, Table 90-8, page 249, room height 9½ ft, width 9 ft, length 10 ft, mounting height 2½ ft from ceiling.

$$\text{Room index} = \frac{2 \times 9 + 10}{4 \times (9.5 - 2.5)} = \frac{28}{28} = 1 = \text{symbol } H$$

In practice, the room index can be found directly from Table 89. Having now selected a luminaire and room index for the room we wish to light, we refer to Table 90 for the coefficient of utilization.

Using item 48 in Table 90-8 again, and a room index of H which we have calculated, we find that if the ceiling reflects 75 per cent of the light and the walls 50 per cent, the coefficient of utilization is 0.26. We note, however, that if the ceiling and walls were darker and the ceiling reflected only 30 per cent and the walls reflected only 10 per cent, the coefficient of utilization would be only 0.10, or we would get only 0.10/0.26, or 38 per cent of the light with the darker ceiling and walls.

Maintenance Factor. The example just selected shows that with a dark ceiling and walls we get much less useful light than with a light ceiling and walls. After a job is installed, not only do the walls and ceiling deteriorate, but the lamps and reflectors as well. For these reasons it is necessary to install sufficient illumination at the start, so that after reasonable deterioration there will be plenty of light to work under. For filament lamps, 90 per cent of the initial lumen output is a fair value of output for the lamps themselves after they have been in average service; and for fluorescent lamps, 80 per cent for the lamps themselves. About another 10 to 20 per cent is lost in the average installation because of dust, dirt, and grease on the ceiling, walls, and reflecting equipment of the luminaire, so that the total average illumination under usual service will run around 60 to 70 per cent of the value at the time of installation. The extra amount of illumination to be added to that actually needed at the time of installation, to take care of depreciation, is determined by means of a factor called the *maintenance factor*. The maintenance factor may be thought of in the same way as the efficiency of a machine.

To determine the input of a machine, one divides the output by the efficiency; in lighting, to determine the amount of lighting to be initially installed, divide the illumination wanted by the maintenance factor.

Maintenance is commonly rated as good, medium, or poor: *good* when the atmosphere is free from smoke, dust, etc., the luminaires are cleaned frequently and the lamps replaced systematically; *medium* when the atmosphere is less clean, cleaning of luminaires only fair, and the lamps are not replaced until they burn out; *poor* when the atmosphere is dirty and the equipment is poorly maintained. Table 88 gives the average illumination maintained on a horizontal plane for 1,000 lamp lumens with various spacings and maintenance factors and coefficients of utilization. For 2,000 lumens, multiply the tabulated values by 2,000/1,000; and for 500 lumens, by 500/1,000, etc. If the area per luminaire is given, rather than the area per lamp, divide the tabulated values by the number of lamps per luminaire. If the area per room is given, rather than the area per lamp, divide the tabulated values by the number of lamps per room.

Problem in Lighting. Before proceeding to the complete calculations of the lighting of an office building, let us solve a simple problem to show the use of formulas and tables.

Problem. An office 12 ft by 18 ft and 12 ft high is to be lighted by direct lighting at an intensity of approximately 30 footcandles. The walls and ceilings are fairly light and the maintenance will be good (*G*). Specify the type of luminaire, the type and size of lamp, and the number of luminaires and their mounting height and spacing.

The relations of the units previously discussed can be expressed in simple basic formulas as follows:

(1) Total lumens needed for a room
$$= \text{area in square feet} \times \text{footcandles}$$

(2) Lumens to be supplied by a given luminaire
$$= \frac{\text{area in square feet} \times \text{footcandles}}{\text{coefficient of utilization} \times \text{maintenance factor}}$$

(3) Number of lamps =
$$\frac{\text{area in square feet} \times \text{footcandles}}{\text{coefficient of utilization} \times \text{maintenance factor} \times \text{lumens per lamp}}$$

In this problem,

(1) Lumens needed $= 12 \times 18 \times 30 = 6,480$ lumens

(2) In order to use formula (2) we need the coefficient of utilization, which involves the room index. Assume that the mounting height is $9\frac{1}{2}$ ft above the floor; then from Table 89 the room index is found to be H. Using this index in Table 90-6, item 3, we find that the coefficient of utilization is 0.33, and that the maintenance factor (G) is 0.75. Substituting in (2),

$$\text{Lumens} = \frac{6,480}{0.33 \times 0.75} = 26,200 \text{ lumens}$$

Referring to Table 84, a 500-watt incandescent lamp gives 10,000 lumens. So

$$(3) \text{ Number of lamps} = \frac{6480}{.33 \times 0.75 \times 10,000} = 2.6 \text{ lamps}$$

If we used two luminaires, each with a 500-watt lamp, we could get only

$$\frac{2 \times 10,000}{26,200} \times 30 = 23 \text{ footcandles}$$

If we used four luminaires, each with a 300-watt lamp at 5,900 lumens, as given in Table 84, we would get

$$\frac{4 \times 5900}{26,200} \times 30 = 27 \text{ footcandles}$$

Where the job warrants, several luminaires, lamps, spacings, and mounting height should be tried and the results tabulated as shown on page 110.

From the tabulation below the choice seems to be between three and four luminaires of Table 90-5, item 2. Four luminaires have been chosen because the distribution will be better than with three. While the footcandles will be higher than specified if white lamps are used, the intensity may be cut down somewhat by using soft white lamps. The layout will be as in Fig. 109.

COMPARISON OF METHODS OF LIGHTING

Type	Lumi-naires	Lamp, watts	MH	RI	CU	MF	Lumens		Foot-can-dles	Watts	Watts per foot-can-dle
							Needed	Sup-plied			
Table 90-6, item 3:incan. general diffuse	2	500	9½	H	0.33	0.75	26,200	20,000	23	1,000	43.5
	3	500	9½	H	0.33	0.75	26,200	30,000	34	1,500	44
	4	500	9½	H	0.33	0.75	26,200	40,000	46	2,000	43.5
	3	300	9½	H	0.33	0.75	26,200	17,700	20	900	45
	4	300	9½	H	0.33	0.75	26,200	23,600	27	1,200	44.5
Table 90-5, item 2: fluor. direct	2	4—40's	11	I	0.35	0.70	26,400	18,480 (white)	20	320	16
	3	4—40's	11	I	0.35	0.70	26,400	27,720	31.5	480	15.2
	4	4—40's	11	I	0.35	0.70	26,400	36,960	42	640	15.3
Table 90-3, item 5: fluor. direct	4	2—40's	9½	H	0.43	0.65	23,200	18,480 (white)	24	320	13.3
Table 90-4, item 4: fluor. direct	4	1—40	12	J	0.32	0.70	29,000	9,240 (white)	9.6	160	16.7
	6	1—40	12	J	0.32	0.70	29,000	13,860	14.3	240	16.8

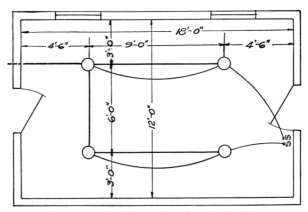

Fig. 109. Lighting plan of a single office.

The heavy full lines represent the conduit, and the heavy curved lines indicate how the switching is to be done.   With the arrangement shown, the lamps near the windows may be turned off on bright days.

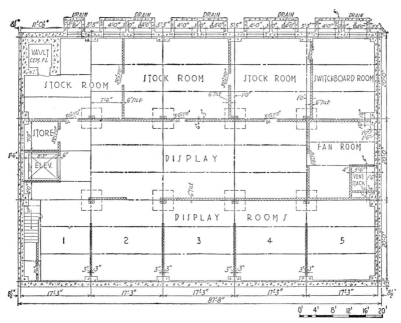

FIG. 110. Office building—basement plan.

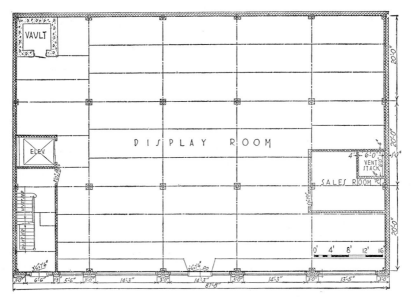

FIG. 111. Office building—first-floor plan.

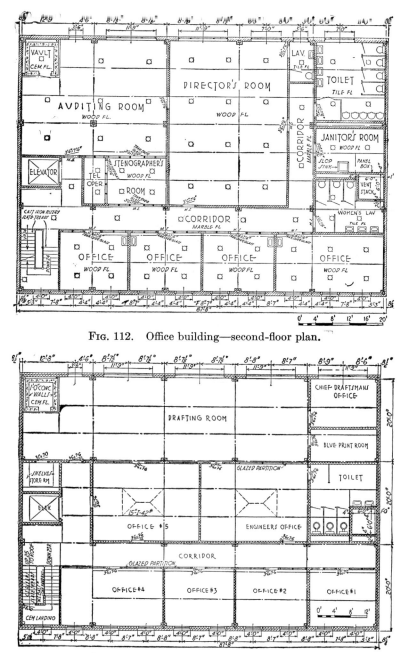

FIG. 112. Office building—second-floor plan.

FIG. 113. Office building—third-floor plan.

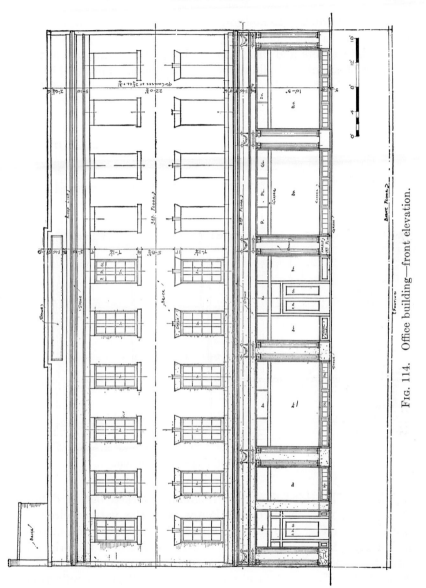

Fig. 114. Office building—front elevation.

Lighting of an Office Building. Many of the problems usually met with in laying out lighting are included in the preparation of the data sheets and drawings needed in the laying out of the lighting of an office building with four floors. Figures 110 to 115 show the floor plans, the elevation, and a section of the

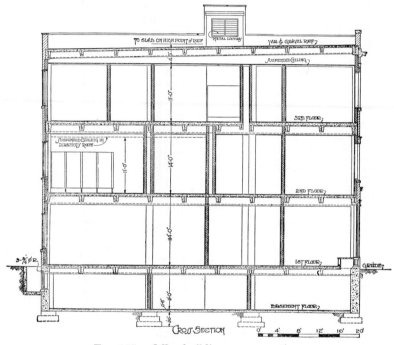

Fig. 115. Office building—cross section.

building. The third floor was originally worked out in detail for lighting with incandescent lamps, and the various circuits are shown in Fig. 116. It is proposed to modernize the installation using fluorescent lamps but to use as many of the original circuits as possible. The owner of the building has agreed to repaint the offices and to use a paint that will give a reflection coefficient for the ceilings of 70 per cent, and for the walls of 50 per cent.

The first step in planning a new installation or in modernizing an old one is to decide on the proper intensity of lighting to use

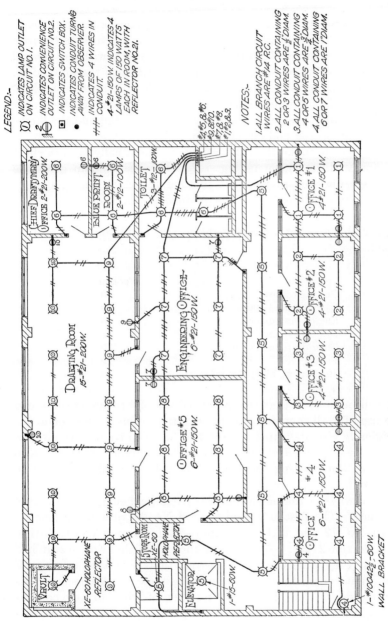

Fig. 116. Lighting plan of office building—third floor.

in the various rooms, and then to select one or more types of luminaires that will be suitable for the kind of work to be done in the various rooms and that will be in keeping with the general character of the building. Having decided upon the luminaires, a preliminary spacing is tried and the lighting intensity is checked. When suitable luminaires have been decided upon and the proper spacing found, the job is then worked up in detail and the lamps definitely located and circuited up.

In order to make the calculations systematically, a data sheet is prepared, as shown in Fig. 117. The last column gives the wattage for each room. The method by which the values for each column are obtained is explained at the lower part of the data sheet.

For this job the following intensities of illumination will be used.

	Footcandles
General offices	30
Corridors and stairs	10
Engineering offices	40
Drafting rooms	50
Chief draftsman's office	30
Vault	20
Store room, blueprint room, toilets	10

It will be noticed that the old circuiting of Figures 118–119 can be used for all rooms except the drafting room. This room was originally circuited up for a total of 3,240 watts on two circuits numbered 9 and 10. With the higher number of footcandles used in the drafting room, a total of 4,800 watts will now be required.

Two ways of taking care of this extra load suggest themselves at once. The first is to pull the old No. 14 wire and replace it with No. 12 and to fuse for more than 15 amp (NEC Article 210, Section 2125). With this method, the lights will be switched just as they were on the old layout that permitted turning off the lights near the windows on bright days. A check on the wiring shows that the largest number of wires in any conduit is six in a 1-in. conduit. Table 61 permits six No. 12 wires in a 1-in. conduit.

DATA ON LIGHTING - OFFICE BLDG. - 3RD FLOOR

m	ROOM	L	W	H	ROOM INDEX	LUMEN-AIRE	FC	K_u	K_m	AREA	LUMENS	LUMEN-AIRES	WATTS
1	OFFICE NO.1	16	13.5	10.5	H		30	.33	.70	216	28,000	8	640
2	OFFICE NO.2	17	13.5	10.5	H		30	.33	.70	230	29,800	8	640
3	OFFICE NO.3	16.5	13.5	10.5	H		30	.33	.70	223	29,000	8	640
4	OFFICE NO.4	24.5	13.5	10.5	H		30	.33	.70	331	43,000	12	960
5	OFFICE NO.5	25.5	18.5	10.5	G		30	.36	.70	472	56,400	16	1280
6	ENG. OFFICE	25.5	18.5	10.5	G		40	.36	.70	472	75,000	20	1600
7	CHF. DRAFT'N.	16	11.5	10.5	1		30	.30	.70	184	22,000	8	640
8	DRAFTING. RM.	68.5	20	10.5	E		50	.46	.70	1370	210,000	30	4200
9	BLUEPRINT RM.	16	8	10.5	J		10	.24	.70	128	7620	2	160
10	STORE ROOM	8	6	10.5	J		10	.24	.70	48	2850	1	80
11	VAULT	6	6	10.5	J		10	.24	.70	36	4270	1	80
12	TOILET	16	17	10.5	H		10	.33	.70	272	1800	3	740
13	CORRIDOR	85	5.75	10.5	J		10	.24	.70	239	29,100	8	640
14	STAIRS	14	9	10.5	J		10	.24	.70	126	7500	2	160
15	ELEVATOR	7	6	10.5	J		10	.24	.70	42	2500	1	80

COL. 5 MOUNTING HEIGHT OF SEMIDIRECT LUMINAIRES ABOVE FLOOR

COL. 12 LUMENS $= \dfrac{AREA \times FC.}{K_u \times K_m}$

COL. 13 USE 2-40 WATT SOFT WHITE LAMPS AT 1760 LUMENS EACH EXCEPT ITEMS 8 & 11. USE 2-40 WATT WHITE IN ITEM 11

COL. 12 ITEM 8 USE 4-40 WATT SOFT WHITE LAMPS.

COL. 1 ITEM 13 SECTION ASSUMED 13'x5.75'x10.5' $RI = \dfrac{2 \times 5.75 + 13}{6 \times 10.5 - 2.5} = 0.5 = J$

FIG. 117. Data on lighting of office building—third floor.

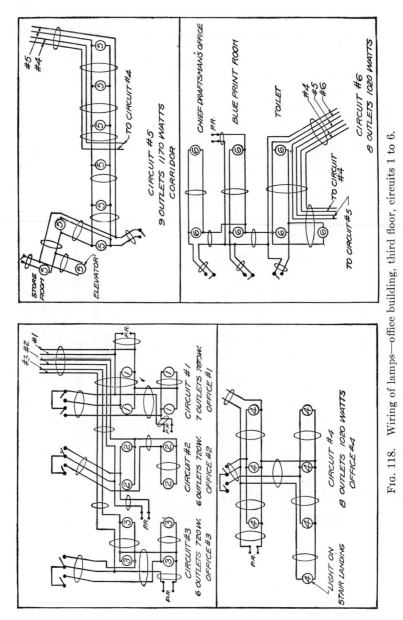

Fig. 118. Wiring of lamps—office building, third floor, circuits 1 to 6.

The second method by which the extra load can be carried is to add an extra circuit for the lamps nearest the chief draftsman's office and use one of the spare switches on the panelboard. With this arrangement, the lights will be switched as shown in Fig. 120. This arrangement will not permit switching off the lights near the windows and leaving the others on. As there are always slack times when all the lights in a drafting room are not needed, pull-cord switches can be installed on each fixture at slight

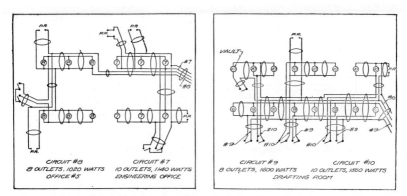

FIG. 119. Wiring of lamps—office building, third floor, circuits 7 to 10.

expense, if desired, and each may then be switched individually at the draftsman's board or desk.

Lighting of Second Floor. The data sheet giving the dimensions of the rooms has been started for this floor and is shown in Fig. 121. The student is to finish this data sheet, using the number of footcandles now considered proper for the various kinds of work done in the rooms. The proper intensities will be found in Table 82. After choosing the proper intensities of illumination, select one or more luminaires to give an up-to-date lighting layout. Circuit up the lamps in accordance with the code and arrange the switching for convenience and in such a manner that lights not needed for overtime work can be switched off.

Lighting of First Floor. The lighting of this floor is left entirely to the student. The floor has a show window for displaying electrical appliances, since the office building is that of an electric company supplying power and light to a large city.

Provide outlets for all the household appliances now in use so that the company can set up a display of a modern electric kitchen.   Look up the rules governing the wiring for electric ranges and any other equipment that may require special outlets. Study also methods of floodlighting any window exhibit, and plan and locate an electric sign suitable for the front of the

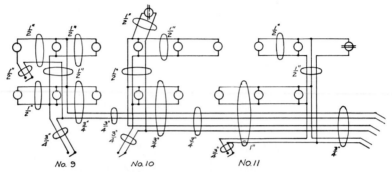

No. 9   No. 10   No. 11

FIG. 120.   Wiring of lamps—office building, new circuits 9, 10, and 11.

DATA ON LIGHTING-OFFICE BLDG.-2ND FLOOR

1	2	3	4	5	6	7	8	9	10	11	12	13	14
ITM	ROOM	L	W	H	ROOM INDEX	LUMEN-AIRE	FC	K_U	K_M	AREA	LUMENS	LUMEN AIRES	WATTS
1	OFFICE NO. 1	25	13.5										
2	OFFICE NO. 2	16.5	13.5										
3	OFFICE NO. 3	16.5	13.5										
4	OFFICE NO. 4	16	13.5										
5	DIRECTORS RM.	27.5	39										
6	AUDITING ROOM	34.5	27.5										
7	STENOG. ROOM	14	11										
8	JANITOR'S RM.	16	10.5										
9	TOILET	16	18.5										
10	WOMEN'S LAV.	16	12.5										
11	SMALL LAV.	9.5	6										
12	TELEPHONE OP.	11	5										
13	VAULT	6	6										
14	CORRIDOR	99	5.5										
15	STAIRS	14	9										

FIG. 121.   Data on lighting of office building—second floor.

building.   Show it on your drawing and provide suitable wiring for it.   It will be noticed that the first floor has eight columns that complicate the problem a little.   Where there are columns in a room, it is generally best to divide the room into bays and consider each bay as a unit.

Lighting of Basement. The lighting of this floor does not involve any problems that have not already been mastered in the planning of the lighting of the other floors. Notice that on this floor, as on the first floor, there are columns to be considered, and plan the lighting so that these will cause as little trouble as possible. With this floor, as with the first, the problem can best be solved by dividing the floor into bays and considering each bay by itself.

CHAPTER 9

INDUSTRIAL PLANT

General. Figures 122 to 128 show the plans of a large modern pumping plant for the oil industry. It is included in this book because it illustrates the method followed in designing any large plant and because it brings in outdoor and indoor construction, underground work, and the use of standard material and equipment, and also that used in vapor-proof and explosion-proof constructions. It is unusual in that it involves the use of 2,300-, 440-, and 120-volt motors.

To carry through a large job of this kind there is a project engineer, an electrical engineer, a civil engineer, and a mechanical engineer. All these men have assistants and draftsmen. The electrical engineers handle everything that involves electrical apparatus and circuits; the civil engineers, the maps of the property, and all foundations and buildings. The mechanical engineers handle all mechanical equipment, such as pumps, compressors, heating and ventilating equipment, piping, and special equipment involving machine-design problems of any kind.

As the job proceeds, each group is supplied with a set of basic plans and elevations of the buildings. On these plans the engineers and draftsmen locate the equipment to be used in their own particular branches of engineering. It is necessary that all groups cooperate very closely. For example, the mechanical engineers must locate their mechanical apparatus properly in relation to the structural features of the building. They must show any motors that operate their apparatus in the proper location on the plans, so that the electrical engineers can provide suitable places for the controllers and carry the wiring to the motors and controllers in the best manner. Further, as the job proceeds and changes of any kind are made, each group must be kept informed of these changes.

With the preliminary plans before them, the electrical engineers can total up the horsepower required for each building and prepare a one-line diagram for the whole job. Wherever possible it is desirable to orient the one-line diagram geographi-

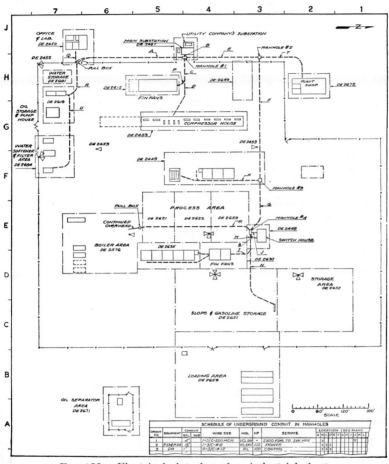

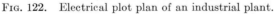

Fig. 122. Electrical plot plan of an industrial plant.

cally in the same direction as the plot plan; that is, the lines on the one-line diagram should run in the same general direction as the lines will run on the actual job. This makes it easy to find things on the drawings as the design proceeds and makes maintenance easy after the job is in operation.

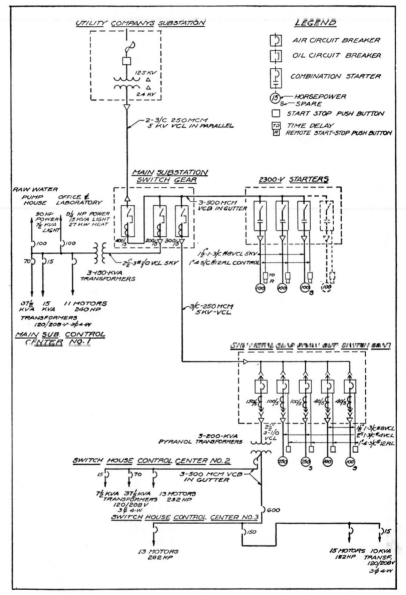

Fig. 123. Partial one-line diagram of an industrial plant.

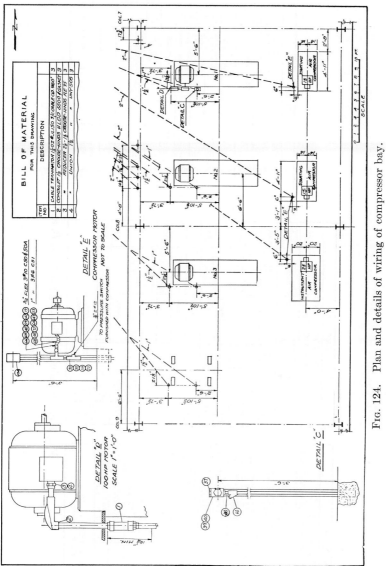

Fig. 124. Plan and details of wiring of compressor bay.

SCHEDULE

LIGHTING PANEL "A"

TYPE DVP 3 PHASE 4 WIRE 120-208 VOLT

CIR. No L1	CIR. No L2	CIR. No L3	BKR. NO/AMP	No. of Fix	No. of Rec.	Misc	Area	Conn Load Watts
1			1/20	3			COMPRESSORS #1 & 2	1500
	3		3/20	3			COMPRESSORS #3 & 4	1500
		5	5/20	3			COMPRESSORS #5 & 6	1500
2			2/20	3			COMPRESSORS #1 & 2	1500
	4		4/20	3			COMPRESSORS #3 & 4	1500
		6	6/15		4		NORTH END OF BUILDING	
7			7/20	1			BETWEEN C.T. I & COMP. HSE	500
	9		9/20	1			BETWEEN C.T. I & COMP. HSE.	1000
		11	11/20	3			COMPRESSORS # 5 & 6	1500
8			8/15	6			NORTH END OUTSIDE	700
	10		10/15	2			V-51 & V-61	300
		12	12/15	16			GG 1, 2, 5 & 8 ON V-51 & V-61	640
4200 W	4300 W	3640 W	CONNECTED LOAD PER PHASE					

SCHEDULE

LIGHTING PANEL "B"

TYPE DVP 3 PHASE 4 WIRE 120-208 VOLT

CIR. No L1	CIR. No L2	CIR. No L3	BKR NO/AMP	No. of Fix.	No. of Rec.	Misc.	Area	Conn Load Watts
1			1/20	3			UTILITY BAYS	1500
	3		3/20					
		5	5/20	3			COMPRESSORS #7 & 8	1500
2			2/20			SPARE		
	4		4/20	3			UTILITY BAYS	1500
		6	6/15			SPARE		
7			7/20			SPARE		
	9		9/20	1			S. EAST PIPING AREA	1000
		11	11/20	3			COMPRESSORS #7 & 8	1500
8			8/15		6		SOUTH END BLDG.	
	10		10/15			SPARE		
		12	12/15	7			S. END OUTSIDE & HANDRAIL MAST	900
1500 W	2500 W	3900 W	CONNECTED LOAD PER PHASE					

SCHEDULE

EMERGENCY LIGHTING PANEL "E"

TYPE DVP 3 PHASE 4 WIRE 120-208 VOLT

CIR. No L1	CIR. No L2	CIR. No L3	BKR NO./AMP	No. of Fix	No. of Rec.	Misc.	Area	Conn. Load Watts
1			1/20	3			COMPRESSORS #1, 3 & 5	1500
	3		3/20	3			COMPRESSORS #2, 4 & 6	1500
		5	5/20	3			UTILITY COS #7 BAYS & FUTURE	1000
2			2/20	2			COMPR #8 FUT. & UTILITY BAYS	1000
	4		4/20	2			FUTURE	
		6	6/15	3			OUTSIDE BLDG	350
7			7/15			ALARM & SHUTDOWN & SHUT DOWN STATION LIGHT		60
	8		8/15					
2560 W	1500 W	1350 W	CONNECTED LOAD PER PHASE		L1 500W, L2 1000W, L3 500W		FUTURE LOAD REQUIRED BY 4 ADDITIONAL BAYS	

FIG. 125. Schedules of lighting panels *A*, *B*, and *C*.

As soon as the number and size of the circuits for each building is decided upon, the design of the panelboards and switchboards can be started. If only panelboards are needed, they are selected by the method outlined for the carpentry shop and the cabinet shop, as explained on page 99. If a switchboard is required, the number of panels, instruments, switches, and circuit breakers is decided upon, and a sketch is submitted to a switchboard manufacturer. Some companies design and detail their own switchboards. This is often done when the company has its own construction men.

At this point in the design there is generally sufficient information available on the various operations to be carried on in the plant to enable the electrical engineers to determine the foot-candles needed for the lighting and to select the luminaires, and to lay out the lighting for the job.

With the preceding general outline of procedure in mind, the details of the pumping station will be considered in order.

Energy is purchased from a public utility company and received at 4160 volts, three-phase, 60-cycle, three-wire, at the main substation shown at the top or west side of the plot plan in Fig. 122.

One-line Diagram. We now refer to the one-line diagram of Fig. 123. At the main substation, the voltage is stepped down from 12,500 volts, three-phase, three-wire, to 2,400 volts, three-wire, and current is transmitted underground through 2 three-conductor cables to the main substation switchgear and from there to a bus. This bus supplies four 100-hp, 2,300-volt motors that drive pumps to supply jacket water for the compressors. A second line supplies three 150-kva transformers that step down the voltage to 480 volts, three-phase, three-wire, to supply the main substation control center 1. From this center are fed 11 motors for the jacket-water fans and air compressors, for the power and raw-water pump house, and for the office and laboratory. From this 480-volt bus, a 37½-kva transformer and a 15-kva transformer are tapped off for lighting.

A third 2,300-volt line supplies four motors and a bank of three 200-kva transformers which step the voltage down to 480 volts, three-phase, three-wire, and supply a large number of motors fed from switch-house control centers 2 and 3.

Having now considered the general plan of distribution and the type of construction used, the electrical circuits and some

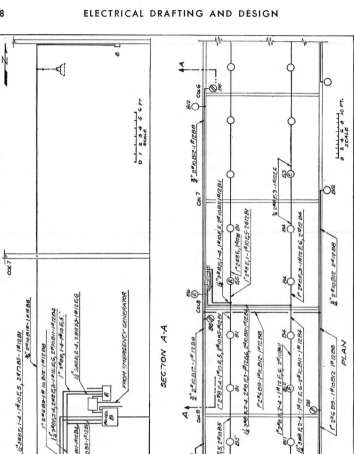

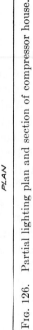

FIG. 126.   Partial lighting plan and section of compressor house.

of the details of the electrical equipment of the compressor house will be considered. Fittings such as are shown by Tables 26 to 40 will be used for ordinary standard construction and those shown by Charts 4 and 5 for apparatus in hazardous locations.

Compressor House Power Circuits. The compressor house contains eight engine-driven compressors as shown by the eight full-line rectangles on the plot plan of Fig. 122. Between compressors 6 and 7 there are three electrically driven pumps, with provision for a fourth pump in the future. At the east side of the building there are three air compressors, which are also electrically driven. The motors and their controls for these compressors constitute the principal electrical equipment of the building between columns 7 and 9.

An enlarged plan of the pump and air compressor section of the building is shown in Fig. 124, which gives the size and location of the conduits and the manner of carrying current to the controls of the motors. The actual fittings to be used and the location of each are shown by the detail drawings lettered details C, D, and E in Fig. 124. From these drawings, a bill of material can be made up and the material ordered for the job. A part of the bill of material is shown in the upper right-hand corner of the drawing.

Using detail D as an example of detailing and listing, we find that 1 is a cable terminator, 2 a condulet, 3 a condulet reducer, and 4 a condulet union.

In making up a bill of material the order is as follows:

ITEM, NAME OF PART, SIZE, MAKE, CATALOGUE NUMBER, QUANTITY REQUIRED (for the whole job).

Thus,

Item	Name of part	Size, in.	Make	Cat. No.	Quantity required
1	Cable terminator	1½	OZ	J1150-3/c, cable OD 0.960 in.	3
2	Condulet	1½	Crouse-Hinds	LBD5500 and gasket	3
3	Condulet reducer	1½	Crouse-Hinds	RE 75	3
4	Condulet union	1½	Crouse-Hinds	UNY 505	3

MANHOLE MATERIAL SCHEDULE							
CONDUIT NO.	COUPLING	CHASE NIPPLE	NIPPLE	REDUCER	PIPE CAP	END BELL	END BELL PLUG
SOUTH SIDE							
A,B,C						4"	4"
45,44,43						2"	
42,41,40						4"	
NORTH SIDE							
E						2"	2"
F,G						4"	4"
43						2"	
EAST SIDE							
H						2"	2"
44,45						2"	
J						4"	4"
40,41						4"	

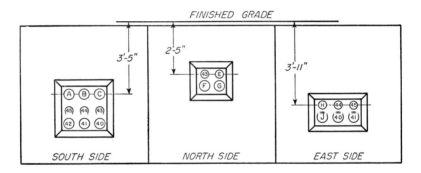

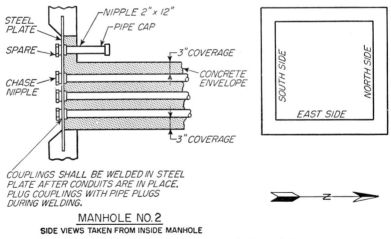

MANHOLE NO. 2

SIDE VIEWS TAKEN FROM INSIDE MANHOLE

FIG. 127.   Details of electrical manhole.

The complete bill of material for the conduit, wire, switches and fittings for the compressor house covers 148 items for the section of the compressor house shown on these drawings. A separate detail drawing is often not required as, for instance, in listing conduit. Since the size of the conduit is given on the plan, the length can be scaled from the plan and a sufficient number of feet can be added to take care of bends and vertical runs. When the runs are complicated, a simple isometric sketch, as explained in Chap. 1, is very useful to enable the draftsman to total up the length of the conduit accurately.

Lighting Circuits. The lighting circuits on this job represent the very latest practice in lighting. For simplicity, only one regular branch circuit and one emergency lighting circuit will be analyzed. The 37½- and the 15-kva transformers previously mentioned, which are connected three-phase, four-wire on the low side, step the voltage down from 480 volts on the high side to 120 volts from each secondary phase wire to neutral. This voltage is for lighting, and the circuits are balanced as nearly as possible across the three phases. The method of balancing the loads is clearly shown by inspection of lighting schedules A, B, and C shown in Fig. 125. From the theory of the three-phase circuit as explained in Fig. 102, the voltage across phase wires is 1.73 times the voltage from any phase wire to neutral, so that with 120 volts to neutral, the phase voltage is $120 \times 1.73 = 208$ volts. Owing to the popularity of this method of distribution, motors are now made for 208 volts, so that while lighting is being taken from phase wires to neutral and is fairly well balanced across the phases, a balanced power load can be taken from the phase wires at the same time.

Emergency Circuit. Panel E is for emergency lighting. There are several such panels lettered E_1, E_2, etc. The emergency panels are similar to the other lighting panels, but supply only a few lamps distributed about the plant in such a way as to make it convenient to work in case the main power goes off. The emergency panel is connected to the middle point of a double-throw switch which is normally thrown on the power circuit. If the power goes off, this double-throw switch automatically transfers the emergency panel to a three-phase generator driven by a steam turbine. The turbine is automatically started by

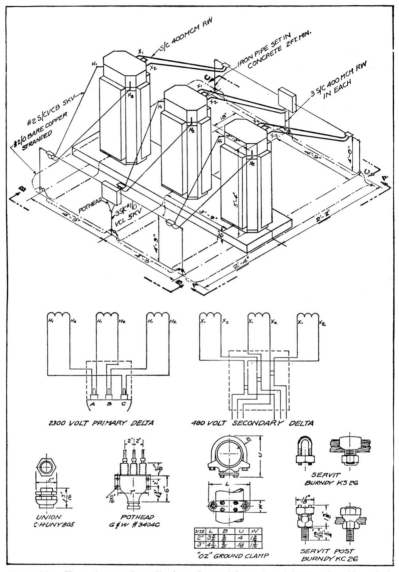

FIG. 128. Transformer installation of 3-150-kva.-2,300/480-volt self-cooled transformers.

a valve actuated by a spring. If the electric power fails, the spring is released and opens the steam valve to the turbine.

Details of Lights. The details of the wiring for panels B and E for the compressor house will next be considered. Since there must be at least four wires in a conduit that feeds three circuits balanced across places and neutral, there may be more than three if the conduit continues on and supplies other lamps as, for instance, certain lamps on the emergency circuit. It is therefore important that a simple system be used for identifying the conduit, the number and size of the wires and the panelboard they are from, and the number of the circuit on the panelboard.

The system is as follows: The first figure gives the conduit size, and the next figure and symbol gives the number of wires and gauge number. A letter following the wire size gives the panelboard, and a figure immediately following this letter gives the number of the circuit on the panelboard. For example, on the conduit run on the west wall of the compressor house of Fig. 126, we find $\frac{3}{4}''$, 2 #10B, 1 #12B 8. This means that the conduit is $\frac{3}{4}$ in. and that there are two No. 10 wires that come from panelboard B and that they are on circuit 12. The same conduit carries one No. 12 wire that is on circuit 8 and also comes from panelboard B. On the long run 6 ft 6 in. east of the center line of the building and just south of column 8 we find

$$1\text{-}1\frac{1}{4}'', 3 \ \#8E_1 \ 2\text{-}4; \ 1 \ \#12E_1 \ 6, \ 2 \ \#10B \ 11, \ 1 \ \#12B \ 4$$

This means that the conduit is $1\frac{1}{4}$ in. and that there are three No. 8 wires on the emergency panelboard E_1 for circuits 2 and 4, one No. 12 wire on panelboard E_1 for circuit 6, two No. 10 wires on panelboard B for circuit 11, and one No. 12 wire on panelboard B for circuit 4.

Manholes. Figure 127 shows the manner of representing manholes and marking conduits. Conduits actually in use are numbered; spare conduits are lettered. Iron conduit is used where the runs are short and where bends are necessary. Kora-duct (a light-weight transite product) is used on straight long runs on this job. All conduit, metal and transite, is enclosed in an envelope of red concrete as shown by the details in Fig. 127. Since all metal conduit must be grounded, and since the details show the conduit welded to an iron plate, all that is necessary to ground the conduit system is to drill and tap the plate for a Servit post and connect this post to the main station ground wire.

Transformers. Figure 128 shows the three 150-kva transformers that step down the 2,300 volts to 480 volts. This isometric sketch is carried out to considerably more detail than the sketch that an engineer would give a draftsman to show him what he had in mind for the arrangement of the transformers. As this transformer installation is a particularly good one, the sketch has been carried to considerable detail to enable the reader to use this installation as an example of a first-class installation, and to detail the job in regular orthographic projection.

IMPORTANT 1951 NEC RULINGS THAT APPLY TO THIS JOB
(Numbers refer to sections)
Review of all rulings that apply to previous topics and the following:

Chapter 2

2302 Service from One Building through Another
2303b Insulation of Service Conductors Underground
2311–2314 Underground Services
2331 Wiring Methods
2333 Individual Conductors Exposed to the Weather
2525 Conductor to Be Grounded
2541 Exposed Metal
2558 Equipment on Structural Metal
2594 Alternating-current and Service Equipment

Chapter 3

3102 Conductor Insulation
3342 Armored Cable—Use

Chapter 5

5012 Transformers and Capacitors
5018 Motors and Generators
5019 Lighting Fixtures, Switches, etc.
5022 Receptacles and Attachment Plugs
5023 Conductor Insulation
5055 Sealing
5066 Grounding

PROBLEMS

1. Why is 2,300 volts used on the 100-hp motors rather than 220 volts?

2. Make a circuit diagram showing how the 37½-kva transformer is connected to transform from 480 volts, three-wire, to 120/208 volts, four-wire.

3. Referring to the partial lighting plan of the compressor house shown in Fig. 126, make a complete wiring diagram of the circuits shown, including connections to panel *B*, the automatic change-over switch, and panel *E*, the emergency circuit panel. Follow the general plan used for circuiting the lamps for the office building shown in Fig. 118.

4. Using the isometric sketch of the three 150-kva transformers of Fig. 128:

(*a*) Make a detail scale drawing showing how you would make the connections inside the primary and secondary junction boxes shown on the sketch.

(*b*) Detail elevations *A-A*, *B-B*, and *C-C* to the scale of $\frac{3}{4}$ in. = 1 ft, using the regular rules for third-angle projection. This job is to include the selection of the proper size of iron pipe or conduit, proper condulets, and the detailing of the primary and secondary junction boxes to give ample room for installing the fittings that you used in making the connections under (*a*).

(*c*) Prepare a complete bill of material for everything on this job except the concrete foundation for the transformers.

TABLES

TABLE 1.   DECIMAL EQUIVALENTS OF FRACTIONS OF AN INCH

$\frac{1}{64} = 0.015625$	$\frac{17}{64} = 0.265625$	$\frac{33}{64} = 0.515625$	$\frac{49}{64} = 0.765625$
$\frac{1}{32} = 0.031250$	$\frac{9}{32} = 0.281250$	$\frac{17}{32} = 0.531250$	$\frac{25}{32} = 0.781250$
$\frac{3}{64} = 0.046875$	$\frac{19}{64} = 0.296875$	$\frac{35}{64} = 0.546875$	$\frac{51}{64} = 0.796875$
$\frac{1}{16} = 0.062500$	$\frac{5}{16} = 0.312500$	$\frac{9}{16} = 0.562500$	$\frac{13}{16} = 0.812500$
$\frac{5}{64} = 0.078125$	$\frac{21}{64} = 0.328125$	$\frac{37}{64} = 0.578125$	$\frac{53}{64} = 0.828125$
$\frac{3}{32} = 0.093750$	$\frac{11}{32} = 0.343750$	$\frac{19}{32} = 0.593750$	$\frac{27}{32} = 0.843750$
$\frac{7}{64} = 0.109375$	$\frac{23}{64} = 0.359375$	$\frac{39}{64} = 0.609375$	$\frac{55}{64} = 0.859375$
$\frac{1}{8} = 0.125000$	$\frac{3}{8} = 0.375000$	$\frac{5}{8} = 0.625000$	$\frac{7}{8} = 0.875000$
$\frac{9}{64} = 0.140625$	$\frac{25}{64} = 0.390625$	$\frac{41}{64} = 0.640625$	$\frac{57}{64} = 0.890625$
$\frac{5}{32} = 0.156250$	$\frac{13}{32} = 0.406250$	$\frac{21}{32} = 0.656250$	$\frac{29}{32} = 0.906250$
$\frac{11}{64} = 0.171875$	$\frac{27}{64} = 0.421875$	$\frac{43}{64} = 0.671875$	$\frac{59}{64} = 0.921875$
$\frac{3}{16} = 0.187500$	$\frac{7}{16} = 0.437500$	$\frac{11}{16} = 0.687500$	$\frac{15}{16} = 0.937500$
$\frac{13}{64} = 0.203125$	$\frac{29}{64} = 0.453125$	$\frac{45}{64} = 0.703125$	$\frac{61}{64} = 0.953125$
$\frac{7}{32} = 0.218750$	$\frac{15}{32} = 0.468750$	$\frac{23}{32} = 0.718750$	$\frac{31}{32} = 0.968750$
$\frac{15}{64} = 0.234375$	$\frac{31}{64} = 0.484375$	$\frac{47}{64} = 0.734375$	$\frac{63}{64} = 0.984375$
$\frac{1}{4} = 0.250000$	$\frac{1}{2} = 0.500000$	$\frac{3}{4} = 0.750000$	

TABLE 2.   INCHES AND FRACTIONS OF AN INCH EXPRESSED AS DECIMALS
OF A FOOT

Inches	Decimals of a foot	Fractions of an inch	Decimals of a foot	Fractions of an inch	Decimals of a foot	Fractions of an inch	Decimals of a foot
1	0.0833	$\frac{1}{32}$	0.0026	$\frac{13}{32}$	0.0339	$\frac{25}{32}$	0.0651
2	0.1667	$\frac{1}{16}$	0.0052	$\frac{7}{16}$	0.0365	$\frac{13}{16}$	0.0677
3	0.2500	$\frac{3}{32}$	0.0078	$\frac{15}{32}$	0.0391	$\frac{27}{32}$	0.0703
4	0.3333	$\frac{1}{8}$	0.0104	$\frac{1}{2}$	0.0417	$\frac{7}{8}$	0.0729
5	0.4167	$\frac{5}{32}$	0.0130	$\frac{17}{32}$	0.0443	$\frac{29}{32}$	0.0755
6	0.5000	$\frac{3}{16}$	0.0156	$\frac{9}{16}$	0.0409	$\frac{15}{16}$	0.0781
7	0.5833	$\frac{7}{32}$	0.0182	$\frac{19}{32}$	0.0495	$\frac{31}{32}$	0.0807
8	0.6667	$\frac{1}{4}$	0.0208	$\frac{5}{8}$	0.0521		
9	0.7500	$\frac{9}{32}$	0.0234	$\frac{21}{32}$	0.0547		
10	0.8333	$\frac{5}{16}$	0.0260	$\frac{11}{16}$	0.0573		
11	0.9167	$\frac{11}{32}$	0.0286	$\frac{23}{32}$	0.0599		
12	1.0000	$\frac{3}{8}$	0.0313	$\frac{3}{4}$	0.0625		

TABLE 3.   TRIGONOMETRICAL FORMULAS

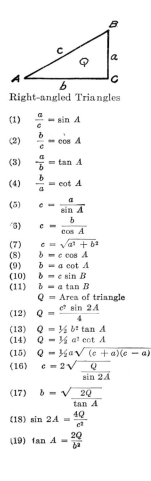

Right-angled Triangles

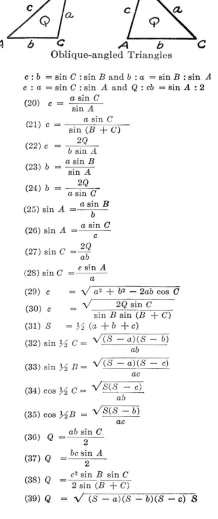

Oblique-angled Triangles

(1) $\dfrac{a}{c} = \sin A$

(2) $\dfrac{b}{c} = \cos A$

(3) $\dfrac{a}{b} = \tan A$

(4) $\dfrac{b}{a} = \cot A$

(5) $c = \dfrac{a}{\sin A}$

(6) $c = \dfrac{b}{\cos A}$

(7) $c = \sqrt{a^2 + b^2}$

(8) $b = c \cos A$

(9) $b = a \cot A$

(10) $b = c \sin B$

(11) $b = a \tan B$

Q = Area of triangle

(12) $Q = \dfrac{c^2 \sin 2A}{4}$

(13) $Q = \tfrac{1}{2} b^2 \tan A$

(14) $Q = \tfrac{1}{2} a^2 \cot A$

(15) $Q = \tfrac{1}{2} a \sqrt{(c + a)(c - a)}$

(16) $c = 2\sqrt{\dfrac{Q}{\sin 2A}}$

(17) $b = \sqrt{\dfrac{2Q}{\tan A}}$

(18) $\sin 2A = \dfrac{4Q}{c^2}$

(19) $\tan A = \dfrac{2Q}{b^2}$

$c : b = \sin C : \sin B$ and $b : a = \sin B : \sin A$
$c : a = \sin C : \sin A$ and $Q : cb = \sin A : 2$

(20) $c = \dfrac{a \sin C}{\sin A}$

(21) $c = \dfrac{a \sin C}{\sin (B + C)}$

(22) $c = \dfrac{2Q}{b \sin A}$

(23) $b = \dfrac{a \sin B}{\sin A}$

(24) $b = \dfrac{2Q}{a \sin C}$

(25) $\sin A = \dfrac{a \sin B}{b}$

(26) $\sin A = \dfrac{a \sin C}{c}$

(27) $\sin C = \dfrac{2Q}{ab}$

(28) $\sin C = \dfrac{c \sin A}{a}$

(29) $c = \sqrt{a^2 + b^2 - 2ab \cos C}$

(30) $c = \sqrt{\dfrac{2Q \sin C}{\sin B \sin (B + C)}}$

(31) $S = \tfrac{1}{2} (a + b + c)$

(32) $\sin \tfrac{1}{2} C = \dfrac{\sqrt{(S - a)(S - b)}}{ab}$

(33) $\sin \tfrac{1}{2} B = \dfrac{\sqrt{(S - a)(S - c)}}{ac}$

(34) $\cos \tfrac{1}{2} C = \dfrac{\sqrt{S(S - c)}}{ab}$

(35) $\cos \tfrac{1}{2} B = \dfrac{\sqrt{S(S - b)}}{ac}$

(36) $Q = \dfrac{ab \sin C}{2}$

(37) $Q = \dfrac{bc \sin A}{2}$

(38) $Q = \dfrac{c^2 \sin B \sin C}{2 \sin (B + C)}$

(39) $Q = \sqrt{(S - a)(S - b)(S - c)\, S}$

TABLE 4. NATURAL TRIGONOMETRIC FUNCTIONS

Angle	sin	cos	tan	cot	sec	csc	Angle
0	.0000	1.0000	.0000	......	1.0000	......	90°
1	.0175	.9998	.0175	57.2900	1.0002	57.2987	89
2	.0349	.9994	.0349	28.6363	1.0006	28.6537	88
3	.0523	.9986	.0524	19.0811	1.0014	19.1073	87
4	.0698	.9976	.0699	14.3007	1.0024	14.3356	86
5	.0872	.9962	.0875	11.4301	1.0038	11.4737	85
6	.1045	.9945	.1051	9.5144	1.0055	9.5668	84
7	.1219	.9925	.1228	8.1443	1.0075	8.2055	83
8	.1392	.9903	.1405	7.1154	1.0098	7.1853	82
9	.1564	.9877	.1584	6.3138	1.0125	6.3925	81
10	.1736	.9848	.1763	5.6713	1.0154	5.7588	80
11	.1908	.9816	.1944	5.1446	1.0187	5.2408	79
12	.2079	.9781	.2126	4.7046	1.0223	4.8097	78
13	.2250	.9744	.2309	4.3315	1.0263	4.4454	77
14	.2419	.9703	.2493	4.0108	1.0306	4.1336	76
15	.2588	.9659	.2679	3.7321	1.0353	3.8637	75
16	.2756	.9613	.2867	3.4874	1.0403	3.6280	74
17	.2924	.9563	.3057	3.2709	1.0457	3.4203	73
18	.3090	.9511	.3249	3.0777	1.0515	3.2361	72
19	.3256	.9455	.3443	2.9042	1.0576	3.0716	71
20	.3420	.9397	.3640	2.7475	1.0642	2.9238	70
21	.3584	.9336	.3839	2.6051	1.0711	2.7904	69
22	.3746	.9272	.4040	2.4751	1.0785	2.6695	68
23	.3907	.9205	.4245	2.3559	1.0864	2.5593	67
24	.4067	.9135	.4452	2.2460	1.0946	2.4586	66
25	.4226	.9063	.4663	2.1445	1.1034	2.3662	65
26	.4384	.8988	.4877	2.0503	1.1126	2.2812	64
27	.4540	.8910	.5095	1.9626	1.1223	2.2027	63
28	.4695	.8829	.5317	1.8807	1.1326	2.1301	62
29	.4848	.8746	.5543	1.8040	1.1434	2.0627	61
30	.5000	.8660	.5774	1.7321	1.1547	2.0000	60
31	.5150	.8572	.6009	1.6643	1.1666	1.9416	59
32	.5299	.8480	.6249	1.6003	1.1792	1.8871	58
33	.5446	.8387	.6494	1.5399	1.1924	1.8361	57
34	.5592	.8290	.6745	1.4826	1.2062	1.7883	56
35	.5736	.8192	.7002	1.4281	1.2208	1.7434	55
36	.5878	.8090	.7265	1.3764	1.2361	1.7013	54
37	.6018	.7986	.7536	1.3270	1.2521	1.6616	53
38	.6157	.7880	.7813	1.2799	1.2690	1.6243	52
39	.6293	.7771	.8098	1.2349	1.2868	1.5890	51
40	.6428	.7660	.8391	1.1918	1.3054	1.5557	50
41	.6561	.7547	.8693	1.1504	1.3250	1.5243	49
42	.6691	.7431	.9004	1.1106	1.3456	1.4945	48
43	.6820	.7314	.9325	1.0724	1.3673	1.4663	47
44	.6947	.7193	.9657	1.0355	1.3902	1.4396	46
45	.7071	.7071	1.0000	1.0000	1.4142	1.4142	45
Angle	cos	sin	cot	tan	csc	sec	Angle

TABLE 5. EQUAL ANGLES
For gauges see Table 9
(*American Institute of Steel Construction*)

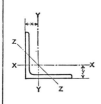

ANGLES
EQUAL LEGS

PROPERTIES FOR DESIGNING

Size	Thickness	Weight per Foot	Area	AXIS X-X AND AXIS Y-Y				AXIS Z-Z
				I	S	r	x or y	r
In.	In.	Lb.	In.²	In.⁴	In.³	In.	In.	In.
3½ x 3½	½	11.1	3.25	3.6	1.5	1.06	1.06	.68
	⁷⁄₁₆	9.8	2.87	3.3	1.3	1.07	1.04	.68
	⅜	8.5	2.48	2.9	1.2	1.07	1.01	.69
	⁵⁄₁₆	7.2	2.09	2.5	.98	1.08	.99	.69
	¼	5.8	1.69	2.0	.79	1.09	.97	.69
3 x 3	½	9.4	2.75	2.2	1.1	.90	.93	.58
	⁷⁄₁₆	8.3	2.43	2.0	.95	.91	.91	.58
	⅜	7.2	2.11	1.8	.83	.91	.89	.58
	⁵⁄₁₆	6.1	1.78	1.5	.71	.92	.87	.59
	¼	4.9	1.44	1.2	.58	.93	.84	.59
	³⁄₁₆	3.71	1.09	.96	.44	.94	.82	.59
2½ x 2½	½	7.7	2.25	1.2	.72	.74	.81	.49
	⅜	5.9	1.73	.98	.57	.75	.76	.49
	⁵⁄₁₆	5.0	1.47	.85	.48	.76	.74	.49
	¼	4.1	1.19	.70	.39	.77	.72	.49
	³⁄₁₆	3.07	.90	.55	.30	.78	.69	.49
2 x 2	⅜	4.7	1.36	.48	.35	.59	.64	.39
	⁵⁄₁₆	3.92	1.15	.42	.30	.60	.61	.39
	¼	3.19	.94	.35	.25	.61	.59	.39
	³⁄₁₆	2.44	.71	.27	.19	.62	.57	.39
	⅛	1.65	.48	.19	.13	.63	.55	.40
1¾ x 1¾	¼	2.77	.81	.23	.19	.53	.53	.34
	³⁄₁₆	2.12	.62	.18	.14	.54	.51	.34
	⅛	1.44	.42	.13	.10	.55	.48	.35
1½ x 1½	¼	2.34	.69	.14	.13	.45	.47	.29
	³⁄₁₆	1.80	.53	.11	.10	.46	.44	.29
	⅛	1.23	.36	.08	.07	.47	.42	.30
1¼ x 1¼	¼	1.92	.56	.08	.09	.37	.40	.24
	³⁄₁₆	1.48	.43	.06	.07	.38	.38	.24
	⅛	1.01	.30	.04	.05	.38	.36	.25
1 x 1	¼	1.49	.44	.04	.06	.29	.34	.20
	³⁄₁₆	1.16	.34	.03	.04	.30	.32	.19
	⅛	.80	.23	.02	.03	.30	.30	.20

Table 6.   I Beams
(American Institute of Steel Construction)

AMERICAN STANDARD BEAMS
DIMENSIONS FOR DETAILING

$c = \frac{1}{2}\,web + \frac{1}{16}''$

Depth of Section	Weight per Foot	Flange		Web		Distance					Grip	Max. Flange Rivet	Usual Gage g
		Width	Mean Thickness	Thickness	Half Thickness	a	T	k	g₁	c			
In.	Lb.	In.	In.	In.	In.	In.	In.	In.	In.	In.	In.	In.	In.
24	120.0	8	1 1/8	13/16	7/16	3 5/8	20 1/8	1 15/16	3 1/4	1/2	1 1/8	1	4
	105.9	7 7/8	1 1/8	5/8	5/16	3 5/8	20 1/8	1 15/16	3 1/4	3/8	1 1/8	1	4
24	100.0	7 1/4	7/8	3/4	3/8	3 1/4	20 3/4	1 5/8	3	7/16	7/8	1	4
	90.0	7 1/8	7/8	5/8	5/16	3 1/4	20 3/4	1 5/8	3	3/8	7/8	1	4
	79.9	7	7/8	1/2	1/4	3 1/4	20 3/4	1 5/8	3	5/16	7/8	1	4
20	95.0	7 1/4	15/16	13/16	7/16	3 1/4	16 1/2	1 3/4	3 1/4	1/2	15/16	1	4
	85.0	7	15/16	11/16	5/16	3 1/4	16 1/2	1 3/4	3 1/4	3/8	7/8	1	4
20	75.0	6 3/8	13/16	5/8	5/16	2 7/8	16 7/8	1 9/16	3	3/8	13/16	7/8	3 1/2
	65.4	6 1/4	13/16	1/2	1/4	2 7/8	16 7/8	1 9/16	3	5/16	3/4	7/8	3 1/2
18	70.0	6 1/4	11/16	3/4	3/8	2 3/4	15 1/4	1 3/8	2 3/4	7/16	11/16	7/8	3 1/2
	54.7	6	11/16	1/2	1/4	2 3/4	15 1/4	1 3/8	2 3/4	5/16	11/16	7/8	3 1/2
15	50.0	5 5/8	5/8	9/16	5/16	2 1/2	12 1/2	1 1/4	2 3/4	3/8	9/16	3/4	3 1/2
	42.9	5 1/2	5/8	7/16	1/4	2 1/2	12 1/2	1 1/4	2 3/4	5/16	9/16	3/4	3 1/2
12	50.0	5 1/2	11/16	11/16	3/8	2 3/8	9 3/8	1 5/16	2 3/4	7/16	11/16	3/4	3
	40.8	5 1/4	11/16	1/2	1/4	2 3/8	9 3/8	1 5/16	2 3/4	5/16	5/8	3/4	3
12	35.0	5 1/8	9/16	7/16	1/4	2 3/8	9 3/4	1 1/8	2 1/2	5/16	1/2	3/4	3
	31.8	5	9/16	3/8	3/16	2 3/8	9 3/4	1 1/8	2 1/2	1/4	1/2	3/4	3·
10	35.0	5	1/2	5/8	5/16	2 1/8	8	1	2 1/2	3/8	1/2	3/4	2 3/4
	25.4	4 5/8	1/2	5/16	3/16	2 1/8	8	1	2 1/2	1/4	1/2	3/4	2 3/4
8	23.0	4 1/8	7/16	7/16	1/4	1 7/8	6 1/4	7/8	2 1/4	5/16	7/16	3/4	2 1/4
	18.4	4	7/16	5/16	3/16	1 7/8	6 1/4	7/8	2 1/4	5/16	7/16	3/4	2 1/4
7	20.0	3 7/8	3/8	7/16	1/4	1 3/4	5 3/8	13/16	2	5/16	3/8	5/8	2 1/4
	15.3	3 5/8	3/8	1/4	1/8	1 3/4	5 3/8	13/16	2	3/16	3/8	5/8	2 1/4
6	17.25	3 5/8	3/8	1/2	1/4	1 1/2	4 1/2	3/4	2	5/16	3/8	5/8	2
	12.5	3 3/8	3/8	1/4	1/8	1 1/2	4 1/2	3/4	2	3/16	5/16		
5	14.75	3 1/4	5/16	1/2	1/4	1 3/8	3 5/8	11/16	2	5/16	5/16	1/2	1 3/4
	10.0	3	5/16	1/4	1/8	1 3/8	3 5/8	11/16	2	3/16	5/16	1/2	1 3/4
4	9.5	2 3/4	5/16	5/16	3/16	1 1/4	2 3/4	5/8	2	1/4	5/16	1/2	1 1/2
	7.7	2 5/8	5/16	3/16	1/8	1 1/4	2 3/4	5/8	2	3/16	5/16		
3	7.5	2 1/2	1/4	3/8	3/16	1 1/8	1 7/8	9/16		1/4	1/4	3/8	1 1/2
	5.7	2 3/8	1/4	3/16	1/8	1 1/8	1 7/8	9/16		3/16	1/4	3/8	1 1/2

Gage g₁ is based on $k + 1\frac{1}{4}''$, to nearest $\frac{1}{4}''$.
Gage g is permissible near ends of beam; elsewhere Specification may require reduction in rivet size.

Table 7.   Channels
(*American Institute of Steel Construction*)

AMERICAN STANDARD CHANNELS — DIMENSIONS FOR DETAILING

Depth of Section	Weight per Foot	Flange Width	Flange Mean Thickness	Web Thickness	Web Half Thickness	a	T	k	g_1	c	Grip	Max. Flange Rivet	Usual Gage g
In.	Lb.	In.	In.	In.	In.	In.	In.	In.	In.	In.	In.	In.	In.
*18	58.0	$4\frac{1}{4}$	$\frac{5}{8}$	$\frac{11}{16}$	$\frac{3}{8}$	$3\frac{1}{2}$	$15\frac{3}{8}$	$\frac{15}{16}$	$2\frac{3}{4}$	$\frac{3}{4}$	$\frac{5}{8}$	1	$2\frac{1}{2}$
	51.9	$4\frac{1}{8}$	$\frac{5}{8}$	$\frac{5}{8}$	$\frac{5}{16}$	$3\frac{1}{2}$	$15\frac{3}{8}$	$\frac{15}{16}$	$2\frac{3}{4}$	$\frac{11}{16}$	$\frac{5}{8}$	1	$2\frac{1}{2}$
	45.8	4	$\frac{5}{8}$	$\frac{1}{2}$	$\frac{1}{4}$	$3\frac{1}{2}$	$15\frac{3}{8}$	$\frac{15}{16}$	$2\frac{3}{4}$	$\frac{9}{16}$	$\frac{5}{8}$	1	$2\frac{1}{2}$
	42.7	4	$\frac{5}{8}$	$\frac{7}{16}$	$\frac{1}{4}$	$3\frac{1}{2}$	$15\frac{3}{8}$	$\frac{15}{16}$	$2\frac{3}{4}$	$\frac{1}{2}$	$\frac{5}{8}$	1	$2\frac{1}{2}$
15	50.0	$3\frac{3}{4}$	$\frac{5}{8}$	$\frac{3}{4}$	$\frac{3}{8}$	3	$12\frac{3}{8}$	$\frac{15}{16}$	$2\frac{3}{4}$	$\frac{13}{16}$	$\frac{5}{8}$	1	$2\frac{1}{4}$
	40.0	$3\frac{1}{2}$	$\frac{5}{8}$	$\frac{9}{16}$	$\frac{1}{4}$	3	$12\frac{3}{8}$	$\frac{15}{16}$	$2\frac{3}{4}$	$\frac{5}{8}$	$\frac{5}{8}$	1	2
	33.9	$3\frac{3}{8}$	$\frac{5}{8}$	$\frac{7}{16}$	$\frac{3}{16}$	3	$12\frac{3}{8}$	$\frac{15}{16}$	$2\frac{3}{4}$	$\frac{1}{2}$	$\frac{5}{8}$	1	2
12	30.0	$3\frac{1}{8}$	$\frac{1}{2}$	$\frac{1}{2}$	$\frac{1}{4}$	$2\frac{5}{8}$	$9\frac{7}{8}$	$\frac{11}{16}$	$2\frac{1}{2}$	$\frac{9}{16}$	$\frac{1}{2}$	$\frac{7}{8}$	$1\frac{3}{4}$
	25.0	3	$\frac{1}{2}$	$\frac{3}{8}$	$\frac{5}{16}$	$2\frac{5}{8}$	$9\frac{7}{8}$	$\frac{11}{16}$	$2\frac{1}{2}$	$\frac{7}{16}$	$\frac{1}{2}$	$\frac{7}{8}$	$1\frac{3}{4}$
	20.7	3	$\frac{1}{2}$	$\frac{5}{16}$	$\frac{1}{8}$	$2\frac{5}{8}$	$9\frac{7}{8}$	$\frac{11}{16}$	$2\frac{1}{2}$	$\frac{3}{8}$	$\frac{1}{2}$	$\frac{7}{8}$	$1\frac{3}{4}$
10	30.0	3	$\frac{7}{16}$	$\frac{11}{16}$	$\frac{3}{8}$	$2\frac{3}{8}$	$8\frac{1}{8}$	$\frac{15}{16}$	$2\frac{1}{2}$	$\frac{3}{4}$	$\frac{7}{16}$	$\frac{3}{4}$	$1\frac{3}{4}$
	25.0	$2\frac{7}{8}$	$\frac{7}{16}$	$\frac{9}{16}$	$\frac{1}{4}$	$2\frac{3}{8}$	$8\frac{1}{8}$	$\frac{15}{16}$	$2\frac{1}{2}$	$\frac{5}{8}$	$\frac{7}{16}$	$\frac{3}{4}$	$1\frac{3}{4}$
	20.0	$2\frac{3}{4}$	$\frac{7}{16}$	$\frac{3}{8}$	$\frac{5}{16}$	$2\frac{3}{8}$	$8\frac{1}{8}$	$\frac{15}{16}$	$2\frac{1}{2}$	$\frac{7}{16}$	$\frac{7}{16}$	$\frac{3}{4}$	$1\frac{1}{2}$
	15.3	$2\frac{5}{8}$	$\frac{7}{16}$	$\frac{1}{4}$	$\frac{1}{8}$	$2\frac{3}{8}$	$8\frac{1}{8}$	$\frac{15}{16}$	$2\frac{1}{2}$	$\frac{5}{16}$	$\frac{7}{16}$	$\frac{3}{4}$	$1\frac{1}{2}$
9	20.0	$2\frac{5}{8}$	$\frac{7}{16}$	$\frac{7}{16}$	$\frac{1}{4}$	$2\frac{1}{4}$	$7\frac{1}{4}$	$\frac{7}{8}$	$2\frac{1}{2}$	$\frac{1}{2}$	$\frac{7}{16}$	$\frac{3}{4}$	$1\frac{1}{2}$
	15.0	$2\frac{1}{2}$	$\frac{7}{16}$	$\frac{5}{16}$	$\frac{3}{16}$	$2\frac{1}{4}$	$7\frac{1}{4}$	$\frac{7}{8}$	$2\frac{1}{2}$	$\frac{3}{8}$	$\frac{7}{16}$	$\frac{3}{4}$	$1\frac{3}{8}$
	13.4	$2\frac{3}{8}$	$\frac{7}{16}$	$\frac{1}{4}$	$\frac{1}{8}$	$2\frac{1}{4}$	$7\frac{1}{4}$	$\frac{7}{8}$	$2\frac{1}{2}$	$\frac{5}{16}$	$\frac{3}{8}$	$\frac{3}{4}$	$1\frac{3}{8}$
8	18.75	$2\frac{1}{2}$	$\frac{3}{8}$	$\frac{1}{2}$	$\frac{1}{4}$	2	$6\frac{3}{8}$	$\frac{13}{16}$	$2\frac{1}{4}$	$\frac{9}{16}$	$\frac{3}{8}$	$\frac{3}{4}$	$1\frac{1}{2}$
	13.75	$2\frac{3}{8}$	$\frac{3}{8}$	$\frac{5}{16}$	$\frac{3}{16}$	2	$6\frac{3}{8}$	$\frac{13}{16}$	$2\frac{1}{4}$	$\frac{3}{8}$	$\frac{3}{8}$	$\frac{3}{4}$	$1\frac{3}{8}$
	11.5	$2\frac{1}{4}$	$\frac{3}{8}$	$\frac{1}{4}$	$\frac{1}{8}$	2	$6\frac{3}{8}$	$\frac{13}{16}$	$2\frac{1}{4}$	$\frac{5}{16}$	$\frac{3}{8}$	$\frac{3}{4}$	$1\frac{3}{8}$
7	14.75	$2\frac{1}{4}$	$\frac{3}{8}$	$\frac{7}{16}$	$\frac{1}{4}$	$1\frac{7}{8}$	$5\frac{3}{8}$	$\frac{13}{16}$	2	$\frac{1}{2}$	$\frac{3}{8}$	$\frac{5}{8}$	$1\frac{1}{4}$
	12.25	$2\frac{1}{4}$	$\frac{3}{8}$	$\frac{5}{16}$	$\frac{3}{16}$	$1\frac{7}{8}$	$5\frac{3}{8}$	$\frac{13}{16}$	2	$\frac{3}{8}$	$\frac{3}{8}$	$\frac{5}{8}$	$1\frac{1}{4}$
	9.8	$2\frac{1}{8}$	$\frac{3}{8}$	$\frac{1}{4}$	$\frac{1}{8}$	$1\frac{7}{8}$	$5\frac{3}{8}$	$\frac{13}{16}$	2	$\frac{5}{16}$	$\frac{3}{8}$	$\frac{5}{8}$	$1\frac{1}{4}$
6	13.0	$2\frac{1}{8}$	$\frac{3}{8}$	$\frac{7}{16}$	$\frac{1}{4}$	$1\frac{3}{4}$	$4\frac{1}{2}$	$\frac{3}{4}$	2	$\frac{1}{2}$	$\frac{5}{16}$	$\frac{5}{8}$	$1\frac{3}{8}$
	10.5	2	$\frac{3}{8}$	$\frac{5}{16}$	$\frac{3}{16}$	$1\frac{3}{4}$	$4\frac{1}{2}$	$\frac{3}{4}$	2	$\frac{3}{8}$	$\frac{3}{8}$	$\frac{5}{8}$	$1\frac{1}{8}$
	8.2	$1\frac{7}{8}$	$\frac{3}{8}$	$\frac{3}{16}$	$\frac{1}{8}$	$1\frac{3}{4}$	$4\frac{1}{2}$	$\frac{3}{4}$	2	$\frac{1}{4}$	$\frac{5}{16}$	$\frac{5}{8}$	$1\frac{1}{8}$
5	9.0	$1\frac{7}{8}$	$\frac{5}{16}$	$\frac{5}{16}$	$\frac{3}{16}$	$1\frac{1}{2}$	$3\frac{5}{8}$	$\frac{11}{16}$	2	$\frac{3}{8}$	$\frac{5}{16}$	$\frac{1}{2}$	$1\frac{1}{8}$
	6.7	$1\frac{3}{4}$	$\frac{5}{16}$	$\frac{3}{16}$	$\frac{1}{8}$	$1\frac{1}{2}$	$3\frac{5}{8}$	$\frac{11}{16}$	2	$\frac{1}{4}$	$\frac{5}{16}$	$\frac{1}{2}$	$1\frac{1}{8}$
4	7.25	$1\frac{3}{4}$	$\frac{5}{16}$	$\frac{5}{16}$	$\frac{3}{16}$	$1\frac{3}{8}$	$2\frac{3}{4}$	$\frac{5}{8}$	2	$\frac{3}{8}$	$\frac{5}{16}$	$\frac{1}{2}$	1
	5.4	$1\frac{5}{8}$	$\frac{5}{16}$	$\frac{3}{16}$	$\frac{1}{8}$	$1\frac{3}{8}$	$2\frac{3}{4}$	$\frac{5}{8}$	2	$\frac{1}{4}$	$\frac{1}{4}$	$\frac{1}{2}$	1
3	6.0	$1\frac{5}{8}$	$\frac{1}{4}$	$\frac{3}{8}$	$\frac{3}{16}$	$1\frac{1}{4}$	$1\frac{3}{4}$	$\frac{5}{8}$		$\frac{7}{16}$	$\frac{5}{16}$	$\frac{1}{2}$	$\frac{7}{8}$
	5.0	$1\frac{1}{2}$	$\frac{1}{4}$	$\frac{1}{4}$	$\frac{1}{8}$	$1\frac{1}{4}$	$1\frac{3}{4}$	$\frac{5}{8}$		$\frac{5}{16}$	$\frac{1}{4}$	$\frac{1}{2}$	$\frac{7}{8}$
	4.1	$1\frac{3}{8}$	$\frac{1}{4}$	$\frac{3}{16}$	$\frac{1}{8}$	$1\frac{1}{4}$	$1\frac{3}{4}$	$\frac{5}{8}$		$\frac{1}{4}$	$\frac{1}{4}$		

*Car and Shipbuilding Channel; not an American Standard.
Gage g_1 is based on $k + 1\frac{1}{4}''$, to nearest $\frac{1}{4}''$.
Gage g is permissible near ends of channel; elsewhere Specification may require reduction in rivet size.

TABLE 8. TEES
(American Institute of Steel Construction)

TEES

DIMENSIONS

AND

PROPERTIES FOR DESIGNING

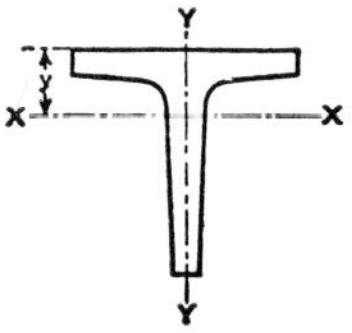

Nominal Size	Weight per Foot	Area	Depth	Width of Flange	Minimum Thickness Flange	Minimum Thickness Stem	AXIS X-X I	AXIS X-X S	AXIS X-X r	AXIS X-X y	AXIS Y-Y I	AXIS Y-Y S	AXIS Y-Y r
In.	Lb.	In.²	In.	In.	In.	In.	In.⁴	In.³	In.	In.	In.⁴	In.³	In.
5 x 3⅛	13.6	4.00	3⅛	5	½	13⁄32	2.7	1.1	.82	.76	5.2	2.1	1.14
5 x 3	11.5	3.37	3	5	⅜	13⁄32	2.4	1.1	.84	.76	3.9	1.6	1.10
4 x 4½	11.2	3.29	4½	4	⅜	⅜	6.3	2.0	1.39	1.31	2.1	1.1	.80
4 x 4	13.5	3.97	4	4	½	½	5.7	2.0	1.20	1.18	2.8	1.4	.84
4 x 3	9.2	2.68	3	4	⅜	⅜	2.0	.90	.86	.78	2.1	1.1	.89
4 x 2½	8.5	2.48	2½	4	⅜	⅜	1.2	.62	.69	.62	2.1	1.0	.92
3 x 3	7.8	2.29	3	3	⅜	⅜	1.84	.86	.89	.88	.89	.60	.63
3 x 3	6.7	1.97	3	3	5⁄16	5⁄16	1.61	.74	.90	.85	.75	.50	.62
3 x 2½	6.1	1.77	2½	3	5⁄16	5⁄16	.94	.51	.73	.68	.75	.50	.65
2½x2½	6.4	1.87	2½	2½	⅜	⅜	1.0	.59	.74	.76	.52	.42	.53
2½x2½	4.6	1.33	2½	2½	¼	¼	.74	.42	.75	.71	.34	.27	.51
2¼x2¼	4.1	1.19	2¼	2¼	¼	¼	.52	.32	.66	.65	.25	.22	.46
2 x 2	4.3	1.26	2	2	5⁄16	5⁄16	.44	.31	.59	.61	.23	.23	.43
2 x 2	3.56	1.05	2	2	¼	¼	.37	.26	.59	.59	.18	.18	.42

TABLE 9.   RIVETS, CONVENTIONAL SIGNS, AND GAUGES FOR ANGLES

DIMENSIONS OF STRUCTURAL RIVETS

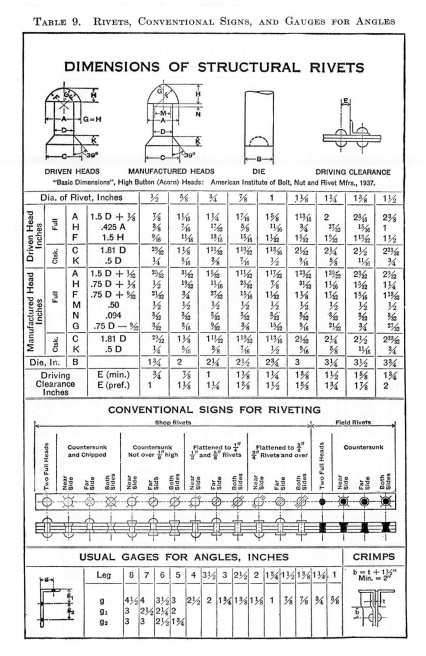

DRIVEN HEADS   MANUFACTURED HEADS   DIE   DRIVING CLEARANCE

"Basic Dimensions", High Button (Acorn) Heads: American Institute of Bolt, Nut and Rivet Mfrs., 1937.

Dia. of Rivet, Inches			$\frac{1}{2}$	$\frac{5}{8}$	$\frac{3}{4}$	$\frac{7}{8}$	1	$1\frac{1}{8}$	$1\frac{1}{4}$	$1\frac{3}{8}$	$1\frac{1}{2}$
Driven Head Inches Full	A	$1.5\,D + \frac{1}{8}$	$\frac{7}{8}$	$1\frac{1}{16}$	$1\frac{1}{4}$	$1\frac{7}{16}$	$1\frac{5}{8}$	$1\frac{13}{16}$	2	$2\frac{3}{16}$	$2\frac{3}{8}$
	H	$.425\,A$	$\frac{3}{8}$	$\frac{7}{16}$	$\frac{17}{32}$	$\frac{5}{8}$	$\frac{11}{16}$	$\frac{3}{4}$	$\frac{27}{32}$	$\frac{15}{16}$	1
	F	$1.5\,H$	$\frac{9}{16}$	$\frac{11}{16}$	$\frac{13}{16}$	$\frac{15}{16}$	$1\frac{1}{16}$	$1\frac{5}{32}$	$1\frac{9}{32}$	$1\frac{13}{32}$	$1\frac{1}{2}$
Ctsk.	C	$1.81\,D$	$\frac{29}{32}$	$1\frac{1}{8}$	$1\frac{11}{32}$	$1\frac{19}{32}$	$1\frac{13}{16}$	$2\frac{1}{32}$	$2\frac{1}{4}$	$2\frac{1}{2}$	$2\frac{23}{32}$
	K	$.5\,D$	$\frac{1}{4}$	$\frac{5}{16}$	$\frac{3}{8}$	$\frac{7}{16}$	$\frac{1}{2}$	$\frac{9}{16}$	$\frac{5}{8}$	$\frac{11}{16}$	$\frac{3}{4}$
Manufactured Head Inches Full	A	$1.5\,D + \frac{1}{2}$	$\frac{25}{32}$	$\frac{31}{32}$	$1\frac{5}{32}$	$1\frac{11}{32}$	$1\frac{17}{32}$	$1\frac{23}{32}$	$1\frac{29}{32}$	$2\frac{3}{32}$	$2\frac{9}{32}$
	H	$.75\,D + \frac{1}{8}$	$\frac{1}{2}$	$\frac{19}{32}$	$\frac{11}{16}$	$\frac{25}{32}$	$\frac{7}{8}$	$\frac{31}{32}$	$1\frac{1}{16}$	$1\frac{5}{32}$	$1\frac{1}{4}$
	F	$.75\,D + \frac{9}{32}$	$\frac{21}{32}$	$\frac{3}{4}$	$\frac{27}{32}$	$\frac{15}{16}$	$1\frac{1}{32}$	$1\frac{1}{8}$	$1\frac{7}{32}$	$1\frac{5}{16}$	$1\frac{13}{32}$
	M	$.50$	$\frac{1}{2}$	$\frac{1}{2}$	$\frac{1}{2}$	$\frac{1}{2}$	$\frac{1}{2}$	$\frac{1}{2}$	$\frac{1}{2}$	$\frac{1}{2}$	$\frac{1}{2}$
	N	$.094$	$\frac{3}{32}$	$\frac{3}{32}$	$\frac{3}{32}$	$\frac{3}{32}$	$\frac{3}{32}$	$\frac{3}{32}$	$\frac{3}{32}$	$\frac{3}{32}$	$\frac{3}{32}$
	G	$.75\,D - \frac{9}{32}$	$\frac{3}{32}$	$\frac{3}{16}$	$\frac{9}{32}$	$\frac{3}{8}$	$\frac{15}{32}$	$\frac{9}{16}$	$\frac{21}{32}$	$\frac{3}{4}$	$\frac{27}{32}$
Ctsk.	C	$1.81\,D$	$\frac{29}{32}$	$1\frac{1}{8}$	$1\frac{11}{32}$	$1\frac{19}{32}$	$1\frac{13}{16}$	$2\frac{1}{32}$	$2\frac{1}{4}$	$2\frac{1}{2}$	$2\frac{23}{32}$
	K	$.5\,D$	$\frac{1}{4}$	$\frac{5}{16}$	$\frac{3}{8}$	$\frac{7}{16}$	$\frac{1}{2}$	$\frac{9}{16}$	$\frac{5}{8}$	$\frac{11}{16}$	$\frac{3}{4}$
Die, In.	B		$1\frac{3}{4}$	2	$2\frac{1}{4}$	$2\frac{1}{2}$	$2\frac{3}{4}$	3	$3\frac{1}{4}$	$3\frac{1}{2}$	$3\frac{3}{4}$
Driving Clearance Inches	E (min.)		$\frac{3}{4}$	$\frac{7}{8}$	1	$1\frac{1}{8}$	$1\frac{1}{4}$	$1\frac{3}{8}$	$1\frac{1}{2}$	$1\frac{5}{8}$	$1\frac{3}{4}$
	E (pref.)		1	$1\frac{1}{8}$	$1\frac{1}{4}$	$1\frac{3}{8}$	$1\frac{1}{2}$	$1\frac{5}{8}$	$1\frac{3}{4}$	$1\frac{7}{8}$	2

CONVENTIONAL SIGNS FOR RIVETING

Shop Rivets — Field Rivets

Two Full Heads | Countersunk and Chipped (Near Side, Far Side, Both Sides) | Countersunk Not over $\frac{1}{8}''$ high (Near Side, Far Side, Both Sides) | Flattened to $\frac{1}{4}''$ — $\frac{1}{2}''$ and $\frac{5}{8}''$ Rivets (Near Side, Far Side, Both Sides) | Flattened to $\frac{3}{8}''$ — $\frac{3}{4}''$ Rivets and over (Near Side, Far Side, Both Sides) | Two Full Heads | Countersunk (Near Side, Far Side, Both Sides)

USUAL GAGES FOR ANGLES, INCHES

Leg	8	7	6	5	4	$3\frac{1}{2}$	3	$2\frac{1}{2}$	2	$1\frac{3}{4}$	$1\frac{1}{2}$	$1\frac{3}{8}$	$1\frac{1}{4}$	1
g	$4\frac{1}{2}$	4	$3\frac{1}{2}$	3	$2\frac{1}{2}$	2	$1\frac{3}{4}$	$1\frac{3}{8}$	$1\frac{1}{8}$	1	$\frac{7}{8}$	$\frac{7}{8}$	$\frac{3}{4}$	$\frac{5}{8}$
g_1	3	$2\frac{1}{2}$	$2\frac{1}{4}$	2										
g_2	3	3	$2\frac{1}{2}$	$1\frac{3}{4}$										

CRIMPS

$b = t + 1\frac{1}{2}''$

Min. = 2″

TABLE 10. GAUGES AND WEIGHTS OF SHEET METAL
(From "Fan Engineering," by permission of the Buffalo Forge Company)

GAUGES AND WEIGHTS OF SHEET METAL

Thickness in Inches. Weight in Lb per Sq Ft (except as noted)

Gauge Number	Manufacturers' Std Sheet Steel			Birmingham Wire Gauge (Copper)		American Wire Brown & Sharpe				
	Thickness*	Weight		Thickness	Wght (Oz)	Thickness	Weight			
		Steel	Galv				Copper	Brass	Aluminum	Magnesium
0000				.454	337¾	.4600	21.27	20.37	6.48	
000				.425	316	.4096	18.94	18.14	5.77	
00				.380	282½	.3648	16.87	16.15	5.14	
0				.340	252¾	.3249	14.39	14.39	4.58	
1				.300	223	.2893	12.81	12.81	4.08	
2				.284	211	.2576	11.41	11.41	3.63	
3	.2391	10.000		.259	192¾	.2294	10.61	10.16	3.23	
4	.2242	9.375		.238	177	.2043	9.450	9.05	2.88	
5	.2092	8.75		.220	163½	.1819	8.410	8.05	2.56	
6	.1943	8.125		.203	151	.1620	7.490	7.17	2.28	
7	.1793	7.500		.180	134	.1443	6.670	6.39	2.03	**
8	.1644	6.875	7.031	.165	122½	.1285	5.940	5.68	1.81	1.18
9	.1495	6.250	6.406	.148	110	.1144	5.290	5.07	1.61	
10	.1345	5.625	5.781	.134	99½	.1019	4.713	4.51	1.44	.940
11	.1196	5.000	5.156	.120	89¼	.0907	4.195	4.02	1.28	
12	.1046	4.375	4.531	.109	81.0	.0808	3.737	3.58	1.14	.746
13	.0897	3.750	3.906	.095	70.62	.0720	3.330	3.19	1.01	
14	.0747	3.125	3.281	.083	61.76	.0641	2.965	2.84	.903	.590
15	.0673	2.812	2.969	.072	53.58	.0571	2.641	2.53	.804	
16	.0598	2.500	2.656	.065	48.00	.0508	2.349	2.25	.716	.470
17	.0538	2.250	2.406	.058	43.16	.0453	2.095	2.01	.638	.415
18	.0478	2.000	2.156	.049	36.48	.0403	1.864	1.78	.568	.369
19	.0418	1.750	1.906	.042	31.25	.0359	1.660	1.59	.506	.332
20	.0359	1.500	1.656	.035	26.00	.0320	1.480	1.42	.450	.295
21	.0329	1.375	1.531	.032	24	.0285	1.318	1.26	.401	.258
22	.0299	1.250	1.406	.028	20.83	.0253	1.170	1.12	.357	.230
23	.0269	1.125	1.281	.025	18.6	.0226	1.045	1.00	.318	.212
24	.0239	1.000	1.156	.022	16.37	.0201	.930	.890	.283	.184
25	.0209	.875	1.031	.020	15	.0179	.828	.793	.252	
26	.0179	.750	.906	.018	13.32	.0159	.735	.706	.225	
27	.0164	.687	.844	.016	12	.0142	.657	.628	.200	
28	.0149	.625	.781	.014	10.42	.0126	.583	.560	.178	
29	.0135	.562	.719	.013	9.67	.0113	.523	.499	.159	
30	.0120	.500	.656	.012	9.00	.0100	.462	.444	.141	
31	.0105	.437	.594	.010	7.44	.0089	.413	.395	.126	
32	.0097	.406	.563	.009	6.70	.0080	.367	.352	.113	
33	.0090	.375	.531	.008	5.95	.0071	.327	.314	.100	
34	.0082	.343	.500	.007	5.20	.0063	.291	.28	.089	
35	.0075	.312		.005	3.73	.0056	.259	.249	.079	
36	.0067	.281		.004	2.98	.0050	.231	.221	.070	
37	.0064	.265				.0045	.205	.197	.063	
38	.0060	.250				.0040	.183	.176	.056	

*Thickness of galvanized sheets approximately .004 inch greater.
**Larger sizes rolled to plate thickness

TABLE 11. DATA ON TWELVE COMMON MACHINE SCREWS
Drawings Actual Size

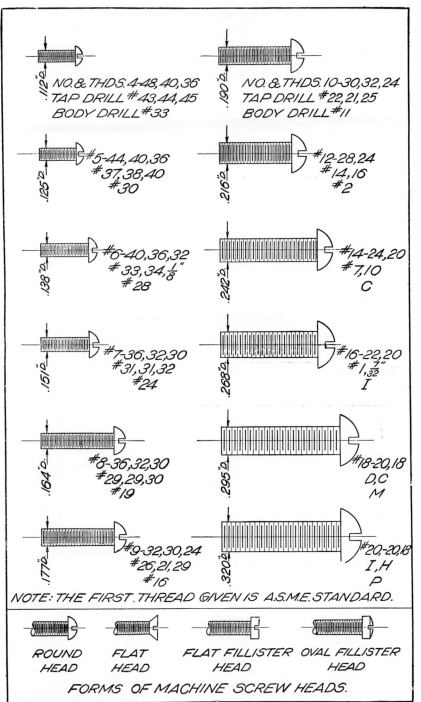

NO.& THDS. 4-48, 40, 36
TAP DRILL #43, 44, 45
BODY DRILL #33
.112"D.

NO.& THDS. 10-30, 32, 24.
TAP DRILL #22, 21, 25
BODY DRILL #11
.190"D.

#5-44, 40, 36
#37, 38, 40
#30
.125"D.

#12-28, 24
#14, 16
#2
.216"D.

#6-40, 36, 32
#33, 34, 1/8"
#28
.138"D.

#14-24, 20
#7, 10
C
.242"D.

#7-36, 32, 30
#31, 31, 32
#24
.151"D.

#16-22, 20
#1, 7/32"
I
.268"D.

#8-36, 32, 30
#29, 29, 30
#19
.164"D.

#18-20, 18
D, C
M
.295"D.

#9-32, 30, 24
#26, 21, 29
#16
.177"D.

#20-20, 18
I, H
P
.320"D.

NOTE: THE FIRST THREAD GIVEN IS A.S.M.E. STANDARD.

ROUND HEAD   FLAT HEAD   FLAT FILLISTER HEAD   OVAL FILLISTER HEAD

FORMS OF MACHINE SCREW HEADS.

Table 12. U. S. Standard Machine Bolts
Franklin Institute Standard

(Data from Locke Insulator Manufacturing Company)

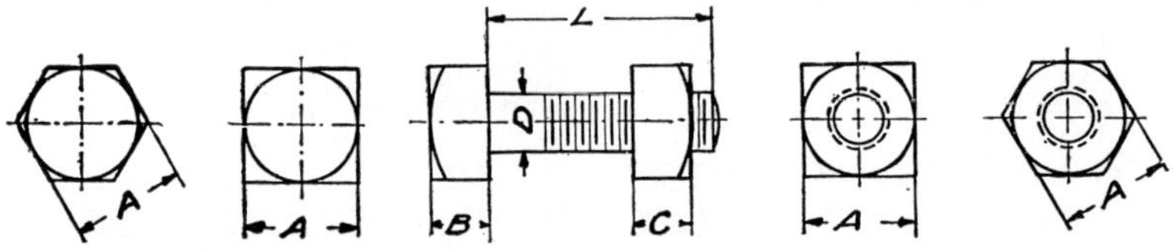

Dimensions in Inches

Size	*A*	*B*	*C*	Number of threads per inch
1/4	1/2	1/4	1/4	20
3/8	11/16	3/8	3/8	16
1/2	7/8	7/16	1/2	13
5/8	1 1/16	9/16	5/8	11
3/4	1 1/4	5/8	3/4	10
7/8	1 7/16	3/4	7/8	9
1	1 5/8	13/16	1	8

Length of Threading, Inches

Length bolt	Diameter of bolt						
	1/4	3/8	1/2	5/8	3/4	7/8	1
1 – 1 1/2	3/4	3/4	1	1 1/4			
1 5/8 – 2	3/4	3/4	1	1 1/4	1 1/2	1 1/2	
2 1/8 – 2 1/2	3/4	3/4	1	1 1/4	1 1/2	1 3/4	
2 5/8 – 3	7/8	7/8	1	1 1/4	1 1/2	1 3/4	1 3/4
3 1/8 – 4	7/8	7/8	1 1/4	1 1/4	1 1/2	1 3/4	1 3/4
4 1/8 – 8	1	1	1 1/4	1 1/2	1 3/4	2	2 1/4
8 1/8 – 12	1	1	1 1/2	1 3/4	2	2 1/4	2 1/2
12 1/8 – 20	1	1	1 1/2	2	2	2 1/4	2 1/2

Lengths not listed are threaded about three times the diameter.
No bolts are threaded closer to head than 1/4 in.

TABLE 13. BUTTON-HEAD CARRIAGE BOLTS

(*Data from "American Electricians' Handbook"*)

Dimensions in Inches

D Diameter	Number of threads per inch	T Thickness of head	S Length of square part	H Diameter of head	W Width of nut	N Thickness of nut	F Across corners of nut
$\frac{1}{4}$	20	$\frac{3}{32}$	$\frac{1}{4}$	$\frac{17}{32}$	$\frac{1}{2}$	$\frac{1}{4}$	$\frac{23}{32}$
$\frac{5}{16}$	18	$\frac{1}{8}$	$\frac{5}{16}$	$\frac{21}{32}$	$\frac{19}{32}$	$\frac{5}{16}$	$\frac{27}{32}$
$\frac{3}{8}$	16	$\frac{5}{32}$	$\frac{3}{8}$	$\frac{25}{32}$	$\frac{11}{16}$	$\frac{3}{8}$	$\frac{31}{32}$
$\frac{1}{2}$	13	$\frac{7}{32}$	$\frac{1}{2}$	$1\frac{1}{32}$	$\frac{7}{8}$	$\frac{1}{2}$	$1\frac{1}{4}$
$\frac{5}{8}$	11	$\frac{9}{32}$	$\frac{5}{8}$	$1\frac{9}{32}$	$1\frac{1}{16}$	$\frac{5}{8}$	$1\frac{1}{2}$
$\frac{3}{4}$	10	$\frac{3}{8}$	$\frac{3}{4}$	$1\frac{9}{16}$	$1\frac{1}{4}$	$\frac{3}{4}$	$1\frac{25}{32}$
$\frac{7}{8}$	9	$\frac{7}{16}$	$\frac{7}{8}$	$1\frac{13}{16}$	$1\frac{7}{16}$	$\frac{7}{8}$	$2\frac{1}{32}$
1	8	$\frac{1}{2}$	1	$2\frac{1}{16}$	$1\frac{5}{8}$	1	$2\frac{19}{64}$

TABLE 14.   PUNCHED WASHERS

(*Data from "American Electricians' Handbook"*)

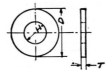

Dimensions in Inches

Diameter bolt	D Outside diameter	T Approximate thickness	H Diameter hole
$\frac{3}{16}$	$\frac{9}{16}$	$\frac{3}{64}$	$\frac{1}{4}$
$\frac{1}{4}$	$\frac{3}{4}$	$\frac{1}{16}$	$\frac{5}{16}$
$\frac{5}{16}$	$\frac{7}{8}$	$\frac{1}{16}$	$\frac{3}{8}$
$\frac{3}{8}$	1	$\frac{5}{64}$	$\frac{7}{16}$
$\frac{7}{16}$	$1\frac{1}{4}$	$\frac{5}{64}$	$\frac{1}{2}$
$\frac{1}{2}$	$1\frac{3}{8}$	$\frac{3}{32}$	$\frac{9}{16}$
$\frac{9}{16}$	$1\frac{1}{2}$	$\frac{3}{32}$	$\frac{5}{8}$
$\frac{5}{8}$	$1\frac{3}{4}$	$\frac{1}{8}$	$\frac{11}{16}$
$\frac{3}{4}$	2	$\frac{1}{8}$	$\frac{13}{16}$
$\frac{7}{8}$	$2\frac{1}{4}$	$\frac{5}{32}$	$\frac{15}{16}$
1	$2\frac{1}{2}$	$\frac{5}{32}$	$1\frac{1}{16}$
$1\frac{1}{8}$	$2\frac{3}{4}$	$\frac{5}{32}$	$1\frac{1}{4}$
$1\frac{1}{4}$	3	$\frac{5}{32}$	$1\frac{3}{8}$
$1\frac{3}{8}$	$3\frac{1}{4}$	$\frac{11}{64}$	$1\frac{1}{2}$
$1\frac{1}{2}$	$3\frac{1}{2}$	$\frac{11}{64}$	$1\frac{5}{8}$
$1\frac{5}{8}$	$3\frac{3}{4}$	$\frac{11}{64}$	$1\frac{3}{4}$
$1\frac{3}{4}$	4	$\frac{11}{64}$	$1\frac{7}{8}$
$1\frac{7}{8}$	$4\frac{1}{4}$	$\frac{11}{64}$	2
2	$4\frac{1}{2}$	$\frac{11}{64}$	$2\frac{1}{8}$

TABLE 15. GIMLET-POINTED LAG SCREWS

(Data from "American Electricians' Handbook")

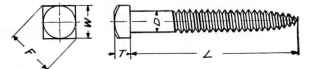

Dimensions in Inches

D Diameter	T Thickness of head	W Width of side of head	F Distance across corners	Clearance bore for body of screw	L
$\frac{1}{4}$	$\frac{3}{16}$	$\frac{3}{8}$	$^{17}\!/_{32}$	$\frac{5}{16}$	Screws increase in length by $\frac{1}{2}$ in. increments from $1\frac{1}{2}$ to and including 8 in. Screws from 8 to 12 in. increase in length by 1-in. increments. Screws of diameters of $\frac{1}{4}$, $\frac{5}{16}$ and $\frac{3}{8}$ in. are made in lengths of $1\frac{1}{2}$ in. to and including 6 in.; $\frac{7}{16}$ in. diameter from $1\frac{1}{2}$ to 9 in. long; $\frac{1}{2}$ in. diameter from $1\frac{1}{2}$ to 12 in.; $\frac{9}{16}$ and $\frac{5}{8}$ in. diameter from 2 to 12 in.; $\frac{3}{4}$ in. diameter from $2\frac{1}{2}$ to 12 in.; $\frac{7}{8}$ in. diameter from 3 to 12 in.; 1 in. diameter from $3\frac{1}{2}$ to 12 in. long.
$\frac{5}{16}$	$^{15}\!/_{64}$	$^{15}\!/_{32}$	$^{21}\!/_{32}$	$\frac{3}{8}$	
$\frac{3}{8}$	$^{9}\!/_{32}$	$^{9}\!/_{16}$	$^{51}\!/_{64}$	$\frac{7}{16}$	
$\frac{1}{2}$	$\frac{3}{8}$	$\frac{3}{4}$	$1\,\frac{1}{16}$	$\frac{9}{16}$	
$\frac{5}{8}$	$^{15}\!/_{32}$	$^{15}\!/_{16}$	$1^{21}\!/_{64}$	$1\frac{1}{16}$	
$\frac{3}{4}$	$^{9}\!/_{16}$	$1\,\frac{1}{8}$	$1^{19}\!/_{32}$	$1\frac{3}{16}$	
$\frac{7}{8}$	$^{21}\!/_{32}$	$1^{15}\!/_{16}$	$1^{55}\!/_{64}$	$1\frac{5}{16}$	
1	$\frac{3}{4}$	$1\,\frac{1}{2}$	$2\,\frac{1}{8}$	$1\frac{1}{16}$	

TABLE 16. WOOD SCREWS

(Dimensions from "American Electricians' Handbook")

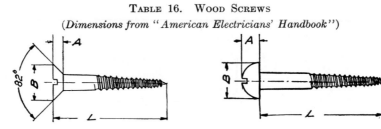

Dimensions in Inches

Screw gage No.	Diameter		Nearest B. & S. gage	Flat head		Round head		Counter bore for head	Clearance		Greatest length L obtainable
	In decimals	In fractions		A	B	A	B		No.	Diameter	
0	0.05784	1/16 −	15	1/16	7/64 +	....	....	....	....	......	3/8
1	0.07100	5/64 −	14	1/16	9/64 −	....	....	....	....	......	1/2
2	0.08416	5/64 +	12	1/16	5/32 +	1/16	13/64	7/32	44	0.086	7/8
3	0.09732	3/32 +	11	1/16	3/16	5/64	13/64	....	....	......	1 1/4
4	0.11048	7/64 +	9	1/16	7/32 −	5/64	13/64	7/32	33	0.113	1 1/2
5	0.12364	1/8	8	1/16	15/64 +	3/32	15/64	....	....	......	2 1/2
6	0.13680	9/64 −	7	5/64	17/64 +	3/32	1/4	17/64	28	0.1415	3
7	0.14996	5/32 −	7	3/32	19/64 −	7/64	3/32	....	....	......	3
8	0.16312	5/32 +	6	7/64	5/16 +	7/64	19/64	5/16	18	0.1695	4
9	0.17628	11/64 +	5	7/64	11/32 +	1/8	21/64	....	....	......	4
10	0.18944	3/16 +	5	7/64	3/8 −	1/8	11/32	23/64	10	0.1935	4
11	0.20260	13/64 −	4	1/8	25/64 +	9/64	3/8	....	....	......	4
12	0.21576	7/32 −	4	1/8	27/64	5/32	25/64	13/32	7/32	0.2188	6
13	0.22892	15/64 −	3	1/8	29/64	5/32	27/64	....	....	......	6
14	0.24208	1/4 −	3	9/64	15/32 +	5/32	29/64	29/64	1/4	0.250	6
15	0.25524	1/4 +	2	9/64	1/2	11/64	29/64	....	....	......	6
16	0.26840	17/64 +	2	5/32	17/32 −	11/64	31/64	....	....	......	6
17	0.28156	9/32	1	5/32	35/64 +	11/64	1/2	....	....	......	6
18	0.29472	19/64 −	1	11/64	37/64	3/16	17/32	35/64	....	0.302	6
19	0.30788	5/16 −	0	3/16	39/64	....	17/32	....	....	......	6
20	0.32104	21/64 −	0	13/64	5/8 +	13/64	9/16	37/64	....	0.323	6
21	0.33420	21/64 +	0	13/64	21/32	13/64	19/32	....	....	......	6
22	0.34736	11/32 +	0	13/64	11/16 −	7/32	5/8	....	....	......	6
23	0.36052	23/64 +	2/0	7/32	45/64 +	7/32	41/64	....	....	......	6
24	0.37368	3/8 −	2/0	7/32	47/64	15/64	21/32	43/64	....	0.377	6
25	0.38684	25/64 −	3/0	7/32	49/64 −	15/64	11/16	....	....	......	6
26	0.40000	13/32 −	3/0	15/64	25/32 +	....	45/64	....	....	......	6
27	0.41316	13/32 +	3/0	15/64	13/16	1/4	23/32	....	....	......	6
28	0.42632	27/64 +	3/0	1/4	27/32	1/4	47/64	....	....	......	6
29	0.43948	7/16 +	4/0	1/4	55/64 +	17/64	3/4	....	....	......	6
30	0.45264	29/64	4/0	17/64	57/64	9/32	25/32	....	....	......	6

TABLE 17. PIPE CHART

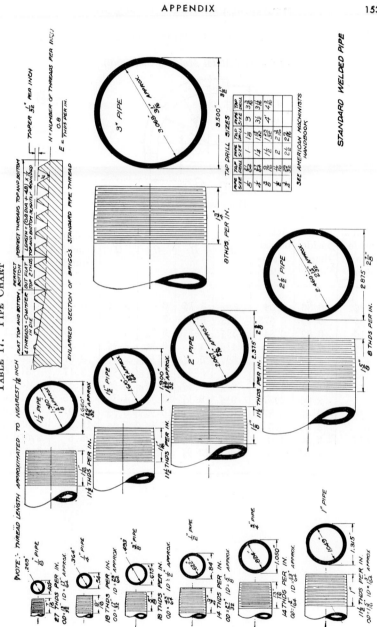

Table 18. Conduit Elbows

(National Metal Molding Company)

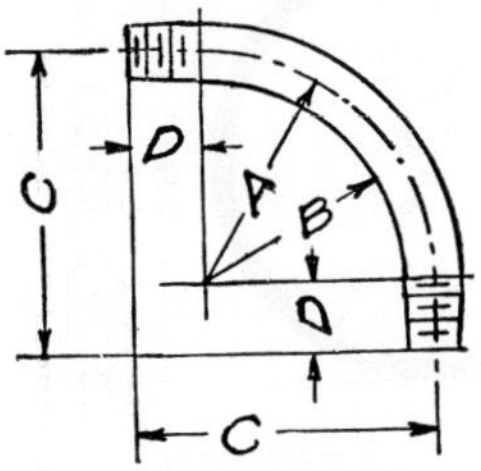

Dimensions in Inches

Nominal inside diameter	Actual inside diameter	Actual outside diameter	*A*	*B*	*C*	*D*	Weight each, pounds	Weight per 100, pounds
¼	0.36	0.54	3¾	3 ½	6	2 ⅜	0.415	41.5
⅜	0.49	0.675	3¾	3 7/16	7	2 ⅜	0.554	55.4
½	0.62	0.84	3¾	3 11/32	6 ¾	3	0.831	83.1
¾	0.82	1.05	4½	4	6 ⅞	2 ⅜	1.11	111.0
1	1.04	1.315	5¾	5 1/16	6 11/16	2 15/16	2.07	207.0
1¼	1.38	1.66	6⅝	5 25/32	9 15/16	3 5/16	3.17	317.0
1½	1.61	1.9	8⅜	7 7/16	11 11/16	3 5/16	4.41	441.0
2	2.06	2.375	9¼	8 ¼	13 ⅞	4 7/16	7.15	715.0
2½	2.46	2.875	10½	9 1/16	15 ¾	6 ¼	13.9	1,390.0
3	3.06	3.5	11¾	10	17 3/16	5 ½	18.5	1,850.0
3½	3.56	4.0	13¾	11 ¾	20 9/16	6 13/16	26.5	2,650.0
4	4.02	4.5	16	13 ¾	23	7	34.7	3,470.0

TABLE 19. PUNCHED STEEL LOCKNUTS

(*Data from "American Electricians' Handbook"*)

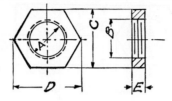

Dimensions in Inches

Nominal size of conduit	Threads per inch	A	B	C		D		E	
$\frac{3}{8}$	18	0.568	0.658	1		1 $\frac{1}{8}''$		$\frac{3}{16}$	
				Oct.	Hex.	Oct.	Hex.	Oct.	Hex.
$\frac{1}{2}$	14	0.701	0.815	1	1 $\frac{1}{16}$	1 $\frac{1}{16}$	1 $\frac{7}{32}$	$\frac{5}{32}$	$\frac{1}{8}$
$\frac{3}{4}$	14	0.911	1.025	1 $\frac{1}{4}$		1 $\frac{7}{16}$		$\frac{5}{32}$	
1	11$\frac{1}{2}$	1.144	1.283	1 $\frac{1}{2}$		1$\frac{29}{32}$		$\frac{3}{16}$	
1$\frac{1}{4}$	11$\frac{1}{2}$	1.488	1.627	2 $\frac{1}{32}$		2 $\frac{5}{16}$		$\frac{3}{16}$	
1$\frac{1}{2}$	11$\frac{1}{2}$	1.727	1.866	2 $\frac{1}{4}$		2 $\frac{9}{16}$		$\frac{3}{16}$	
2	11$\frac{1}{2}$	2.223	2.339	2$\frac{23}{32}$		3 $\frac{1}{8}$		$\frac{7}{32}$	
2$\frac{1}{2}$	8	2.620	2.820	3 $\frac{1}{4}$		3 $\frac{3}{4}$		$\frac{1}{4}$	
				Oct.	Hex.	Oct.	Hex.	Oct.	Hex.
3	8	3.241	3.441	4$\frac{1}{32}$	3$\frac{11}{16}$	4$\frac{1}{16}$	4	1$\frac{1}{32}$	1$\frac{7}{32}$

TABLE 20. MALLEABLE IRON BUSHINGS

(*Data from "American Electricians' Handbook"*)

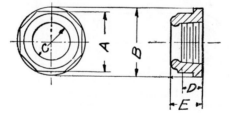

Dimensions in Inches

Nominal size of conduit	A	B	C	D	E
$\frac{3}{8}$	$\frac{25}{32}$	$\frac{27}{32}$	$\frac{15}{32}$	$\frac{3}{16}$	$\frac{11}{32}$
$\frac{1}{2}$	$\frac{15}{16}$	1 $\frac{1}{32}$	$\frac{19}{32}$	$\frac{1}{4}$	$\frac{13}{32}$
$\frac{3}{4}$	1 $\frac{5}{32}$	1 $\frac{1}{4}$	$\frac{3}{4}$	$\frac{1}{4}$	$\frac{15}{32}$
1	1$\frac{13}{32}$	1$\frac{17}{32}$	$\frac{31}{32}$	$\frac{5}{16}$	$\frac{17}{32}$
1$\frac{1}{4}$	1$\frac{11}{16}$	1$\frac{29}{32}$	1 $\frac{5}{16}$	$\frac{3}{8}$	$\frac{19}{32}$
1$\frac{1}{2}$	1$\frac{31}{32}$	2 $\frac{5}{32}$	1$\frac{17}{32}$	$\frac{13}{32}$	$\frac{5}{8}$
2	2$\frac{15}{32}$	2$\frac{11}{16}$	1$\frac{15}{16}$	$\frac{13}{32}$	2$\frac{1}{32}$
2$\frac{1}{2}$	2 $\frac{7}{8}$	3 $\frac{5}{32}$	2$\frac{11}{32}$	$\frac{15}{32}$	$\frac{3}{4}$
3	3$\frac{17}{32}$	3$\frac{25}{32}$	2$\frac{27}{32}$	$\frac{17}{32}$	$\frac{7}{8}$

TABLE 21. CONDUIT NIPPLES

(Data from "American Electricians' Handbook")

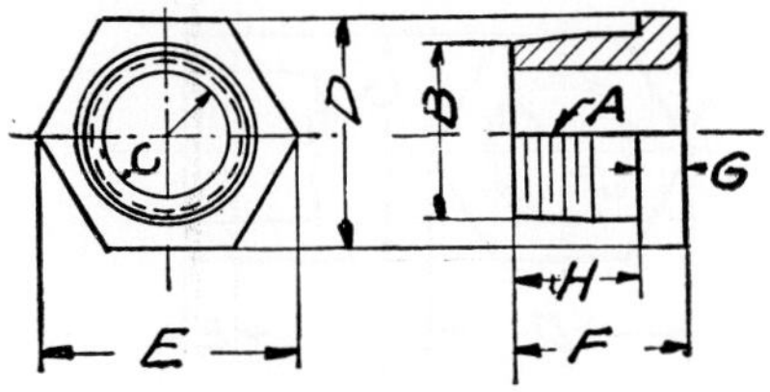

Dimensions in Inches

Size of conduit	*A* Threads per inch	*B* Diam. of threads	*C*	*D*	*E*	*F*	*G*	*H*
1/2	14.0	0.815	0.62	1.00	1.15	0.62	0.12	0.50
3/4	14.0	1.025	0.82	1.25	1.44	0.81	0.19	0.62
1	11.5	1.283	1.04	1.37	1.59	0.94	0.25	0.69
1 1/4	11.5	1.626	1.38	1.75	2.02	1.06	0.25	0.81
1 1/2	11.5	1.866	1.61	2.00	2.31	1.12	0.31	0.81
2	11.5	2.339	2.06	2.50	2.89	1.31	0.31	1.00
2 1/2	8.0	2.819	2.46	3.00	3.46	1.44	0.37	1.06
3	8.0	3.441	3.06	3.75	4.33	1.50	0.37	1.12
3 1/2	8.0	3.938	3.54	4.25	4.91	1.62	0.44	1.19

TABLE 22. COUPLINGS

(Dimensions from "American Electricians' Handbook")

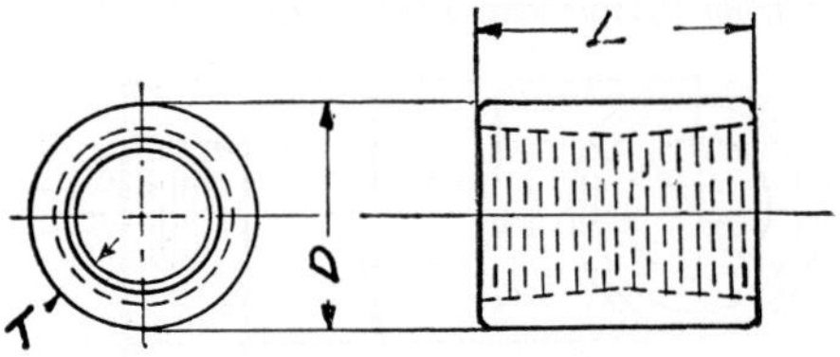

Dimensions in Inches

D Outside diameter	*L* Length	*T* Thickness	Weight of 100 pounds
1 3/32	1 5/16	1/4	15 1/2
1 11/32	1 9/16	19/64	25 1/2
1 21/32	1 3/4	11/32	40 1/2
2	1 15/16	11/32	57 1/2
2 9/32	2 3/16	3/8	71 1/4
2 27/32	2 5/16	1 15/32	132
3 9/32	2 11/16	17/32	185
4 1/64	3	33/64	300
4 1/2	2 1/8	1/2	400
5 3/32	3 1/8	1/2	412

TABLE 23. SPACING FOR CONDUITS WITH LOCKNUTS OR NIPPLES

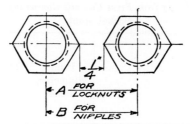

Dimensions in Inches

Conduit size	Locknut		Nipples B
	A	Shape	
½	1 $\frac{5}{32}$	Hex.	1 $\frac{7}{16}$
½	1 $\frac{5}{16}$	Oct.	
¾	1$\frac{11}{16}$	Hex.	1$\frac{23}{32}$
1	1$\frac{31}{32}$	Hex.	1$\frac{27}{32}$
1¼	2 $\frac{9}{16}$	Hex.	2 $\frac{9}{32}$
1½	2$\frac{13}{16}$	Hex.	2 $\frac{9}{16}$
2	3 $\frac{3}{8}$	Hex.	3 $\frac{5}{32}$
2½	4	Hex.	3$\frac{23}{32}$
3	4 ¼	Hex.	4$\frac{19}{32}$
3	4$\frac{15}{16}$	Oct.	
3½	. . . . .	. . . .	5 $\frac{5}{32}$

¼ in. between locknuts and nipples is the minimum recommended. If this is increased or decreased, then A or B must be changed by the same amount.

The ½- and 3-in. sizes of locknuts come in both the hexagonal and octagonal shapes. Others hexagonal only.

For sizes of locknuts, see Table 19; for sizes of nipples, Table 21.

TABLE 24.   DIMENSIONS OF FIBRE CONDUIT
(Data from Fibre Conduit Company)
Socket Joint

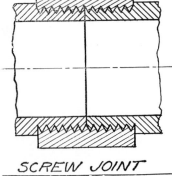

	Inside diameter, inches	Thickness of wall, inch	Approximate weight per foot, net pounds
	1	$\frac{1}{4}$	0.40
	$1\frac{1}{2}$	$\frac{1}{4}$	0.70
	2	$\frac{1}{4}$	0.90
	$2\frac{1}{2}$	$\frac{1}{4}$	1.10
	3	$\frac{1}{4}$	1.30
	$3\frac{1}{2}$	$\frac{1}{4}$	1.50
	4	$\frac{1}{4}$	1.85

SOCKET JOINT

Harrington Joint

	Inside diameter, inches	Thickness of wall, inch	Approximate weight per foot, net pounds
	2	$\frac{1}{4}$	0.95
	$2\frac{1}{2}$	$\frac{1}{4}$	1.20
	3	$\frac{1}{4}$	1.40
	$3\frac{1}{2}$	$\frac{1}{4}$	1.65
	4	$\frac{1}{4}$	2.00

HARRINGTON JOINT

Screw Joint

	Inside diameter, inches	Thickness of wall, inch	Approximate weight per foot, net pounds
	$1\frac{1}{2}$	$\frac{5}{16}$	1.00
	2	$\frac{3}{8}$	1.50
	$2\frac{1}{2}$	$\frac{3}{8}$	1.90
	3	$\frac{7}{16}$	2.50
	$3\frac{1}{2}$	$\frac{7}{16}$	3.00
	4	$\frac{1}{2}$	3.70

SCREW JOINT

TABLE 25. FIBRE CONDUIT FITTINGS
(*The Fibre Conduit Co.*)

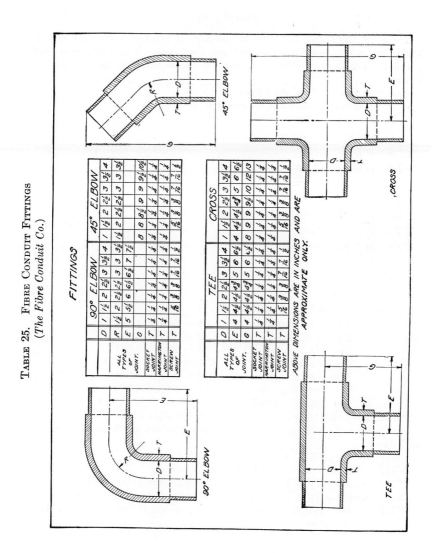

ABOVE DIMENSIONS ARE IN INCHES AND ARE APPROXIMATE ONLY.

CONDULETS

The condulets shown are a few of the popular types of a complete line of wiring devices made by the Crouse-Hinds Company. The company is prepared to furnish engineering information on its complete line of wiring devices.

How to Remember Condulet Types.

A   is first and looks like an inverted *A*
B   is Bent (90 deg)
C   looks like a Canoe
E   is End
LB   is L turning Back
LF   is L turning Front
LL   is L with L at Left
LR   is L with L at Right
LBB   is L Bent Back
LFB   is L Bent Front
T   is letter T
U   is letter U
X   is letter X

Crouse-Hinds Catalogue Numbering

1 = ½-in. conduit
2 = ¾-in. conduit
3 = 1-in. conduit
4 = 1¼-in. conduit
5 = 1½-in. conduit
6 = 2-in. conduit
7 = 2½-in. conduit

8 = 3-in. conduit
9 = 3½-in. conduit
10 = 4-in. conduit
011 = 4½-in. conduit
012 = 5-in. conduit
014 = 6-in. conduit

All obround condulets have a "7" as the last digit.

Application of the System. The catalogue numbers are to be interpreted as follows:

A17   means a ½-in. Type A obround condulet.
LB37   means a 1-in. Type LB obround condulet.
T367   means a Type T, run 1-in., tap 2-in., obround condulet.
T417   means a Type T, run 1¼-in., tap ½-in., obround condulet.
X417   means Type X (clockwise facing opening), 1¼-in. run, ½-in. tap, and repeat.

TABLE 26.   CROUSE-HINDS CONDULETS—TYPE A

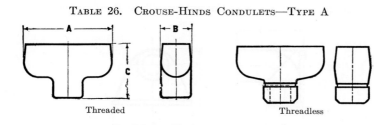

Threaded   Threadless

DIMENSIONS IN INCHES

Cat. No.	Size	A	B	C
A17	$\frac{1}{2}$	$3\frac{5}{8}$	$1\frac{5}{16}$	$2\frac{1}{4}$
A27	$\frac{3}{4}$	$4\frac{1}{4}$	$1\frac{1}{2}$	$2\frac{1}{2}$
A37	1	5	$1\frac{3}{4}$	$2\frac{7}{8}$
A47	$1\frac{1}{4}$	$5\frac{1}{2}$	$2\frac{3}{16}$	$3\frac{5}{16}$
A57	$1\frac{1}{2}$	6	$2\frac{7}{16}$	$3\frac{11}{16}$
A67	2	7	3	$5\frac{1}{4}$
A77	$2\frac{1}{2}$	9	$4\frac{1}{4}$	6
A87	3	9	$4\frac{1}{4}$	$6\frac{13}{16}$
A97	$3\frac{1}{2}$	11	$5\frac{1}{4}$	$7\frac{13}{16}$
A107	4	11	$5\frac{1}{4}$	$8\frac{5}{16}$
A0127	5	$11\frac{1}{2}$	$7\frac{3}{8}$	$8\frac{1}{2}$
A0147	6	$11\frac{1}{2}$	$7\frac{3}{8}$	$10\frac{1}{4}$

TABLE 27.   CROUSE-HINDS CONDULETS—TYPE B—ONE-PIECE

Dimensions in Inches

Cat. No.	Size	A	B	C
B17	$\frac{1}{2}$	$3\frac{11}{16}$	$2\frac{1}{4}$	$1\frac{3}{8}$
B27	$\frac{3}{4}$	$4\frac{5}{16}$	$2\frac{7}{16}$	$1\frac{5}{8}$
B37	1	5	$2\frac{3}{4}$	$1\frac{7}{8}$

TABLE 28. CROUSE-HINDS CONDULETS—TYPE B—TWO-PIECE

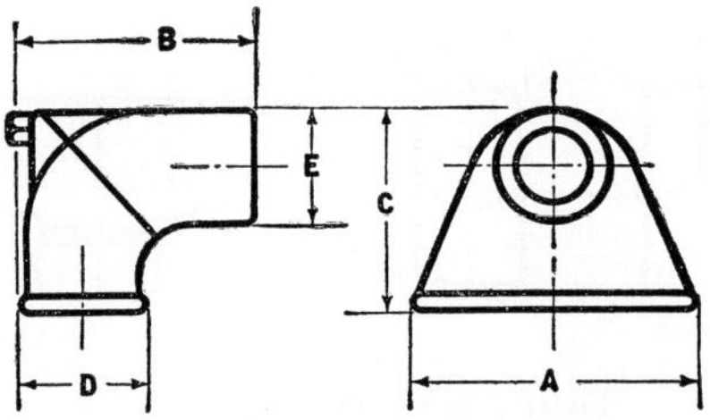

Dimensions in Inches

Cat. No.	Size	*A*	*B*	*C*	*D*	*E*
*B*47	1¼	5¾	4⅝	4 1/16	2 7/16	2 3/16
*B*57	1½	6¼	5 1/16	4 7/16	2 11/16	2 7/16
*B*67	2	7¼	5 9/16	5	3¼	3
*B*77	2½	9¼	7 5/16	6⅜	4½	3½
*B*87	3	9¼	7 5/16	6⅜	4½	4¼
*B*97	3½	11¼	9 11/16	8⅜	5½	4¾
*B*107	4	11¼	9 11/16	8⅜	5½	5¼
*B*0127	5	12	14⅛	12 9/16	7⅞	6½
*B*0147	6	12	14⅛	12 9/16	7⅞	7⅝

TABLE 29. CROUSE-HINDS CONDULETS—TYPE C

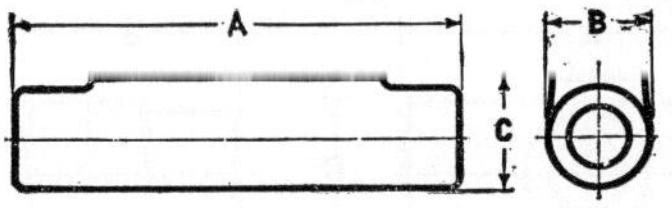

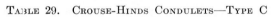

Dimensions in Inches

Cat. No.	Size	*A*	*B*	*C*
*C*187	⅛	2 7/16	1 3/16	¾
*C*287	¼	3½	1	1⅛
*C*387	⅜	4⅜	1⅛	1¼
*C*17	½	5⅜	1⅜	1⅜
*C*27	¾	6	1 9/16	1⅝
*C*37	1	7	1¾	1⅞
*C*47	1¼	7 7/16	2 3/16	2 5/16
*C*57	1½	8 3/16	2 7/16	2 9/16
*C*67	2	9 3/16	3	3⅛
*C*77	2½	11¾	4¼	3⅝
*C*87	3	11¾	4¼	4⅜
*C*97	3½	14 5/16	5¼	4⅞
*C*107	4	14 5/16	5¼	5⅜

TABLE 30.   CROUSE-HINDS CONDULETS—TYPE E

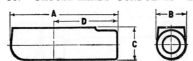

Dimensions in Inches

Cat. No.	Size	A	B	C	D
E17	½	4 9/16	1 3/8	1 3/8	2 3/4
E27	3/4	5 3/16	1 9/16	1 5/8	3
E37	1	6	1 3/4	1 7/8	3 1/2
E47	1 1/4	6 1/2	2 3/16	2 5/16	3 3/4
E57	1 1/2	7 1/8	2 7/16	2 9/16	4 1/8
E67	2	8 1/8	3	3 1/8	4 5/8
E77	2 1/2	10 3/8	4 1/4	3 5/8	5 7/8
E87	3	10 3/8	4 1/4	4 3/8	5 7/8
E97	3 1/2	12 11/16	5 1/4	4 7/8	7 1/8
E107	4	12 11/16	5 1/4	5 3/8	7 1/8

TABLE 31.   CROUSE-HINDS CONDULETS—TYPE F

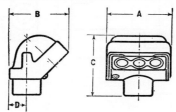

Dimensions in Inches

Cat. No.	Size	A	B	C	D
F163	½	2 15/16	2 3/4	2 5/8	1 3/16
F263	3/4	2 15/16	2 3/4	2 5/8	1 5/16
F363	1	3 5/16	2 15/16	2 13/16	1 1/16
F463	1 1/4	3 13/16	3 15/16	3 9/16	1 1/4
F563	1 1/2	4 13/16	5	4 1/16	1 3/8
F663	2	6 5/8	6 7/16	4 5/8	1 11/16

TABLE 32.   CROUSE-HINDS CONDULETS—TYPE LF

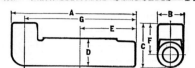

Dimensions in Inches

Cat. No.	Size	A	B	C	D	E	F	G
LF17	$\frac{1}{2}$	$6\frac{1}{8}$	$\frac{15}{16}$	$2\frac{1}{8}$	$1\frac{3}{4}$	$2\frac{3}{4}$	$1\frac{1}{2}$	$5\frac{1}{2}$
LF27	$\frac{3}{4}$	7	$1\frac{1}{2}$	$2\frac{3}{8}$	$1\frac{5}{8}$	$3\frac{1}{16}$	$1\frac{5}{8}$	$6\frac{1}{4}$
LF37	1	$8\frac{1}{16}$	$1\frac{3}{4}$	$2\frac{3}{4}$	$1\frac{7}{8}$	$3\frac{1}{2}$	$1\frac{7}{8}$	$7\frac{3}{16}$
LF47	$1\frac{1}{4}$	$9\frac{1}{16}$	$2\frac{3}{16}$	$3\frac{3}{16}$	$2\frac{5}{16}$	$3\frac{3}{4}$	$2\frac{1}{16}$	$7\frac{13}{16}$
LF57	$1\frac{1}{2}$	$9\frac{15}{16}$	$2\frac{7}{16}$	$3\frac{9}{16}$	$2\frac{9}{16}$	$4\frac{1}{8}$	$2\frac{5}{16}$	$8\frac{11}{16}$
LF67	2	$11\frac{1}{2}$	3	$4\frac{1}{8}$	$3\frac{1}{8}$	$4\frac{5}{8}$	$2\frac{9}{16}$	10
LF777	$2\frac{1}{2}$	$14\frac{3}{8}$	$4\frac{1}{4}$	$4\frac{7}{8}$	$3\frac{5}{8}$	$5\frac{7}{8}$	$3\frac{1}{8}$	$12\frac{5}{8}$
LF87	3	$15\frac{1}{8}$	$4\frac{1}{4}$	$5\frac{5}{8}$	$3\frac{3}{4}$	$5\frac{7}{8}$	$3\frac{1}{2}$	13
LF97	$3\frac{1}{2}$	$18\frac{3}{16}$	$5\frac{1}{4}$	$6\frac{7}{16}$	$4\frac{7}{8}$	$7\frac{3}{16}$	$4\frac{1}{16}$	$15\frac{13}{16}$
LF107	4	$18\frac{11}{16}$	$5\frac{1}{4}$	$6\frac{15}{16}$	$5\frac{3}{8}$	$7\frac{3}{16}$	$4\frac{5}{16}$	$16\frac{1}{16}$

TABLE 33.   CROUSE-HINDS CONDULETS—TYPE LB

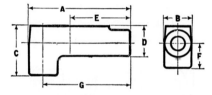

Dimensions in Inches

Cat. No.	Size	A	B	C	D	E	F	G
LB187	$\frac{1}{8}$	2	$\frac{3}{4}$	$1\frac{3}{16}$	$\frac{3}{4}$	$1\frac{1}{4}$	$\frac{3}{4}$	$1\frac{11}{16}$
LB287	$\frac{1}{4}$	$2\frac{15}{16}$	$\frac{7}{8}$	$1\frac{11}{16}$	$1\frac{1}{8}$	$1\frac{3}{4}$	1	$2\frac{1}{2}$
LB387	$\frac{3}{8}$	$3\frac{5}{8}$	1	2	$1\frac{1}{4}$	$2\frac{3}{16}$	$1\frac{1}{4}$	$3\frac{1}{8}$
LB17	$\frac{1}{2}$	$4\frac{9}{16}$	$1\frac{5}{16}$	$2\frac{1}{4}$	$1\frac{3}{8}$	$2\frac{3}{4}$	$1\frac{1}{2}$	$3\frac{15}{16}$
LB27	$\frac{3}{4}$	$5\frac{3}{16}$	$1\frac{1}{2}$	$2\frac{1}{2}$	$1\frac{5}{8}$	$3\frac{1}{16}$	$1\frac{5}{8}$	$4\frac{7}{16}$
LB37	1	6	$1\frac{3}{4}$	$2\frac{7}{8}$	$1\frac{7}{8}$	$3\frac{1}{2}$	$1\frac{7}{8}$	$5\frac{1}{8}$
LB47	$1\frac{1}{4}$	$6\frac{1}{2}$	$2\frac{3}{16}$	$3\frac{5}{16}$	$2\frac{5}{16}$	$3\frac{3}{4}$	$2\frac{1}{16}$	$5\frac{3}{8}$
LB57	$1\frac{1}{2}$	$7\frac{1}{8}$	$2\frac{7}{16}$	$3\frac{11}{16}$	$2\frac{9}{16}$	$4\frac{1}{8}$	$2\frac{5}{16}$	$5\frac{7}{8}$
LB67	2	$8\frac{1}{8}$	3	$4\frac{1}{4}$	$3\frac{1}{8}$	$4\frac{5}{8}$	$2\frac{5}{8}$	$6\frac{5}{8}$
LB77	$2\frac{1}{2}$	$10\frac{3}{8}$	$4\frac{1}{4}$	5	$3\frac{5}{8}$	$5\frac{7}{8}$	$3\frac{1}{8}$	$8\frac{5}{8}$
LB87	3	$10\frac{3}{8}$	$4\frac{1}{4}$	$5\frac{3}{4}$	$4\frac{3}{8}$	$5\frac{7}{8}$	$3\frac{1}{2}$	$8\frac{1}{4}$
LB97	$3\frac{1}{2}$	$12\frac{11}{16}$	$5\frac{1}{4}$	$6\frac{9}{16}$	$4\frac{7}{8}$	$7\frac{3}{16}$	$4\frac{1}{16}$	$10\frac{5}{16}$
LB107	4	$12\frac{11}{16}$	$5\frac{1}{4}$	$7\frac{1}{16}$	$5\frac{3}{8}$	$7\frac{3}{16}$	$4\frac{5}{16}$	$10\frac{1}{16}$

TABLE 34.   CROUSE-HINDS CONDULETS—TYPE LBD

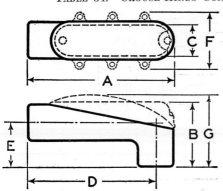

Dimensions

Cat. No.	Size	A	B	C	D	E	F	G
LBD1100	½	5	2⁵⁄₁₆	1¼	4⅜	1½	—	—
LBD2200	¾	6¼	2½	1½	5½	1⅝	—	—
LBD3300	1	6¼	2⅞	1¾	5⅜	1⅞	—	—
LBD4400	1¼	8⅝	—	2³⁄₁₆	7½	2¹⁄₁₆	3½	4¼
LBD5500	1½	12⁷⁄₁₆	—	3	11³⁄₁₆	2⅜	4⅝	5⁷⁄₁₆
LBD6600	2	12⁷⁄₁₆	—	3	10¹⁵⁄₁₆	2⅝	4⅝	5⁷⁄₁₆
LBD7700	2½	17	—	4¼	15³⁄₁₆	3⁵⁄₁₆	5¹³⁄₁₆	7¼
LBD8800	3	17	—	4¼	14⅞	3¹¹⁄₁₆	5¹³⁄₁₆	7¼
LBD9900	3½	22¹⁄₁₆	—	5¼	19⁷⁄₁₆	4¼	7⅜	9¾
LBD10900	4	22¹⁄₁₆	—	5¼	19⁷⁄₁₆	4¼	7⅜	9¾
LBD011	4½	32⁷⁄₁₆	—	6½	29³⁄₁₆	5⅛	8⅝	12⅜
LBD012	5	32⁷⁄₁₆	—	6½	29³⁄₁₆	5⅛	8⅝	12⅜
LBD014	6	41½	—	7⅝	37¹¹⁄₁₆	5⅝	9¾	15

Table 35. Crouse-Hinds Condulets—Type T

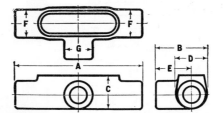

Dimensions in Inches

Cat. No.	Size	A	B	C	D	E	F	G
T187	$\frac{1}{8}$-$\frac{1}{8}$-$\frac{1}{8}$	$2\frac{7}{16}$	$1\frac{1}{4}$	$\frac{3}{4}$	$\frac{13}{16}$	$\frac{7}{8}$	$\frac{5}{8}$	$\frac{5}{8}$
T287	$\frac{1}{4}$-$\frac{1}{4}$-$\frac{1}{4}$	$3\frac{1}{2}$	$1\frac{9}{16}$	$1\frac{1}{8}$	1	$1\frac{1}{16}$	$\frac{7}{8}$	$\frac{7}{8}$
T387	$\frac{3}{8}$-$\frac{3}{8}$-$\frac{3}{8}$	$4\frac{3}{8}$	$1\frac{7}{8}$	$1\frac{1}{4}$	$1\frac{1}{8}$	$1\frac{5}{16}$	1	1
T17	$\frac{1}{2}$-$\frac{1}{2}$-$\frac{1}{2}$	$5\frac{5}{8}$	$2\frac{7}{16}$	$1\frac{3}{4}$	$1\frac{9}{16}$	$1\frac{11}{16}$	$1\frac{1}{4}$	$1\frac{1}{4}$
T127	$\frac{1}{2}$-$\frac{1}{2}$-$\frac{3}{4}$	$5\frac{5}{8}$	$2\frac{7}{16}$	$1\frac{3}{4}$	$1\frac{9}{16}$	$1\frac{11}{16}$	$1\frac{1}{4}$	$1\frac{1}{2}$
T137	$\frac{1}{2}$-$\frac{1}{2}$-1	$5\frac{5}{8}$	$2\frac{9}{16}$	$1\frac{7}{8}$	$1\frac{9}{16}$	$1\frac{13}{16}$	$1\frac{1}{4}$	$1\frac{3}{4}$
T217	$\frac{3}{4}$-$\frac{3}{4}$-$\frac{1}{2}$	$6\frac{1}{4}$	$2\frac{5}{8}$	2	$1\frac{3}{4}$	$1\frac{3}{4}$	$1\frac{1}{2}$	$1\frac{1}{4}$
T27	$\frac{3}{4}$-$\frac{3}{4}$-$\frac{3}{4}$	$6\frac{1}{4}$	$2\frac{5}{8}$	2	$1\frac{3}{4}$	$1\frac{3}{4}$	$1\frac{1}{2}$	$1\frac{1}{2}$
T237	$\frac{3}{4}$-$\frac{3}{4}$-1	$6\frac{1}{4}$	$2\frac{3}{4}$	2	$1\frac{3}{4}$	$1\frac{7}{8}$	$1\frac{1}{2}$	$1\frac{3}{4}$
T257	$\frac{3}{4}$-$\frac{3}{4}$-$1\frac{1}{2}$	$6\frac{1}{4}$	$2\frac{7}{8}$	$2\frac{9}{16}$	$1\frac{3}{4}$	2	$1\frac{1}{2}$	$2\frac{7}{16}$
T317	1-1-$1\frac{1}{2}$	$7\frac{1}{4}$	$2\frac{7}{8}$	$2\frac{1}{4}$	2	$1\frac{7}{8}$	$1\frac{3}{4}$	$1\frac{1}{2}$
T327	1-1-$\frac{3}{4}$	$7\frac{1}{4}$	$2\frac{7}{8}$	$2\frac{1}{4}$	2	$1\frac{7}{8}$	$1\frac{3}{4}$	$1\frac{1}{2}$
T37	1-1-1	$7\frac{1}{4}$	3	$2\frac{1}{4}$	2	$2\frac{1}{16}$	$1\frac{3}{4}$	$1\frac{3}{4}$
T367	1-1-2	$7\frac{1}{4}$	$3\frac{1}{8}$	$3\frac{1}{8}$	2	$2\frac{1}{8}$	$1\frac{3}{4}$	2
T417	$1\frac{1}{4}$-$1\frac{1}{4}$-$\frac{1}{2}$	$7\frac{7}{16}$	$3\frac{1}{16}$	$2\frac{9}{16}$	$2\frac{3}{16}$	$1\frac{15}{16}$	$2\frac{3}{16}$	$1\frac{1}{4}$
T427	$1\frac{1}{4}$-$1\frac{1}{4}$-$\frac{3}{4}$	$7\frac{7}{16}$	$3\frac{1}{16}$	$2\frac{9}{16}$	$2\frac{3}{16}$	$1\frac{15}{16}$	$2\frac{3}{16}$	$1\frac{1}{2}$
T437	$1\frac{1}{4}$-$1\frac{1}{4}$-1	$7\frac{7}{16}$	$3\frac{3}{16}$	$2\frac{9}{16}$	$2\frac{3}{16}$	$2\frac{1}{16}$	$2\frac{3}{16}$	$1\frac{3}{4}$
T47	$1\frac{1}{4}$-$1\frac{1}{4}$-$1\frac{1}{4}$	$7\frac{7}{16}$	$3\frac{3}{16}$	$2\frac{9}{16}$	$2\frac{3}{16}$	$2\frac{1}{16}$	$2\frac{3}{16}$	$2\frac{7}{16}$
T457	$1\frac{1}{4}$-$1\frac{1}{4}$-$1\frac{1}{2}$	$7\frac{7}{16}$	$3\frac{5}{16}$	$2\frac{9}{16}$	$2\frac{3}{16}$	$2\frac{3}{16}$	$2\frac{3}{16}$	$2\frac{7}{16}$
T467	$1\frac{1}{4}$-$1\frac{1}{4}$-2	$7\frac{7}{16}$	$3\frac{5}{16}$	$3\frac{1}{8}$	$2\frac{3}{16}$	$2\frac{9}{16}$	$2\frac{3}{16}$	3
T517	$1\frac{1}{2}$-$1\frac{1}{2}$-$\frac{1}{2}$	$8\frac{3}{16}$	$3\frac{5}{16}$	$2\frac{9}{16}$	$2\frac{7}{16}$	$2\frac{1}{16}$	$2\frac{7}{16}$	$1\frac{1}{4}$
T527	$1\frac{1}{2}$-$1\frac{1}{2}$-$\frac{3}{4}$	$8\frac{3}{16}$	$3\frac{5}{16}$	$2\frac{9}{16}$	$2\frac{7}{16}$	$2\frac{1}{16}$	$2\frac{7}{16}$	$1\frac{1}{2}$
T537	$1\frac{1}{2}$-$1\frac{1}{2}$-1	$8\frac{3}{16}$	$3\frac{7}{16}$	$2\frac{9}{16}$	$2\frac{7}{16}$	$2\frac{3}{16}$	$2\frac{7}{16}$	$1\frac{3}{4}$
T547	$1\frac{1}{2}$-$1\frac{1}{2}$-$1\frac{1}{4}$	$8\frac{3}{16}$	$3\frac{7}{16}$	$2\frac{9}{16}$	$2\frac{7}{16}$	$2\frac{3}{16}$	$2\frac{7}{16}$	$2\frac{7}{16}$
T57	$1\frac{1}{2}$-$1\frac{1}{2}$-$1\frac{1}{2}$	$8\frac{3}{16}$	$3\frac{9}{16}$	$2\frac{9}{16}$	$2\frac{7}{16}$	$2\frac{5}{16}$	$2\frac{7}{16}$	$2\frac{7}{16}$
T567	$1\frac{1}{2}$-$1\frac{1}{2}$-2	$8\frac{3}{16}$	$3\frac{9}{16}$	$3\frac{1}{8}$	$2\frac{7}{16}$	$2\frac{5}{16}$	$2\frac{7}{16}$	3
T617	2-2-$\frac{1}{2}$	$9\frac{3}{16}$	$3\frac{7}{8}$	$3\frac{1}{8}$	3	$2\frac{3}{8}$	3	$1\frac{1}{4}$
T627	2-2-$\frac{3}{4}$	$9\frac{3}{16}$	$3\frac{7}{8}$	$3\frac{1}{8}$	3	$2\frac{3}{8}$	3	$1\frac{1}{2}$
T637	2-2-1	$9\frac{3}{16}$	4	$3\frac{1}{8}$	3	$2\frac{1}{2}$	3	$1\frac{3}{4}$
T647	2-2-$1\frac{1}{4}$	$9\frac{3}{16}$	4	$3\frac{1}{8}$	3	$2\frac{1}{2}$	3	$2\frac{3}{16}$
T657	2-2-$1\frac{1}{2}$	$9\frac{3}{16}$	$4\frac{1}{8}$	$3\frac{1}{8}$	3	$2\frac{5}{8}$	3	$2\frac{7}{16}$
T67	2-2-2	$9\frac{3}{16}$	$4\frac{1}{8}$	$3\frac{1}{8}$	3	$2\frac{5}{8}$	3	3
T7577	$2\frac{1}{2}$-$2\frac{1}{2}$-$1\frac{1}{2}$	$11\frac{3}{4}$	$5\frac{5}{16}$	$3\frac{5}{8}$	$4\frac{1}{4}$	$3\frac{3}{16}$	$3\frac{1}{2}$	$2\frac{7}{16}$
T7677	$2\frac{1}{2}$-$2\frac{1}{2}$-2	$11\frac{3}{4}$	$5\frac{5}{16}$	$3\frac{5}{8}$	$4\frac{1}{4}$	$3\frac{3}{16}$	$3\frac{1}{2}$	3
T77	$2\frac{1}{2}$-$2\frac{1}{2}$-$2\frac{1}{2}$	$11\frac{3}{4}$	$5\frac{5}{8}$	$3\frac{5}{8}$	$4\frac{1}{4}$	$3\frac{1}{2}$	$3\frac{1}{2}$	$3\frac{1}{2}$
T867	3-3-2	$11\frac{3}{4}$	$5\frac{5}{8}$	$4\frac{3}{8}$	$4\frac{1}{4}$	$3\frac{3}{16}$	$4\frac{1}{4}$	3
T87	3-3-3	$11\frac{3}{4}$	$5\frac{5}{8}$	$4\frac{3}{8}$	$4\frac{1}{4}$	$3\frac{1}{2}$	$4\frac{1}{4}$	$4\frac{1}{4}$
T977	$3\frac{1}{2}$-$3\frac{1}{2}$-$2\frac{1}{2}$	$14\frac{5}{16}$	$6\frac{5}{8}$	$4\frac{7}{8}$	$5\frac{1}{4}$	4	$4\frac{3}{4}$	$3\frac{1}{2}$
T97	$3\frac{1}{2}$-$3\frac{1}{2}$-$3\frac{1}{2}$	$14\frac{5}{16}$	$6\frac{15}{16}$	$4\frac{7}{8}$	$5\frac{1}{4}$	$4\frac{5}{16}$	$4\frac{3}{4}$	$4\frac{3}{4}$
T107	4-4-4	$14\frac{5}{16}$	$6\frac{15}{16}$	$5\frac{3}{8}$	$5\frac{1}{4}$	$4\frac{5}{16}$	$5\frac{1}{4}$	$5\frac{1}{4}$

TABLE 36. CROUSE-HINDS CONDULETS—TYPE TB

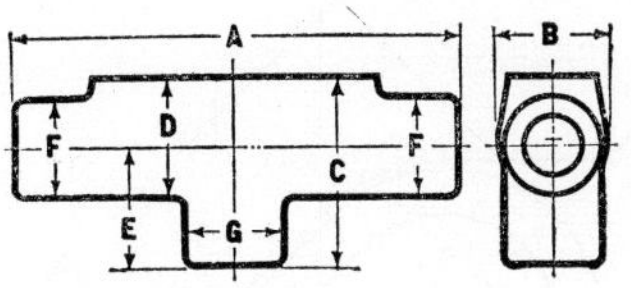

Dimensions in Inches

Cat. No.	Size	*A*	*B*	*C*	*D*	*E*	*F*	*G*
*TB*187	1/8–1/8–1/8	2 7/16	13/16	1 3/16	3/4	3/4	5/8	5/8
*TB*287	1/4–1/4–1/4	3 1/2	1	1 3/4	1 1/8	1 1/16	7/8	7/8
*TB*387	3/8–3/8–3/8	4 3/8	1 1/8	2	1 1/4	1 1/4	1	1
*TB*17	1/2–1/2–1/2	5 5/8	1 9/16	2 5/8	1 3/4	1 1/2	1 1/4	1 1/4
*TB*27	3/4–3/2–3/4	6 1/4	1 3/4	2 7/8	2	1 5/8	1 1/2	1 1/2
*TB*237	3/4–3/4–1	6 1/4	1 3/4	3	2	1 3/4	1 1/2	1 3/4
*TB*317	1–1–1/2	7 1/4	2	3 1/8	2 1/4	1 3/4	1 3/4	1 1/4
*TB*327	1–1–3/4	7 1/4	2	3 1/8	2 1/4	1 3/4	1 3/4	1 1/2
*TB*37	1–1–1	7 1/4	2	3 1/4	2 1/4	1 7/8	1 3/4	1 3/4
*TB*47	1 1/4–1 1/4–1 1/4	7 7/16	2 3/16	3 5/16	2 5/16	2 1/16	2 3/16	2 3/16
*TB*57	1 1/2–1 1/2–1 1/2	8 3/16	2 7/16	3 11/16	2 9/16	2 5/16	2 7/16	2 7/16
*TB*67	2–2–2	9 3/16	3	4 1/4	3 1/8	2 5/8	3	3
*TB*77	2 1/2–2 1/2–2 1/2	11 3/4	4 1/4	5	3 5/8	3 1/8	3 1/2	3 1/2
*TB*87	3–3–3	11 3/4	4 1/4	5 3/4	4 3/8	3 1/2	4 1/4	4 1/4
*TB*97	3 1/2–3 1/2–3 1/2	14 5/16	5 1/4	6 9/16	4 7/8	4 1/16	4 3/4	4 3/4
*TB*107	4–4–4	14 5/16	5 1/4	7 1/16	5 3/8	4 5/16	5 1/4	5 1/4

TABLE 37.   CROUSE-HINDS CONDULETS—TYPE U

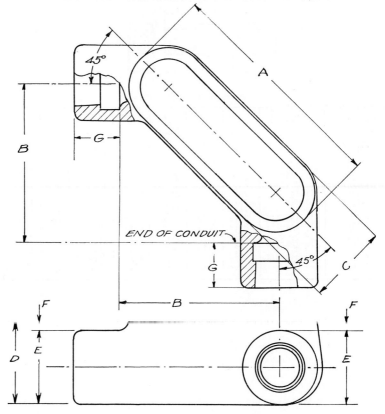

CATALOG	SIZE OF	DIMENSIONS						
NUMBER	CONDUIT	A	B	C	D	E	F	G
U 187	1/8	1½	1	23/32	3/4	5/8	1/8	7/16
U 287	1/4	2¼	1 9/16	7/8	1 3/32	7/8	7/32	1/2
U 387	3/8	2¾	2	1	1 7/32	1	7/32	5/8
U 17	1/2	3⅝	2½	1 5/16	1 3/8	1¼	1/8	3/4
U 27	3/4	4¼	2 13/16	1½	1 5/8	1½	1/8	3/4
U 37	1	5	3¼	1 3/4	1 7/8	1 3/4	1/8	7/8
U 47	1¼	5½	3½	2 3/16	2 5/16	2 3/16	1/8	7/8
U 57	1½	6	3 13/16	2 7/16	2 9/16	2 7/16	1/8	1
U 67	2	7	4⅜	3	3 1/8	3	1/8	1
U 77	2½	9	5 7/8	4¼	3 5/8	3½	1/8	1 5/16
U 87	3	9	5½	4¼	4 3/8	4¼	1/8	1 5/16
U 97	3½	11	7	5¼	4 7/8	4 3/4	1/8	1 5/8
U 107	4	11	5	5¼	5 3/8	5¼	1/8	1 5/8

TABLE 38. CROUSE-HINDS CONDULETS—TYPE X

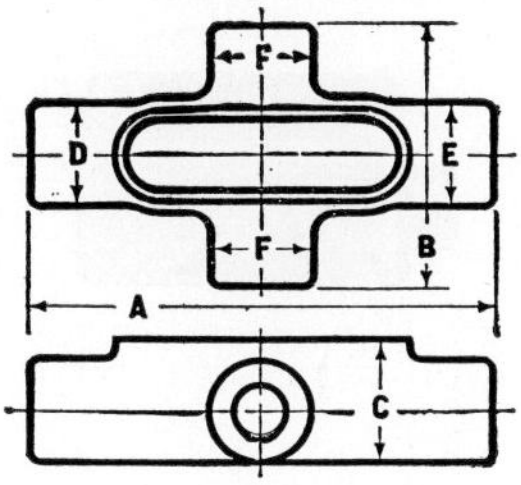

Dimensions in Inches

Cat. No.	Size	*A*	*B*	*C*	*D*	*E*	*F*
*X*17	½–½–½–½	5⅝	3 5/16	1¾	1¼	1¼	1¼
*X*21117	¾–½–½–½	6¼	3½	2	1½	1¼	1¼
*X*217	¾–¾–½–½	6¼	3½	2	1½	1½	1¼
*X*27	¾–¾–¾–¾	6¼	3½	2	1½	1½	1½
*X*317	1–1–½–½	7¼	3¾	2¼	1¾	1¾	1¼
*X*327	1–1–¾–¾	7¼	3¾	2¼	1¾	1¾	1½
*X*37	1–1–1–1	7¼	4	2¼	1¾	1¾	1¾
*X*417	1¼–1¼–½–½	7 7/16	3⅞	2 5/16	2 3/16	2 3/16	1¼
*X*47	1¼–1¼–1¼–1¼	7 7/16	4⅛	2 5/16	2 3/16	2 3/16	2 3/16
*X*527	1½–1½–¾–¾	8 3/16	4⅛	2 9/16	2 7/16	2 7/16	1½
*X*57	1½–1½–1½–1½	8 3/16	4⅝	2 9/16	2 7/16	2 7/16	2 7/16
*X*67	2–2–2–2	9 3/16	5 3/16	3⅛	3	3	3
*X*77	2½–2½–2½–2½	11¾	7	3⅝	3½	3½	3½
*X*87	3–3–3–3	11¾	7	4⅜	4¼	4¼	4¼

TABLE 39.   CROUSE-HINDS CONDULETS—TYPE FS AND FD

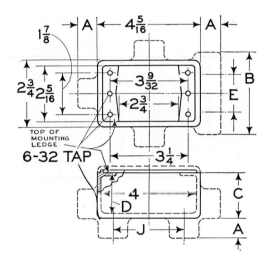

Series	Size	A	B	C	D	E	J
FS	$\frac{1}{2}$	$\frac{7}{8}$	$2\frac{3}{4}$	$1\frac{7}{8}$	$1\frac{11}{16}$	$1\frac{1}{2}$	$3\frac{1}{32}$
FS	$\frac{3}{4}$	$\frac{7}{8}$	3	$1\frac{7}{8}$	$1\frac{11}{16}$	$1\frac{1}{2}$	$2\frac{25}{32}$
FS	1	1	$3\frac{1}{2}$	$1\frac{7}{8}$	$1\frac{11}{16}$	$1\frac{3}{4}$	$2\frac{17}{32}$
FD	$\frac{1}{2}$	$\frac{7}{8}$	$2\frac{3}{4}$	$2\frac{11}{16}$	$2\frac{15}{32}$	$1\frac{1}{2}$	
FD	$\frac{3}{4}$	$\frac{7}{8}$	3	$2\frac{11}{16}$	$2\frac{15}{32}$	$1\frac{1}{2}$	
FD	1	1	$3\frac{3}{8}$	$2\frac{11}{16}$	$2\frac{15}{32}$	$1\frac{5}{8}$	

TABLE 40. CROUSE-HINDS CONDULETS—TYPE SK

**Crouse-Hinds Condulets
Type SK**

For use in concealed work in concrete
May be used in floors, walls and ceilings.

Take $3\frac{1}{4}''$ octagonal box, round base devices
Condulets provided with lugs for nailing to forms

	SK 12 $\frac{1}{2}''$ SKC 12 22 $\frac{3}{4}''$ 22 32 $1''$ 32 2" deep		
	SK 13 $\frac{1}{2}''$ SKC 13 23 $\frac{3}{4}''$ 23 33 $1''$ 33 3" deep		
	SKL 12 $\frac{1}{2}''$ SKT 12 22 $\frac{3}{4}''$ 22 32 $1''$ 32 2" deep		
	SK 13 $\frac{1}{2}''$ SKT 13 23 $\frac{3}{4}''$ 23 33 $1''$ 33 3" deep		
	SKX 12 $\frac{1}{2}''$ — 22 $\frac{3}{4}''$ — 32 $1''$ — 2" deep		
	SKX 13 $\frac{1}{2}''$ — 23 $\frac{3}{4}''$ — 33 $1''$ — 3" deep		
 Blank Cover $2-\frac{3}{4}''$Screw centers	 **Hub Cover** SK 83 $\frac{3}{8}''$Hub 84 $\frac{1}{2}''$Hub 86 $\frac{3}{4}''$Hub		 **Gasket**

TABLE 41. DATA ON A TYPICAL HIGH-GRADE SUSPENSION INSULATOR
(Lapp Insulator Company)

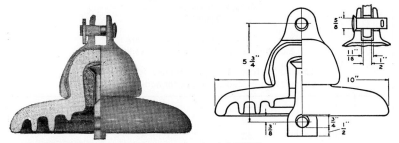

M & E strength 15,000 lb, Routine test 6,000 lb.
Impact strength 55 in.-lb, Leakage distance 11.5 in.
Dry flashover voltage 80,000 volts, Wet flashover voltage 50,000 volts.
Impulse flashover voltage Pos 1.5 × 40, 125,000 volts.
Impulse flashover voltage Neg 1.5 × 40, 130,000 volts.
Net weight, 11 lb each.

String Flashover Data on Lapp No. 8100 Suspension Insulators

Units in string	Dry	Wet	1.5 × 40		Units in string	Dry	Wet	1.5 × 40	
			Pos	Neg				Pos	Neg
2	155	90	250	250	11	640	455	1025	1015
3	215	130	355	340	12	690	490	1105	1105
4	270	170	440	415	13	735	525	1185	1190
5	325	215	525	495	14	785	565	1265	1275
6	380	255	610	585	15	830	600	1345	1360
7	435	295	695	670	16	875	630	1425	1445
8	485	335	780	760	17	920	660	1505	1530
9	540	375	860	845	18	965	690	1585	1615
10	590	415	945	930	19	1010	720	1665	1700
					20	1055	750	1745	1785

TABLE 42. DEAD-END INSULATORS
(Lapp Insulator Company)

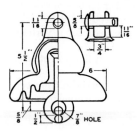

6605

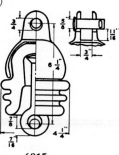

6815

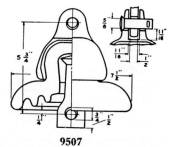

10604   **9507**

Catalogue number	6605	6815	10604	9507
M & E strength, lb	10,000	10,000	15,000	15,000
Routine tension test, lb	4,000	4,000	6,000	6,000
Leakage distance, inches	7	6.5	8.25	8.25
Dry flashover voltage				
1 unit	60,000	50,000	65,000	65,000
2 units	115,000	95,000	125,000	125,000
Wet flashover voltage				
1 unit	30,000	30,000	35,000	35,000
2 units	55,000	50,000	60,000	60,000
Impulse flashover voltage, pos 1.5 × 40				
1 unit	100,000	85,000	115,000	115,000
2 units	200,000	170,000	210,000	210,000
Impulse flashover voltage, neg 1.5 × 40				
1 unit	100,000	85,000	115,000	115,000
2 units	180,000	165,000	210,000	210,000
Net weight, each, lb	5.25	6	8	8
Packed weight, each, lb	6	7	10	10
Standard package	12	12	6	6
Cubic feet per 1,000	190	190	284	284

The 15,000-lb insulators Nos. 10604 and 9507 are extensively used in strings of one to three units for dead-ending the intermediate voltage transmission lines and for lower voltage circuits where higher factors of safety are desired. Head size identical with the standard No. 8200 and 8100 series.

The 10,000-lb insulators Nos 6605 and 6815 are used for a variety of applications.

No. 6605 is used in dead-ending rural and distribution lines, in strings of one or two units.

No. 6815 is identical with No. 6605, except that it carries a "fog type" shell. Used under dirt conditions. Small diameter is convenient where close spacing of lines is necessary.

It cannot be overemphasized that the permanence and security of such insulators are just as important as of transmission-line insulators.

Shells are extra-heavy to reduce breakage from stones and bullets and to withstand rough handling.

TABLE 43. STANDARD LINE POSTS
(Lapp Insulator Company)

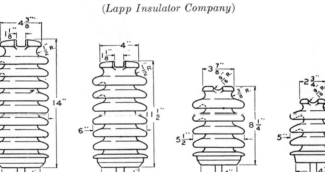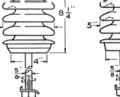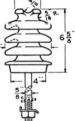

| 9345—1¾″ stud | 9335—1¾″ stud | 9325—1¾″ stud | 9320—1¾″ stud |
9445—7″ stud	9435—7″ stud.	9425—7″ stud	9420—7″ stud

	9345	9335	9325	9320
Catalog number, short stud units..................	9345	9335	9325	9320
Catalog number, long stud units..................	9445	9435	9425	9420
Recommended line voltage, kv	45	35	25	20
Striking distance, inches......	12.25	9.5	6.5	5
Dry flashover voltage.........	125,000	110,000	80,000	70,000
Wet flashover voltage.........	100,000	85,000	60,000	50,000
Impulse flashover voltage, pos 1.5 × 40.................	210,000	180,000	130,000	100,000
Impulse flashover voltage, neg 1.5 × 40.................	260,000	205,000	155,000	125,000
Leakage distance, inches......	29	22	14	10
Mechanical strength, lb.......	2,800	2,800	2,800	2,800
Net weight, each, lb..........	25.5	18	11.5	7.5

TABLE 43. STANDARD LINE POSTS. (*Continued*)

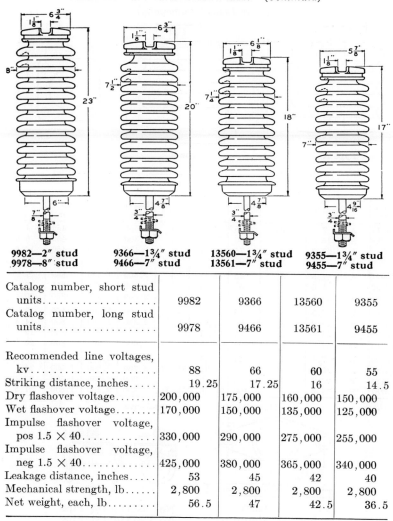

	9982—2″ stud 9978—8″ stud	9366—1¾″ stud 9466—7″ stud	13560—1¾″ stud 13561—7″ stud	9355—1¾″ stud 9455—7″ stud
Catalog number, short stud units...................	9982	9366	13560	9355
Catalog number, long stud units...................	9978	9466	13561	9455
Recommended line voltages, kv.....................	88	66	60	55
Striking distance, inches.....	19.25	17.25	16	14.5
Dry flashover voltage........	200,000	175,000	160,000	150,000
Wet flashover voltage........	170,000	150,000	135,000	125,000
Impulse flashover voltage, pos 1.5 × 40.............	330,000	290,000	275,000	255,000
Impulse flashover voltage, neg 1.5 × 40.............	425,000	380,000	365,000	340,000
Leakage distance, inches.....	53	45	42	40
Mechanical strength, lb......	2,800	2,800	2,800	2,800
Net weight, each, lb.........	56.5	47	42.5	36.5

TABLE 44. INDOOR SWITCH AND BUS SUPPORTS
(Lapp Insulator Company)

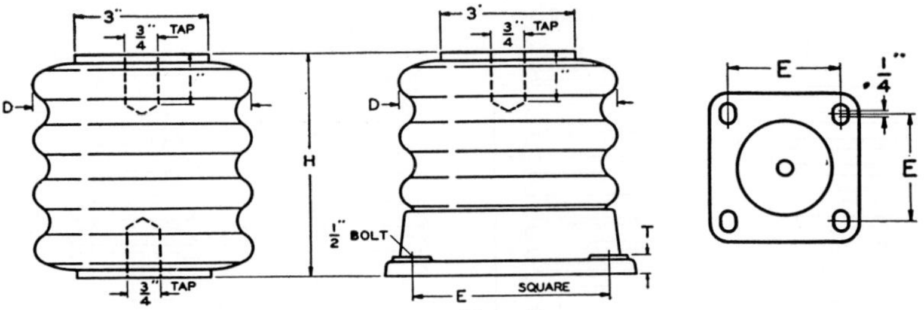

Type A **Type B**

Cat. No.	Type	Voltage rating	Strength class	Dry flash-over, kv	Dimensions, in.				Cantilever strength, lb.			Approx. pkd. wt., lb, ea.
					H	D	E	T	Top + 1 in.	Top + 2½ in.	Top + 5 in.	
14777	A	7.5	2	45	3⅜	4			1,500	900	450	4.5
10988	A	15.0	2	60	5	4			1,300	850	450	6.5
10989	A	23.0	2	75	6½	4½			1,100	750	450	10.5
10990	A	34.5	2	100	10	4½			800	600	450	14
10991	A	7.5	3	45	3⅝	5			2,500	1,500	850	7
10992	A	15.0	3	60	5	5			2,250	1,450	850	10
13748	A	23.0	3	75	6½	5½			2,050	1,350	850	20
9734	B	7.5	3	45	4½	5	4½	½	2,500	1,500	850	13
10637	B	15.0	3	60	5¾	5	4¾	½	2,250	1,450	850	14.5
13782	B	23.0	3	75	7⅛	5½	5	½	2,050	1,350	850	19
13783	B	34.5	3	100	10	5½	5	½	1,600	1,200	850	25
13784	B	7.5	4	45	5⅛	6	5¼	9/16	3,950	2,600	1,500	19
13785	B	15.0	4	60	6⅛	6	5¼	9/16	3,700	2,500	1,500	23
13786	B	23.0	4	75	7½	6½	5½	9/16	3,300	2,350	1,500	27
13787	B	34.5	4	100	10	6½	5½	9/16	2,800	2,100	1,500	31.5

Mountings for Type A Units Above

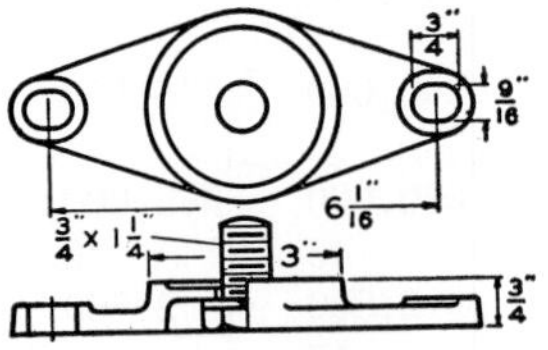

No. 10603
For Flat Mounting

Malleable iron base, black enameled, for mounting Type A units above on flat surface. A ¾-in. cap screw supplied with each unit. This base will develop the full strength of these insulators.

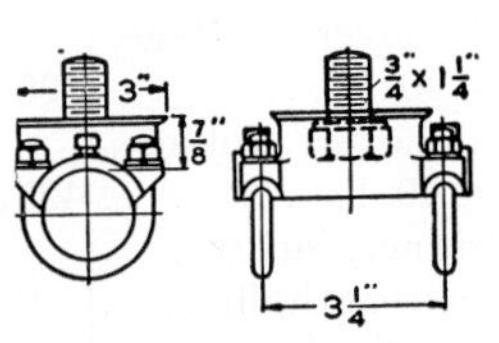

No. 9851 for 1¼" Pipe
No. 13414 for 1½" Pipe

Malleable iron base, black enameled, for mounting Type A units above to IPS pipe. A ¾-in. cap screw supplied with each unit. After bolting in place an auxiliary set screw is driven into the pipe, thus greatly increasing the strength of the mounting.

TABLE 45.   STANDARD TUBES—LOCKE

(Data from Locke Insulator Manufacturing Company)

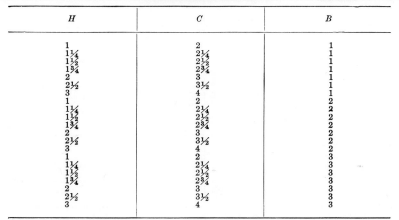

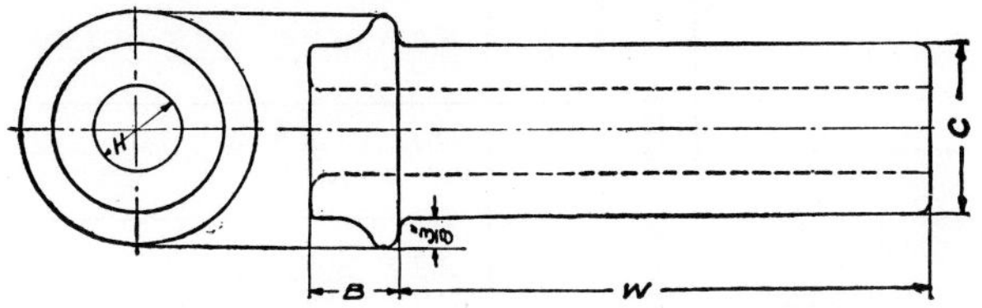

Dimensions in Inches

H	C	B
1	2	1
1¼	2¼	1
1½	2½	1
1¾	2¾	1
2	3	1
2½	3½	1
3	4	1
1	2	2
1¼	2¼	2
1½	2½	2
1¾	2¾	2
2	3	2
2½	3½	2
3	4	2
1	2	3
1¼	2¼	3
1½	2½	3
1¾	2¾	3
2	3	3
2½	3½	3
3	4	3

Standard sizes are furnished with dimension *W* either 4, 6, 10, 12, 14, 16, 18, 20, 22, or 24 in.   Always specify *W*.

TABLE 46. CONNECTORS FOR FLAT BAR TO FLAT BAR

For a complete line of triangular and square connectors, see Catalogue No. 52.

(Burndy Engineering Company, Inc.)

Type AF

WIDTH OF BUS BARS		CATALOG NUMBER			DIMENSIONS IN INCHES				
RUN A	TAP AA	Both Halves Bronze Durium Bolts	½ Bronze, ½ Galv. Malleable Iron Galv. Steel Bolts	Both Halves Galv. Malleable Iron Galv. Steel Bolts	J	L	W	Y	Z*
1"	1"	AFB11	AFR11	AFM11	3/8	2 5/16	2 5/16	13/16	3/4
2"	1"	AFB21	AFR21	AFM21	3/8	3 5/16	2 5/16	13/16	3/4
2"	2"	AFB22	AFR22	AFM22	3/8	3 5/16	3 5/16	1	3/4
3"	1"	AFB31	AFR31	AFM31	3/8	4 5/16	2 5/16	1	3/4
3"	2"	AFB32	AFR32	AFM32	3/8	4 5/16	3 5/16	15/16	3/4
3"	3"	AFB33	AFR33	AFM33	3/8	4 5/16	4 5/16	15/16	1 1/4
4"	2"	AFB42	AFR42	AFM42	3/8	5 5/16	3 5/16	15/16	1 1/4
4"	3"	AFB43	AFR43	AFM43	1/2	5 3/4	4 3/4	1 1/8	1 1/4
4"	4"	AFB44	AFR44	AFM44	1/2	5 3/4	5 3/4	1 1/8	1 1/4
5"	2"	AFB52	AFR52	AFM52	1/2	6 3/4	3 3/4	1 1/8	1 1/4
5"	3"	AFB53	AFR53	AFM53	1/2	6 3/4	4 3/4	1 1/8	1 1/4
5"	4"	AFB54	AFR54	AFM54	1/2	6 3/4	5 3/4	1 1/8	1 1/4
5"	5"	AFB55	AFR55	AFM55	5/8	7 1/8	7 1/8	1 1/2	1 1/4
6"	2"	AFB62	AFR62	AFM62	1/2	7 3/4	3 3/4	1 1/8	1 1/4
6"	3"	AFB63	AFR63	AFM63	1/2	7 3/4	4 3/4	1 1/8	1 1/4
6"	4"	AFB64	AFR64	AFM64	1/2	7 3/4	5 3/4	1 1/8	1 1/4
6"	5"	AFB65	AFR65	AFM65	5/8	8 1/8	7 1/8	1 1/2	1 1/4
6"	6"	AFB66	AFR66	AFM66	5/8	8 1/8	8 1/8	1 1/2	1 1/4

TABLE 47. CONNECTORS FOR FLAT BAR TO CABLE

For a complete line of triangular and square connectors, see Catalogue No. 52.

(*Burndy Engineering Company, Inc.*)

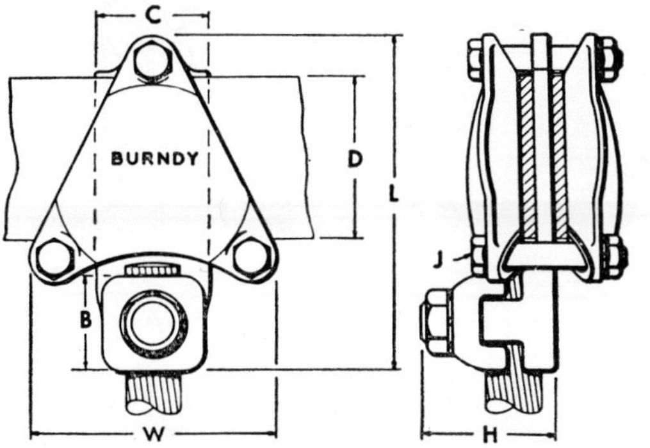

TYPE QAF

CABLE RANGE		WIDTH OF BUS BARS	Type QAF (A-Clamp)		DIMENSIONS IN INCHES					
MIN.	MAX.	D	½ Bronze, ½ Galv. Malleable Iron	All Bronze	B	C	H	J	L	W
#4 Str.	#1 Str.	2″	QAFR1C-2	QAFB1C-2	7/8	1	1	3/8	4 3/16	2 5/16
#4 Str.	#1 Str.	3″	QAFR1C-3	QAFB1C-3	7/8	1	1	3/8	5 1/4	2 5/16
#4 Str.	#1 Str.	4″	QAFR1C-4	QAFB1C-4	7/8	2	1	3/8	5 3/4	3 5/16
1/0 Str.	2/0 Str.	2″	QAFR26-2	QAFB26-2	15/16	1	1 1/8	3/8	4 5/16	2 5/16
1/0 Str.	2/0 Str.	3″	QAFR26-3	QAFB26-3	15/16	1	1 1/8	3/8	5 5/16	2 5/16
1/0 Str.	2/0 Str.	4″	QAFR26-4	QAFB26-4	15/16	2	1 1/8	3/8	5 7/8	3 5/16
3/0 Str.	4/0 Str.	2″	QAFR28-2	QAFB28-2	1 1/16	1	1 5/16	3/8	4 1/2	2 5/16
3/0 Str.	4/0 Str.	3″	QAFR28-3	QAFB28-3	1 1/16	1	1 5/16	3/8	5 1/2	2 5/16
3/0 Str.	4/0 Str.	4″	QAFR28-4	QAFB28-4	1 1/16	2	1 5/16	3/8	6	3 5/16
250 Mcm	350 Mcm	2″	QAFR31-2	QAFB31-2	1 3/16	2	1 11/16	3/8	4 5/16	3 5/16
250 Mcm	350 Mcm	3″	QAFR31-3	QAFB31-3	1 3/16	2	1 11/16	3/8	5 5/16	3 5/16
250 Mcm	350 Mcm	4″	QAFR31-4	QAFB31-4	1 3/16	2	1 11/16	3/8	6 5/16	3 5/16
400 Mcm	500 Mcm	2″	QAFR34-2	QAFB34-2	1 3/8	2	1 15/16	3/8	4 13/16	3 5/16
400 Mcm	500 Mcm	3″	QAFR34-3	QAFB34-3	1 3/8	2	1 15/16	3/8	5 13/16	3 5/16
400 Mcm	500 Mcm	4″	QAFR34-4	QAFB34-4	1 3/8	2	1 15/16	3/8	6 13/16	3 5/16
600 Mcm	800 Mcm	2″	QAFR40-2	QAFB40-2	1 5/8	2	2 5/16	3/8	5 1/8	3 5/16
600 Mcm	800 Mcm	3″	QAFR40-3	QAFB40-3	1 5/8	2	2 5/16	3/8	6 1/8	3 5/16
600 Mcm	800 Mcm	4″	QAFR40-4	QAFB40-4	1 5/8	2	2 5/16	3/8	7 1/8	3 5/16
850 Mcm	1000 Mcm	2″	QAFR44-2	QAFB44-2	1 3/4	2	2 1/2	3/8	5 3/8	3 5/16
850 Mcm	1000 Mcm	3″	QAFR44-3	QAFB44-3	1 3/4	3	2 1/2	3/8	6 3/16	4 5/16
850 Mcm	1000 Mcm	4″	QAFR44-4	QAFB44-4	1 3/4	3	2 1/2	1/2	7 7/16	4 3/4
850 Mcm	1000 Mcm	5″	QAFR44-5	QAFB44-5	1 3/4	3	2 1/2	1/2	8 7/16	4 3/4
1100 Mcm	1500 Mcm	3″	QAFR46-3	QAFB46-3	2	3	2 7/8	3/8	6 1/2	4 5/16
1100 Mcm	1500 Mcm	4″	QAFR46-4	QAFB46-4	2	3	2 7/8	1/2	7 3/4	4 3/4
1100 Mcm	1500 Mcm	5″	QAFR46-5	QAFB46-5	2	3	2 7/8	1/2	8 3/4	4 3/4
1600 Mcm	2000 Mcm	4″	QAFR48-4	QAFB48-4	2 3/8	4	3 3/16	1/2	8 3/16	5 3/4
1600 Mcm	2000 Mcm	5″	QAFR48-5	QAFB48-5	2 3/8	4	3 3/16	1/2	9 3/16	5 3/4
1600 Mcm	2000 Mcm	6″	QAFR48-6	QAFB48-6	2 3/8	4	3 3/16	1/2	10 3/16	5 3/4

TABLE 48. CONNECTORS FOR CABLE TO CABLE

For a complete line of Type QT connectors to 2,000 MCM to 2,000 MCM, see Catalogue No. 52.

(Burndy Engineering Company, Inc.)

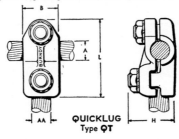

QUICKLUG
Type **QT**

CABLE SIZE		CATALOG NUMBER	DIMENSIONS IN INCHES		
RUN A	TAP AA		B	H	L
#2 Str.	#2 Str.	QT2C2C	$^{13}\!/_{16}$	$1\frac{1}{8}$	2
#1 Str.	#2 Str.	QT1C2C	$^{13}\!/_{16}$	$1\frac{1}{8}$	2
#1 Str.	#1 Str.	QT1C1C	$^{13}\!/_{16}$	$1\frac{1}{8}$	2
1/0 Str.	#2 Str.	QT252C	$^{13}\!/_{16}$	$1^{3}\!/_{16}$	$2\frac{1}{8}$
1/0 Str.	#1 Str.	QT251C	$^{13}\!/_{16}$	$1^{3}\!/_{16}$	$2\frac{1}{8}$
1/0 Str.	1/0 Str.	QT2525	1	$1\frac{1}{4}$	$2^{5}\!/_{16}$
2/0 Str.	#2 Str.	QT262C	$^{13}\!/_{16}$	$1^{3}\!/_{16}$	$2\frac{1}{8}$
2/0 Str.	#1 Str.	QT261C	$^{13}\!/_{16}$	$1^{3}\!/_{16}$	$2\frac{1}{8}$
2/0 Str.	1/0 Str.	QT2625	1	$1\frac{1}{4}$	$2^{5}\!/_{16}$
2/0 Str.	2/0 Str.	QT2626	1	$1\frac{1}{4}$	$2^{5}\!/_{16}$
3/0 Str.	#2 Str.	QT272C	$^{13}\!/_{16}$	$1\frac{1}{4}$	$2^{5}\!/_{16}$
3/0 Str.	#1 Str.	QT271C	$^{13}\!/_{16}$	$1\frac{1}{4}$	$2^{5}\!/_{16}$
3/0 Str.	1/0 Str.	QT2725	1	$1^{5}\!/_{16}$	$2\frac{3}{8}$
3/0 Str.	2/0 Str.	QT2726	1	$1^{5}\!/_{16}$	$2\frac{3}{8}$
3/0 Str.	3/0 Str.	QT2727	$1\frac{1}{8}$	$1^{7}\!/_{16}$	$2\frac{1}{2}$
4/0 Str.	#2 Str.	QT282C	$^{13}\!/_{16}$	$1\frac{1}{4}$	$2^{5}\!/_{16}$
4/0 Str.	#1 Str.	QT281C	$^{13}\!/_{16}$	$1\frac{1}{4}$	$2^{5}\!/_{16}$
4/0 Str.	1/0 Str.	QT2825	1	$1^{5}\!/_{16}$	$2\frac{3}{8}$
4/0 Str.	2/0 Str.	QT2826	1	$1^{5}\!/_{16}$	$2\frac{3}{8}$
4/0 Str.	3/0 Str.	QT2827	$1\frac{1}{8}$	$1^{7}\!/_{16}$	$2\frac{1}{2}$
4/0 Str.	4/0 Str.	QT2828	$1\frac{1}{8}$	$1^{7}\!/_{16}$	$2\frac{1}{2}$
250 Mcm	#2 Str.	QT292C	$^{13}\!/_{16}$	$1^{5}\!/_{16}$	$2\frac{3}{8}$
250 Mcm	#1 Str.	QT291C	$^{13}\!/_{16}$	$1^{5}\!/_{16}$	$2\frac{3}{8}$
250 Mcm	1/0 Str.	QT2925	1	$1\frac{3}{8}$	$2^{9}\!/_{16}$
250 Mcm	2/0 Str.	QT2926	1	$1\frac{3}{8}$	$2^{9}\!/_{16}$
250 Mcm	3/0 Str.	QT2927	$1\frac{1}{8}$	$1\frac{1}{2}$	$2^{11}\!/_{16}$
250 Mcm	4/0 Str.	QT2928	$1\frac{1}{8}$	$1\frac{1}{2}$	$2^{11}\!/_{16}$
250 Mcm	250 Mcm	QT2929	$1\frac{3}{8}$	$1^{11}\!/_{16}$	$2\frac{7}{8}$
300 Mcm	#2 Str.	QT302C	$^{13}\!/_{16}$	$1^{5}\!/_{16}$	$2\frac{3}{8}$
300 Mcm	#1 Str.	QT301C	$^{13}\!/_{16}$	$1^{5}\!/_{16}$	$2\frac{3}{8}$
300 Mcm	1/0 Str.	QT3025	1	$1\frac{3}{8}$	$2^{9}\!/_{16}$
300 Mcm	2/0 Str.	QT3026	1	$1\frac{3}{8}$	$2^{9}\!/_{16}$
300 Mcm	3/0 Str.	QT3027	$1\frac{1}{8}$	$1\frac{1}{2}$	$2^{11}\!/_{16}$
300 Mcm	4/0 Str.	QT3028	$1\frac{1}{8}$	$1\frac{1}{2}$	$2^{11}\!/_{16}$
300 Mcm	250 Mcm	QT3029	$1\frac{3}{8}$	$1^{11}\!/_{16}$	$2\frac{7}{8}$
300 Mcm	300 Mcm	QT3030	$1\frac{3}{8}$	$1^{11}\!/_{16}$	$2\frac{7}{8}$
350 Mcm	#2 Str.	QT312C	$^{13}\!/_{16}$	$1^{5}\!/_{16}$	$2\frac{3}{8}$
350 Mcm	#1 Str.	QT311C	$^{13}\!/_{16}$	$1^{5}\!/_{16}$	$2\frac{3}{8}$
350 Mcm	1/0 Str.	QT3125	1	$1\frac{3}{8}$	$2^{9}\!/_{16}$
350 Mcm	2/0 Str.	QT3126	1	$1\frac{3}{8}$	$2^{9}\!/_{16}$
350 Mcm	3/0 Str.	QT3127	$1\frac{1}{8}$	$1\frac{1}{2}$	$2^{11}\!/_{16}$
350 Mcm	4/0 Str.	QT3128	$1\frac{1}{8}$	$1\frac{1}{2}$	$2^{11}\!/_{16}$
350 Mcm	250 Mcm	QT3129	$1\frac{3}{8}$	$1^{11}\!/_{16}$	$2\frac{7}{8}$
350 Mcm	300 Mcm	QT3130	$1\frac{3}{8}$	$1^{11}\!/_{16}$	$2\frac{7}{8}$
350 Mcm	350 Mcm	QT3131	$1\frac{3}{8}$	$1^{11}\!/_{16}$	$2\frac{7}{8}$

TABLE 48. CONNECTORS FOR CABLE TO CABLE. (*Continued*)

| CABLE SIZE | | CATALOG NUMBER | DIMENSIONS IN INCHES | | |
RUN A	TAP AA		B	H	L
400 Mcm	# 2 Str.	QT322C	$^{13}\!/_{16}$	$1\frac{3}{8}$	$2\frac{1}{2}$
400 Mcm	# 1 Str.	QT321C	$^{13}\!/_{16}$	$1\frac{3}{8}$	$2\frac{1}{2}$
400 Mcm	1/0 Str.	QT3225	1	$1\frac{7}{16}$	$2^{11}\!/_{16}$
400 Mcm	2/0 Str.	QT3226	1	$1\frac{7}{16}$	$2^{11}\!/_{16}$
400 Mcm	3/0 Str.	QT3227	$1\frac{1}{8}$	$1\frac{9}{16}$	$2^{13}\!/_{16}$
400 Mcm	4/0 Str.	QT3228	$1\frac{1}{8}$	$1\frac{9}{16}$	$2^{13}\!/_{16}$
400 Mcm	250 Mcm	QT3229	$1\frac{3}{8}$	$1\frac{3}{4}$	3
400 Mcm	300 Mcm	QT3230	$1\frac{3}{8}$	$1\frac{3}{4}$	3
400 Mcm	350 Mcm	QT3231	$1\frac{3}{8}$	$1\frac{3}{4}$	3
400 Mcm	400 Mcm	QT3232	$1\frac{9}{16}$	$1\frac{7}{8}$	$3\frac{5}{16}$
500 Mcm	# 2 Str.	QT342C	$^{13}\!/_{16}$	$1\frac{3}{8}$	$2\frac{1}{2}$
500 Mcm	# 1 Str.	QT341C	$^{13}\!/_{16}$	$1\frac{3}{8}$	$2\frac{1}{2}$
500 Mcm	1/0 Str.	QT3425	1	$1\frac{7}{16}$	$2^{11}\!/_{16}$
500 Mcm	2/0 Str.	QT3426	1	$1\frac{7}{16}$	$2^{11}\!/_{16}$
500 Mcm	3/0 Str.	QT3427	$1\frac{1}{8}$	$1\frac{9}{16}$	$2^{13}\!/_{16}$
500 Mcm	4/0 Str.	QT3428	$1\frac{1}{8}$	$1\frac{9}{16}$	$2^{13}\!/_{16}$
500 Mcm	250 Mcm	QT3429	$1\frac{3}{8}$	$1\frac{3}{4}$	3
500 Mcm	300 Mcm	QT3430	$1\frac{3}{8}$	$1\frac{3}{4}$	3
500 Mcm	350 Mcm	QT3431	$1\frac{3}{8}$	$1\frac{3}{4}$	3
500 Mcm	400 Mcm	QT3432	$1\frac{9}{16}$	2	$3\frac{5}{16}$
500 Mcm	500 Mcm	QT3434	$1\frac{9}{16}$	2	$3\frac{5}{16}$
600 Mcm	# 2 Str.	QT362C	$^{13}\!/_{16}$	$1\frac{9}{16}$	$2^{11}\!/_{16}$
600 Mcm	# 1 Str.	QT361C	$^{13}\!/_{16}$	$1\frac{9}{16}$	$2^{11}\!/_{16}$
600 Mcm	1/0 Str.	QT3625	1	$1\frac{5}{8}$	$2\frac{7}{8}$
600 Mcm	2/0 Str.	QT3626	1	$1\frac{5}{8}$	$2\frac{7}{8}$
600 Mcm	3/0 Str.	QT3627	$1\frac{1}{8}$	$1^{11}\!/_{16}$	3
600 Mcm	4/0 Str.	QT3628	$1\frac{1}{8}$	$1^{11}\!/_{16}$	3
600 Mcm	250 Mcm	QT3629	$1\frac{3}{8}$	$1\frac{7}{8}$	$3\frac{3}{16}$
600 Mcm	300 Mcm	QT3630	$1\frac{3}{8}$	$1\frac{7}{8}$	$3\frac{3}{16}$
600 Mcm	350 Mcm	QT3631	$1\frac{3}{8}$	$1\frac{7}{8}$	$3\frac{3}{16}$
600 Mcm	400 Mcm	QT3632	$1\frac{9}{16}$	2	$3\frac{1}{2}$
600 Mcm	500 Mcm	QT3634	$1\frac{9}{16}$	2	$3\frac{1}{2}$
600 Mcm	600 Mcm	QT3636	$1^{13}\!/_{16}$	$2\frac{5}{16}$	$3^{15}\!/_{16}$
700 Mcm	# 2 Str.	QT382C	$^{13}\!/_{16}$	$1\frac{9}{16}$	$2^{11}\!/_{16}$
700 Mcm	# 1 Str.	QT381C	$^{13}\!/_{16}$	$1\frac{9}{16}$	$2^{11}\!/_{16}$
700 Mcm	1/0 Str.	QT3825	1	$1\frac{5}{8}$	$2\frac{7}{8}$
700 Mcm	2/0 Str.	QT3826	1	$1\frac{5}{8}$	$2\frac{7}{8}$
700 Mcm	3/0 Str.	QT3827	$1\frac{1}{8}$	$1^{11}\!/_{16}$	3
700 Mcm	4/0 Str.	QT3828	$1\frac{1}{8}$	$1^{11}\!/_{16}$	3
700 Mcm	250 Mcm	QT3829	$1\frac{3}{8}$	$1\frac{7}{8}$	$3\frac{3}{16}$
700 Mcm	300 Mcm	QT3830	$1\frac{3}{8}$	$1\frac{7}{8}$	$3\frac{3}{16}$
700 Mcm	350 Mcm	QT3831	$1\frac{3}{8}$	$1\frac{7}{8}$	$3\frac{3}{16}$
700 Mcm	400 Mcm	QT3832	$1\frac{9}{16}$	2	$3\frac{1}{2}$
700 Mcm	500 Mcm	QT3834	$1\frac{9}{16}$	2	$3\frac{1}{2}$
700 Mcm	600 Mcm	QT3836	$1^{13}\!/_{16}$	$2\frac{5}{16}$	$3^{15}\!/_{16}$
700 Mcm	700 Mcm	QT3838	$1^{13}\!/_{16}$	$2\frac{5}{16}$	$3^{15}\!/_{16}$
750 Mcm	# 2 Str.	QT392C	$^{13}\!/_{16}$	$1\frac{9}{16}$	$2^{11}\!/_{16}$
750 Mcm	# 1 Str.	QT391C	$^{13}\!/_{16}$	$1\frac{9}{16}$	$2^{11}\!/_{16}$
750 Mcm	1/0 Str.	QT3925	1	$1\frac{5}{8}$	$2\frac{7}{8}$
750 Mcm	2/0 Str.	QT3926	1	$1\frac{5}{8}$	$2\frac{7}{8}$
750 Mcm	3/0 Str.	QT3927	$1\frac{1}{8}$	$1^{11}\!/_{16}$	3
750 Mcm	4/0 Str.	QT3928	$1\frac{1}{8}$	$1^{11}\!/_{16}$	3
750 Mcm	250 Mcm	QT3929	$1\frac{3}{8}$	$1\frac{7}{8}$	$3\frac{3}{16}$
750 Mcm	300 Mcm	QT3930	$1\frac{3}{8}$	$1\frac{7}{8}$	$3\frac{3}{16}$
750 Mcm	350 Mcm	QT3931	$1\frac{3}{8}$	$1\frac{7}{8}$	$3\frac{3}{16}$
750 Mcm	400 Mcm	QT3932	$1\frac{9}{16}$	2	$3\frac{1}{2}$
750 Mcm	500 Mcm	QT3934	$1\frac{9}{16}$	2	$3\frac{1}{2}$

TABLE 49. CONNECTOR, CABLE TO LUG

For a complete line of Type QA-B connectors, see Catalogue No. 52.

(*Burndy Engineering Company, Inc.*)

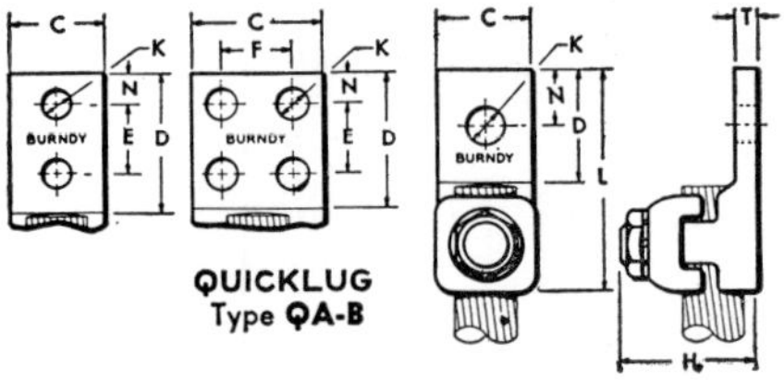

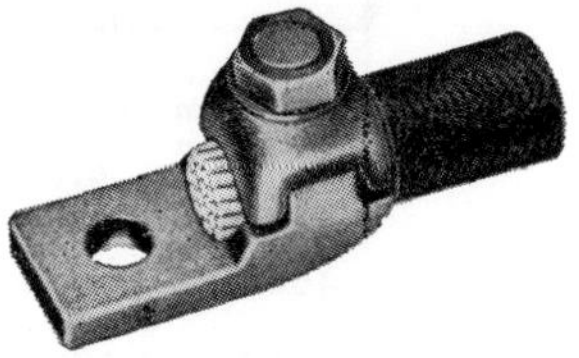

CABLE RANGE				NO. OF HOLES IN PAD	CATALOG NUMBER	DIMENSIONS IN INCHES							
COMMERCIAL AWG		NAVY											
MIN.	MAX.	MIN.	MAX.			C	D	E&F	H	K	L	N	T
#14 Sol.	#8 Str.	3	14	1	QA8C-B	9/16	9/16	—	11/16	7/32	1 3/8	9/32	5/32
#14 Sol.	#8 Str.	3	14	2	QA8C-2B	9/16	1 3/16	5/8	11/16	7/32	2	5/16	5/32
#6 Sol.	#4 Str.	23	40†	1	QA4C-B	5/8	5/8	—	3/4	9/32	1 7/16	5/16	3/16
#6 Sol.	#4 Str.	23	40†	2	QA4C-2B	5/8	1 3/16	5/8	3/4	9/32	2	5/16	3/16
#4 Str.	#1 Str.	40	75	1	QA1C-B	5/8	3/4	—	1	9/32	1 3/4	11/32	7/32
#4 Str.	#1 Str.	40	75	2	QA1C-2B	5/8	1 9/16	7/8	1	11/32	2 9/16	11/32	7/32
1/0 Str.	2/0 Str.	100	125	1	QA26-B	13/16	15/16	—	1 1/8	13/32	2	7/16	7/32
1/0 Str.	2/0 Str.	100	125	2	QA26-2B	13/16	1 15/16	1	1 1/8	13/32	3	7/16	7/32
3/0 Str.	4/0 Str.	150	200	1	QA28-B	1	1 1/16	—	1 5/16	13/32	2 1/4	17/32	1/4
3/0 Str.	4/0 Str.	150	200	2	QA28-2B	1	2	1	1 5/16	13/32	3 3/16	7/16	1/4
3/0 Str.	4/0 Str.	150	200	2	QA28-2N*	1	3 1/8	1 3/4	1 5/16	9/16	4 5/16	5/8	1/4
250 Mcm	350 Mcm	250	350	1	QA31-B	[illegible]	[illegible]	—	1 11/16	17/32	2 11/16	11/16	5/16
250 Mcm	350 Mcm	250	350	2	QA31-2B	1 3/16	2	1	1 11/16	13/32	3 5/16	7/16	5/16
250 Mcm	350 Mcm	250	350	2	QA31-2N*	1 3/16	3 1/8	1 3/4	1 11/16	9/16	4 7/16	5/8	5/16
400 Mcm	500 Mcm	400	500	1	QA34-B	1 3/8	1 5/8	—	1 15/16	17/32	3 3/16	13/16	5/16
400 Mcm	500 Mcm	400	500	2	QA34-2B	1 3/8	2	1	1 15/16	13/32	3 9/16	7/16	5/16
400 Mcm	500 Mcm	400	500	2	QA34-2N*	1 3/8	3 1/8	1 3/4	1 15/16	9/16	4 11/16	5/8	5/16
400 Mcm	500 Mcm	400	500	4	QA34-4B	1 7/8	1 15/16	1	1 15/16	7/16	3 1/2	7/16	5/16
600 Mcm	800 Mcm	650	800	1	QA40-B	1 5/8	1 7/8	—	2 5/16	11/16	3 11/16	15/16	3/8
600 Mcm	800 Mcm	650	800	2	QA40-2B	1 5/8	2 1/8	1 1/8	2 5/16	7/16	3 15/16	1/2	3/8
600 Mcm	800 Mcm	650	800	2	QA40-2N*	1 5/8	3	1 3/4	2 5/16	9/16	4 13/16	5/8	3/8
600 Mcm	800 Mcm	650	800	4	QA40-4B	1 7/8	1 15/16	1	2 5/16	7/16	3 3/4	7/16	3/8
600 Mcm	800 Mcm	650	800	4	QA40-4N*	3	3 1/16	1 3/4	2 5/16	9/16	4 7/8	5/8	3/8
850 Mcm	1000 Mcm	1000	1000	1	QA44-B	1 7/8	2	—	2 1/2	11/16	3 15/16	1	1/2
850 Mcm	1000 Mcm	1000	1000	2	QA44-2B	1 7/8	2 5/16	1 1/4	2 1/2	9/16	4 1/4	17/32	1/2
850 Mcm	1000 Mcm	1000	1000	2	QA44-2N*	1 7/8	3	1 3/4	2 1/2	9/16	4 15/16	5/8	1/2
850 Mcm	1000 Mcm	1000	1000	4	QA44-4B	2 1/8	2 3/16	1 1/8	2 1/2	7/16	4 1/8	1/2	1/2
850 Mcm	1000 Mcm	1000	1000	4	QA44-4N*	3	3 1/16	1 3/4	2 1/2	9/16	5	5/8	1/2
1100 Mcm	1500 Mcm	1300	1300	1	QA46-B	2 1/8	2 1/8	—	2 7/8	13/16	4 3/8	1 1/16	9/16
1100 Mcm	1500 Mcm	1300	1300	2	QA46-2B	2 1/8	2 5/8	1 3/8	2 7/8	9/16	4 7/8	5/8	9/16
1100 Mcm	1500 Mcm	1300	1300	2	QA46-2N*	2 1/8	3	1 3/4	2 7/8	9/16	5 1/4	5/8	9/16
1100 Mcm	1500 Mcm	1300	1300	4	QA46-4B	2 1/2	2 5/8	1 3/8	2 7/8	9/16	4 7/8	9/16	1/2
1100 Mcm	1500 Mcm	1300	1300	4	QA46-4N*	3	3 1/8	1 3/4	2 7/8	9/16	5 3/8	5/8	1/2
1600 Mcm	2000 Mcm	1600	2000	1	QA48-B	2 1/2	2 3/8	—	3 3/16	13/16	5	1 3/16	5/8
1600 Mcm	2000 Mcm	1600	2000	2	QA48-2B	2 1/2	2 3/4	1 1/2	3 3/16	9/16	5 3/8	5/8	5/8
1600 Mcm	2000 Mcm	1600	2000	2	QA48-2N*	2 1/2	3	1 3/4	3 3/16	9/16	5 5/8	5/8	5/8
1600 Mcm	2000 Mcm	1600	2000	4	QA48-4B	2 5/8	2 3/4	1 1/2	3 3/16	9/16	5 3/8	7/16	5/8
1600 Mcm	2000 Mcm	1600	2000	4	QA48-4N*	3	3 1/8	1 3/4	3 3/16	9/16	5 3/4	5/8	5/8

TABLE 50. HYLUGS*
(Burndy Engineering Company, Inc.)

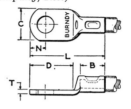

Fig. I   Fig. 2   Fig. 3

Fig. I—Split type insulation grip.
Fig. 2—Without insulation grip.
Fig. 3—Closed insulation grip for sealing navy cables.

Conductor Sizes			For use on screw size	Catalogue number	Fig. No.	Net wt. Lb. per M	Dimensions, inches						
Coml. AWG & aircraft AN	Navy	Solid wire AWG					B	C	D	L App.	N	T App.	ID of insulation grip
22–18	$\frac{3}{8}$–1$\frac{1}{2}$	22–18	4	YAV18-T4	2	1.5	$\frac{1}{4}$	$\frac{3}{16}$	$\frac{9}{32}$	$\frac{19}{32}$	$\frac{3}{32}$	$\frac{1}{32}$	
			4	YAV18-H4	1	2.0	$\frac{1}{4}$	$\frac{3}{16}$	$\frac{9}{32}$	$\frac{3}{4}$	$\frac{3}{32}$	$\frac{1}{32}$	0.125
			4 or 5	YAV18-L11	2	3.6	$\frac{1}{4}$	$\frac{9}{32}$	$\frac{13}{16}$	$\frac{13}{16}$	$\frac{5}{32}$	$\frac{1}{32}$	
20–14	2–5	20–12	6, 7, or 8	YAV14-T1	2	2.6	$\frac{1}{4}$	$\frac{5}{16}$	$\frac{7}{16}$	$\frac{3}{4}$	$\frac{5}{32}$	$\frac{3}{64}$	
				YAV14-H1	1	3.5	$\frac{1}{4}$	$\frac{5}{16}$	$\frac{7}{16}$	$\frac{29}{32}$	$\frac{5}{32}$	$\frac{3}{64}$	0.160
20–14	2–5	20–12	8, 9, or 10	YAV14-L25	2	2.9	$\frac{1}{4}$	$\frac{3}{8}$	$\frac{15}{32}$	$\frac{13}{16}$	$\frac{3}{16}$	$\frac{1}{32}$	
				YAG14-HL25	3	3.7	$\frac{1}{4}$	$\frac{3}{8}$	$\frac{15}{32}$	$\frac{15}{16}$	$\frac{3}{16}$	$\frac{1}{32}$	0.124
				YAV14-L12	2	4.6	$\frac{1}{4}$	$\frac{3}{8}$	$\frac{13}{16}$	$\frac{13}{16}$	$\frac{3}{16}$	$\frac{1}{32}$	
				YAG14-HL12	3	5.1	$\frac{1}{4}$	$\frac{3}{8}$	$\frac{13}{16}$	$\frac{15}{16}$	$\frac{3}{16}$	$\frac{1}{32}$	0.124
12–10	6–9	11–9	8, 9, or 10	YAV10-L34	2	4.2	$\frac{5}{16}$	$\frac{3}{8}$	$\frac{3}{8}$	$\frac{25}{32}$	$\frac{3}{16}$	$\frac{1}{16}$	
				YAV10-L36	2	4.6	$\frac{5}{16}$	$\frac{5}{16}$	$\frac{7}{16}$	$\frac{27}{32}$	$\frac{5}{32}$	$\frac{1}{16}$	
9	14	8–7	4, 5, or 6	YAV9C-L38	2	6.5	$\frac{5}{16}$	$\frac{5}{16}$	$1\frac{1}{16}$	$\frac{13}{16}$	$\frac{5}{16}$	$\frac{5}{64}$	
			8, 9 or 10	YAV9C-L6	2	7.7	$\frac{5}{16}$	$\frac{3}{8}$	$\frac{3}{4}$	$1\frac{1}{4}$	$\frac{3}{8}$	$\frac{1}{16}$	
9	14	8–7	$\frac{1}{4}$	YAV9C-T12	2	7.0	$\frac{5}{16}$	$\frac{7}{16}$	$\frac{9}{16}$	$1\frac{1}{16}$	$\frac{1}{4}$	$\frac{3}{64}$	
			$\frac{5}{16}$	YAV9C-T4	2	7.1	$\frac{5}{16}$	$\frac{17}{32}$	$\frac{21}{32}$	$1\frac{1}{8}$	$\frac{5}{16}$	$\frac{3}{64}$	

* This table, greatly abridged to save space, gives a few of the solderless lugs of the "Hident" line. For complete data on sizes up to 2,000 MCM, and tools for making the "dent," see Catalogue No. Y-46.

TABLE 51. GROUND CONNECTORS
For a complete line of ground connectors, see Catalogue No. G-47.
(*Burndy Engineering Company, Inc.*)

Type GAR

Parallel or 90° Cable Connection to Rod or Pipe With the Same Connector

This ground connector is used for connecting the ground bus, either parallel to, or at right angles to rod or pipe. Easily installed, the connection is completed by merely tightening the two nuts on the U-bolt. High copper alloy cast body with silicon bronze U-bolts, nuts, and lockwashers, permit entire connection to be buried in the ground without danger of corrosion.

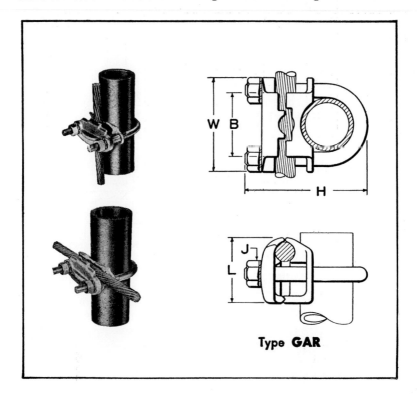

Type **GAR**

TABLE 51. GROUND CONNECTORS. (*Continued*)

DRIVEN		CONDUCTOR RANGE		CATALOG NUMBER	DIMENSIONS IN INCHES				
ROD	PIPE (IPS)	MIN.	MAX.		B	H	J	L	W
1/2"	1/4"	#8 Sol.	#4 Str.	GAR114C	1 1/2	2 1/2	3/8	1 5/16	1 7/8
1/2"	1/4"	#4 Sol.	2/0 Str.	GAR1126	1 1/2	2 1/2	3/8	1 9/16	1 7/8
1/2"	1/4"	2/0 Sol.	250 Mcm	GAR1129	1 3/4	2 1/2	3/8	1 13/16	1 7/8
5/8" or 3/4"	3/8"	#8 Sol.	#4 Str.	GAR644C	1 1/2	2 13/16	3/8	1 5/16	2 1/16
5/8" or 3/4"	3/8"	#4 Sol.	2/0 Str.	GAR6426	1 1/2	2 13/16	3/8	1 9/16	2 1/16
5/8" or 3/4"	3/8"	2/0 Sol.	250 Mcm	GAR6429	1 3/4	2 13/16	3/8	1 13/16	2 1/16
5/8" or 3/4"	3/8"	300 Mcm	500 Mcm	GAR6434	2	3 7/16	1/2	2 1/4	2 7/16
5/8" or 3/4"	3/8"	550 Mcm	750 Mcm	GAR6439	2	3 7/16	1/2	2 9/16	2 7/16
7/8" or 1"	1/2" or 3/4"	#8 Sol.	#4 Str.	GAR144C	1 1/2	2 11/16	3/8	1 5/16	2 3/8
7/8" or 1"	1/2" or 3/4"	#4 Sol.	2/0 Str.	GAR1426	1 1/2	2 11/16	3/8	1 9/16	2 3/8
7/8" or 1"	1/2" or 3/4"	2/0 Sol.	250 Mcm	GAR1429	1 3/4	3	3/8	1 13/16	2 3/8
7/8" or 1"	1/2" or 3/4"	300 Mcm	500 Mcm	GAR1434	2	3 11/16	1/2	2 3/8	2 3/4
7/8" or 1"	1/2" or 3/4"	550 Mcm	750 Mcm	GAR1439	2 1/8	3 11/16	1/2	2 9/16	2 3/4
....	1"	#8 Sol.	#4 Str.	GAR154C	1 3/4	2 13/16	3/8	1 5/16	2 5/8
....	1"	#4 Sol.	2/0 Str.	GAR1526	1 3/4	2 13/16	3/8	1 9/16	2 5/8
....	1"	2/0 Sol.	250 Mcm	GAR1529	1 3/4	3 5/16	3/8	1 13/16	2 5/8
....	1"	300 Mcm	500 Mcm	GAR1534	2 3/16	4 1/2	1/2	2 3/8	3
....	1"	550 Mcm	750 Mcm	GAR1539	2 3/16	4 1/2	1/2	2 9/16	3
....	1-1/4"	#8 Sol.	#4 Str.	GAR164C	1 7/8	3 1/2	3/8	1 5/16	3
....	1-1/4"	#4 Sol.	2/0 Str.	GAR1626	1 7/8	3 1/2	3/8	1 9/16	3
....	1-1/4"	2/0 Sol.	250 Mcm	GAR1629	1 7/8	3 1/2	3/8	1 13/16	3
....	1-1/4"	300 Mcm	500 Mcm	GAR1634	2 3/16	4 3/16	1/2	2 3/8	3 3/8
....	1-1/4"	550 Mcm	750 Mcm	GAR1639	2 7/16	5	5/8	2 3/4	3 3/4
....	1-1/2"	#8 Sol.	#4 Str.	GAR174C	2 5/16	4	3/8	1 5/16	3 1/4
....	1-1/2"	#4 Sol.	2/0 Str.	GAR1726	2 5/16	4	3/8	1 9/16	3 1/4
....	1-1/2"	2/0 Sol.	250 Mcm	GAR1729	2 5/16	4	3/8	1 13/16	3 1/4
....	1-1/2"	300 Mcm	500 Mcm	GAR1734	2 1/2	4 5/8	1/2	2 3/8	2 5/8
....	1-1/2"	550 Mcm	750 Mcm	GAR1739	2 3/4	5 3/16	5/8	2 3/4	4
....	2"	#8 Sol.	#4 Str.	GAR184C	2 3/4	4 3/16	3/8	1 5/16	3 11/16
....	2"	#4 Sol.	2/0 Str.	GAR1826	2 3/4	4 3/16	3/8	1 9/16	3 11/16
....	2"	2/0 Sol.	250 Mcm	GAR1829	2 3/4	4 3/16	3/8	1 13/16	3 11/16
....	2"	300 Mcm	500 Mcm	GAR1834	2 3/4	5 3/16	1/2	2 3/8	4 1/16
....	2"	550 Mcm	750 Mcm	GAR1839	3	5 7/16	5/8	2 3/4	4 7/16

TABLE 52. CONDUCTOR INSULATIONS FOR INDOOR USE
(*Westinghouse Data Book*)

Trade Name	Type Letter	Maximum Operating Temperature	Insulation	Voltage Range	Outer Covering	Use
Code	R	50C (122F)	Code Grade Rubber	0-5000	Moisture-Resistant Flame-Retardant Fibrous Covering	General Use
Moisture-Resistant	RW	60C (140F)	Moisture-Resistant Rubber	0-5000	Moisture-Resistant Flame-Retardant Fibrous Covering	General Use or in Wet Locations
Performance	RP	60C (140F)	Performance Grade Rubber	0-5000	Moisture-Resistant Flame-Retardant Fibrous Covering	General Use
Heat-Resistant	RH	75C (167F)	Heat-Resistant Grade Rubber	0-5000	Moisture-Resistant Flame-Retardant Fibrous Covering	General Use
Small Diameter Building Wire (Heat-Resistant)	RHT	75C (167F)	Heat-Resistant Grade Rubber	0-600	Moisture-Resistant Flame-Retardant Fibrous Covering	General Use
Small Diameter Building Wire (Performance)	RPT	60C (140F)	Performance Grade Rubber	0-600	Moisture-Resistant Flame-Retardant Fibrous Covering	Rewiring Existing Raceways
Type RU Wire	RU	60C (140F)	90 Per Cent Unmilled Grainless Rubber	0-600	Moisture-Resistant Flame-Retardant Fibrous Covering	Rewiring Existing Raceways, and New Wiring for the Duration
Solid Synthetic	SN	60C (140F)	Solid Flame-Retardant Moisture-Resistant Synthetic Compound	0-600	None	Rewiring Existing Raceways, and New Wiring for the Duration

Insulation Type	Code	Temperature	Material	Voltage	Outer Covering	Application
Asbestos Synthetic	SNA	90C (194F)	Synthetic and Felted Asbestos	0-600	Cotton Braid	Switchboard Wiring
Varnished Cambric	V	85C (185F)	Varnished Cambric	0-28000	Fibrous Covering or Lead Sheath	Dry Locations Only Unless Lead Sheathed Smaller than No. 6 by Special Permission
Asbestos Varnished Cambric	AVA	110C (230F)	Impregnated Asbestos and Varnished Cambric	0-5000	Asbestos Braid	General Use Dry Locations
Asbestos Varnished Cambric	AVB	90C (194F)	Same as Type AVA	0-5000	Flame-Retardant Cotton Braid	General Use Dry Locations
Asbestos Varnished Cambric	AVL	110C (230F)	Same as Type AVA	0-5000	Lead Sheath	General Use Wet Locations
Asbestos	A	200C (392F)	Felted Asbestos	0-300	With or Without Asbestos Braid	Dry Locations only. Not for General Conduit Installation. In Raceways, only as Leads to or within apparatus. If without Braid or Moisture Resistant Treatment, Limited to 300 Volts.
Impregnated Asbestos	AI	125C (257F)	Impregnated Felted Asbestos	0-600	With or Without Impregnated Asbestos Braid	
Paper		85C (185F)	Paper	All Voltages	Lead Sheath	Service Entrance and Special Use
Slow Burning	SB	90C (194F)	3 Braids Impregnated Fire-Retardant Thread	0-600	Outer Cover Finished Smooth and Hard	For Use Only in Dry Locations
Slow Burning Weatherproof	SBW	90C (194F)	2 Layers Impregnated Cotton Thread	0-600	Outer Fire-Retardant Coating	For Use Only in Dry Locations
Weatherproof	WP	80C (176F)	At Least Three Cotton Braids or Equivalent Impregnated	—	—	May be Used for Interior Wiring Only by Special Permission
Ozone-Resistant	—	Manufacturer's Recommendation	Ozone-Resistant Rubber	0-28000	Braid or Lead	General Use as Type R, RW, RP or RH

TABLE 53. INSTALLATION REQUIREMENTS
(*Westinghouse Data Book*)

Construction Feature	Non-Hazardous	Class I Semi-Hazardous	Class I Hazardous	Class II, III, IV Hazardous
Is reinforced concrete vault required:				
(1) For transformers containing a liquid that will burn:				
(a) If in buildings?	Yes	Yes	Yes	Yes
(b) If outdoors?	No	No	Yes	Yes
(2) For transformers containing a liquid that will not burn:				
(a) If in buildings?	No, but flue from pressure vent required if poorly ventilated.	No, but flue from pressure vent required if poorly ventilated.	No, but either (1) in explosion-proof enclosure (2) in fire resistive room with unpierced walls.	No, (1) may place in area if dust-tight with dust-tight terminal enclosures. (2) or in dust-tight fire resistive room.
(b) If outdoors?	No	No	No, same as above.	No, same as above.

		Rigid conduit with vapor-proof fittings.	Rigid conduit with threaded explosion-proof joints and fittings.	Class II: Rigid conduit with dust-tight fittings. Class III: Rigid conduit with threaded joint. Class IV: Same as III where machinery is located. Open wiring in storage sections.
Type of wiring method required?	No special restrictions. Several methods permitted.			
Is sealing of conduit runs required?	No	Yes	Yes	No
Type of enclosure required:				
(1) For overcurrent devices	No special restrictions.	Explosion-proof enclosures or approved.	Explosion-proof enclosures or approved.	Dust-tight enclosures or mounted in separate dust-tight room.
(2) For motors and generators	No special restrictions.	Generally explosion resisting; sometimes splashproof, occasionally open type.	Explosion-proof.	Dust-tight, either totally-enclosed, totally-enclosed fan-cooled, or totally-enclosed pipe ventilated.
(3) For lighting fixtures	No special restrictions.	Vapor-proof.	Explosion-proof.	Dust-tight.
(4) For motor controllers	No special restrictions.	Explosion-proof or oil immersed, weather-resisting enclosure.	Explosion-proof or approved.	Dust-tight.

TABLE 54. CURRENT-CARRYING CAPACITIES OF CONDUCTORS
ALLOWABLE CURRENT-CARRYING CAPACITIES OF CONDUCTORS IN AMPERES
Not more than three conductors in raceway or cable, room temp. 30°C—86°F
1951 National Electrical Code

Size AWG, MCM	Rubber Type R, Type RW, Type RU (14-2). Thermo-plastic Type T (14-4/0)	Rubber Type RH	Paper Thermo-plastic asbestos Type TA. Var-Cam Type V. Asbestos Var-Cam Type AVB	Asbestos Var-Cam Type AVA, Type AVL	Impreg-nated asbestos Type AI (14-8) Type AIA	Asbestos Type A (14-8) Type AA
14	15	15	25	30	30	30
12	20	20	30	35	40	40
10	30	30	40	45	50	55
8	40	45	50	60	65	70
6	55	65	70	80	85	95
4	70	85	90	105	115	120
3	80	100	105	120	130	145
2	95	115	120	135	145	165
1	110	130	140	160	170	190
0	125	150	155	190	200	225
00	145	175	185	215	230	250
000	165	200	210	245	265	285
0000	195	230	235	275	310	340
250	215	255	270	315	335	
300	240	285	300	345	380	
350	260	310	325	390	420	
400	280	335	360	420	450	
500	320	380	405	470	500	
600	355	420	455	525	545	
700	385	460	490	560	600	
750	400	475	500	580	620	
800	410	490	515	600	640	
900	435	520	555			
1,000	455	545	585	680	730	
1,250	495	590	645			
1,500	520	625	700	785		
1,750	545	650	735			
2,000	560	665	775	840		

°C	°F	Correction Factor for Room Temperatures over 30°C, 86°F				
40	104	0.82	0.88	0.90	0.94	0.95	
45	113	0.71	0.82	0.85	0.90	0.92	
50	122	0.58	0.75	0.80	0.87	0.89	
55	131	0.41	0.67	0.74	0.83	0.86	
60	140	....	0.58	0.67	0.79	0.83	0.91
70	158	....	0.35	0.52	0.71	0.76	0.87
75	167	....	....	0.43	0.66	0.72	0.86
80	176	....	....	0.30	0.61	0.69	0.84
90	194	....	....	....	0.50	0.61	0.80
100	212	....	....	....	....	0.51	0.77
120	248	....	....	....	....	....	0.69
140	284	....	....	....	....	....	0.59

TABLE 55. PROPERTIES OF COPPER CONDUCTORS
1951 National Electrical Code

Size AWG	Area cir mils	Concentric lay stranded conductors		Bare conductors		D-C resistance ohms/M ft. At 25 C., 77 F.	
		No. wires	Dia. each wire, In.	Dia., In.	*Area Sq. In.	Bare Cond.	Tin'd. Cond.
18	1,624	Solid	0.0403	0.0403	0.0013	6.510	6.77
16	2,583	Solid	0.0508	0.0508	0.0020	4.094	4.25
14	4,107	Solid	0.0641	0.0641	0.0032	2.575	2.68
12	6,530	Solid	0.0808	0.0808	0.0051	1.619	1.69
10	10,380	Solid	0.1019	0.1019	0.0081	1.018	1.06
8	16,510	Solid	0.1285	0.1285	0.0130	0.641	0.660
6	26,250	7	0.0612	0.184	0.027	0.410	0.426
4	41,740	7	0.0772	0.232	0.042	0.259	0.269
3	52,640	7	0.0867	0.260	0.053	0.205	0.213
2	66,370	7	0.0974	0.292	0.067	0.162	0.169
1	83,690	19	0.0664	0.332	0.087	0.129	0.134
0	105,500	19	0.0745	0.373	0.109	0.102	0.106
00	133,100	19	0.0837	0.418	0.137	0.0811	0.0844
000	167,800	19	0.0940	0.470	0.173	0.0642	0.0668
0000	211,600	19	0.1055	0.528	0.219	0.0509	0.0524
	250,000	37	0.0822	0.575	0.260	0.0431	0.0444
	300,000	37	0.0900	0.630	0.312	0.0360	0.0371
	350,000	37	0.0973	0.681	0.364	0.0308	0.0318
	400,000	37	0.1040	0.728	0.416	0.0270	0.0278
	500,000	37	0.1162	0.814	0.520	0.0216	0.0225
	600,000	61	0.0992	0.893	0.626	0.0180	0.0185
	700,000	61	0.1071	0.964	0.730	0.0154	0.0159
	750,000	61	0.1109	0.998	0.782	0.0144	0.0148
	800,000	61	0.1145	1.031	0.835	0.0135	0.0139
	900,000	61	0.1215	1.093	0.938	0.0120	0.0124
	1,000,000	61	0.1280	1.152	1.042	0.0108	0.0111
	1,250,000	91	0.1172	1.289	1.305	0.00864	0.00890
	1,500,000	91	0.1284	1.412	1.566	0.00719	0.00740
	1,750,000	127	0.1174	1.526	1.829	0.00617	0.00636
	2,000,000	127	0.1255	1.631	2.089	0.00539	0.00555

Multiplying Factors for Converting D-C Resistance to A-C Resistance*

Size, cir mils	Multiplying factor	
	25 cycles	60 cycles
250,000	....	1.005
300,000	....	1.006
350,000	....	1.009
400,000	....	1.011
500,000	....	1.018
600,000	1.005	1.025
700,000	1.006	1.034
750,000	1.007	1.039
800,000	1.008	1.044
900,000	1.010	1.055
1,000,000	1.012	1.067
1,250,000	1.019	1.102
1,500,000	1.027	1.142
1,750,000	1.037	1.185
2,000,000	1.048	1.233

* Area given is that of a circle having a diameter equal to the over-all diameter of a stranded conductor.

The values given in the table are those given in Circular 31 of the National Bureau of Standards except that those shown in the last column are those given in Specification B33 of the American Society for Testing Materials.

The resistance values given in the last two columns are applicable only to direct current. When conductors larger than No. 4/0 are used with alternating current, the following multiplying factors should be used to compensate for skin effect.

NOTES ON THE B & S GAUGE WIRE TABLE FOR COPPER WIRE

The following facts are useful in working with the B & S gauge system of numbering wires. A No. 4/0 wire is a large wire and a No. 40 is a very small wire. Above 4/0 the wire size is given in circular mils. A circular mil is the area of a circle 1/1,000 in. in diameter. Since the area of a circle is only 0.7854 (roughly 0.8) as much as the area of a square whose distance across flats is the same as the diameter of the circle inscribed in it, the area of one circular mil is only 0.7854 as much as the area of one square mil.

To find the size of a flat bus bar that would have the same cross-sectional area as a 4/0 solid wire, the calculations would be, 211,600 (area of a No. 4/0 wire in cir mils) $\times$ 0.7854 = 166,191 sq mils. In one square inch there are 1,000 $\times$ 1,000 = 1,000,000 square mils, so there would need to be 166,191/1,000,000 = 0.166191 sq. in. If the bar were $\frac{1}{8}$ in. thick (0.125 in.), its width would need to be 0.166/0.125 = 1.328 in., or about $1\frac{5}{16}$ in.

For rough estimating, a wire $\frac{1}{10}$ in. in diameter has 10,000 cir mils (10,380) and a resistance of 1 ohm (0.9989) per thousand feet. Or, to put it another way, it takes a thousand feet of No. 10 wire to give an ohm.

In going three numbers in the table, the cross-sectional area of a wire is doubled or halved. For example, a No. 7 wire has twice the area of a No. 10, or 20,000 cir mils (20,820), and a No. 13 wire has 5,000 cir mils (5,178), or half the area of a No. 10. Also, for rough estimating,

$$\text{Resistance (in ohms)} = \frac{22 \times \text{distance one way (in feet)}}{\text{area in circular mils}}$$

For example, a run of 500 ft of No. 8 wire will have

$$(22 \times 500)/16,510 = 0.665 \text{ ohm.}$$

The wire table gives 0.6282 ohm at 68°F and 0.7023 ohm at 122°F.

Bare wire, when suspended in air, radiates heat readily and can carry a much larger current than is allowed by the National Electrical Code for insulated wire as used in buildings.

When used in generators, motors, transformers, etc., the code rules for buildings do not apply. The size of wire is determined by experience by allowing a certain number of circular mils for each ampere that the wire is to carry. This varies with the nature of the apparatus and ranges somewhere around 500 to 1,000 cir mils per amp, depending on ventilation, etc. Taking a very liberal value of 1,000 cir mils per amp and a current of 50 amp, 50 $\times$ 1,000, or 50,000, cir mils would be required. From the table, this would be about a No. 3 wire. The National Electrical Code would allow 145 amp for rubber insulation (Type RH) and 155 amp for varnished cambric (Type V) insulation, if the wire were to be used in buildings.

Wire may be either solid or stranded. Solid wire goes up to No. 4/0; and, from there on, unless it is special or for bus bars, it is stranded. Small wire may be stranded for certain kinds of work, as, for example, ordinary lamp cord.

TABLE 56. MAGNET WIRE
(Data from Standard Handbook for Electrical Engineers, McGraw-Hill Book Company, Inc.)

A.W.G. B&S. No.	CIR. MILS	OHMS 1000FT 20°C 68°F	DIAM. ENAMEL	SINGLE COTTON COVERED	SINGLE SILK COVERED	ENAMEL AND COTTON	ENAMEL AND SILK
8	16510	0.6282	0.1310"	0.1365"		0.139"	
9	13090	.7921	.1169	.1214		.1239	
10	10380	.9989	.1044	.1079		.1104	
11	8234	1.260	.0932	.0957		.0982	
12	6530	1.588	.0833	.0858		.0883	
13	5178	2.003	.0745	.0770		.0795	
14	4107	2.525	.0666	.0691		.0716	
15	3257	3.184	.0596	.0621		.0646	
16	2583	4.016	.0528	.0558	0.0528	.0578	0.0548
17	2048	5064	.0473	.0503	.0473	.0523	.0493
18	1624	6.385	.0423	.0453	.0423	.0473	.0443
19	1288	8.051	.0379	.0409	.0379	.0429	.0399
20	1022	10.15	.0338	.0370	.0340	.0388	.0358
21	810.1	12.80	.0303	.0335	.0305	.0353	.0323
22	642.4	16.14	.0271	.0298	.0273	.0316	.0291
23	509.5	20.36	.0241	.0271	.0246	.0286	.0261
24	404	25.67	.0216	.0246	.0221	.0261	.0236
25	320.4	32.37	.0194	.0224	.0199	.0239	.0214
26	254.1	40.81	.0171	.0204	.0179	.0216	.0191
27	201.5	51.47	.0154	.0187	.0162	.0199	.0174
28	159.8	64.90	.0138	.0171	.0146	.0183	.0158
29	126.7	81.83	.0125	.0158	.0133	.017	.0145
30	100.50	103.2	.0112	.0145	.0120	.0157	.0132
31	79.70	130.1	.0099	.0134	.0109	.0144	.0119
32	63.21	164.1	.0090	.0125	.0100	.0135	.011
33	50.13	206.9	.0079	.0116	.0091	.0124	.0099
34	39.75	260.9	.0071	.0108	.0083	.0116	.0091
35	31.52	329	.0063	.0101	.0076	.0108	.0083
36	25.00	414.8	.0057	.0090	.0070	.0087	.0077
37	19.83	523.1	.0051	.0085	.0065	.0091	.0071
38	15.72	659.6	.0046	.0080	.0060	.0080	.0066
39	12.47	831.8	.0040	.0075	.0055	.008	.006
40	9.888	1049	.0036	.0071	.0051	.0076	.0056
41			.0032				
42			.0029				
43			.0026				
44			.0024				

TABLE 57.   NAVY, COMMERCIAL, AND AIRCRAFT CABLE DATA
(*Burndy Engineering Company, Inc.*)

NAVY CABLE

STANDARD SIZE DESIGNATION	NOMINAL STRAND DIAMETER INCHES	DIAMETER OVER STRANDED CONDUCTOR INCHES	AREA OF STRANDED CONDUCTOR CIR. MILS
⅜ (1)	0.025	0.025	642
*½ (21)	.005	*.028	525
1 (19)	.007	.036	950
1 (1)	.032	.032	1,024
1 (7)	.0126	.039	1,120
1-½ (1)	.040	040	1,600
*1-½ (16)	.010	*.049	1,616
*1-½ (41)	.0063	*.049	1,640
2-½ (1)	.051	.051	2,601
*2-½ (26)	.010	*.061	2,626
3 (7)	.020	.061	2,828
3 (19)	.0126	.065	3,040
4 (1)	.064	.064	4,110
4 (7)	.025	.076	4,494
*4 (41)	.010	*.077	4,141
5 (19)	.0159	.080	4,826
6 (1)	.081	.081	6,530
6 (7)	.0305	.0915	6,512
6 (19)	.0179	.090	6,088
*6 (65)	.010	*.097	6,565
8 (1)	.091	.091	8,280
9 (7)	.036	.108	9,030
*9 (90)	.010	*.120	9,090
13 (1)	.114	.114	13,100
14 (7)	.045	.136	14,350
*14 (140)	.010	*.145	14,140
21 (1)	.144	.144	20,736
23 (7)	.057	.171	22,820
**23 (228)	.010	**.180	22,826
30 (19)	.040	.202	30,780
**30 (304)	.010	**.220	30,400
40 (19)	.045	.226	38,950
**42 (209)	.014	**.260	42,218
50 (19)	.051	.254	49,020
60 (37)	.040	.282	59,940
75 (37)	.045	.317	75,850
100 (61)	.040	.363	98,820
125 (61)	.045	.407	125,050
150 (61)	.051	.457	157,380
**153 (760)	.014	**.500	153,520
200 (61)	.057	.514	198,860
250 (61)	.064	.577	250,710
**253 (1254)	.014	**.660	253,310
300 (91)	.057	.628	296,660
350 (91)	.062	.682	350,000
400 (127)	.057	.742	414,020
**400 (2052)	.014	**.825	400,500
500 (127)	.064	.833	521,970
650 (127)	.072	.936	657,860
**672 (3330)	.014	**.985	672,660
800 (127)	.081	1.051	829,310
**814 (4033)	.014	**1.255	814,666
1000 (127)	.091	1.187	1,046,000
1300 (127)	.1019	1.325	1,318,000
1600 (127)	.114	1.480	1,662,000
2000 (127)	.1285	1.670	2,097,000

TABLE 57. NAVY, COMMERCIAL, AND AIRCRAFT CABLE DATA. *(Continued)*

COMMERCIAL CABLE

	CONDUCTOR SIZE		NUMBER AND SIZE OF STRANDS	DIAMETER OVER COPPER ── INCHES
	AWG	CIRCULAR MILS		
SOLID WIRE	30	100	....	0.010 0
	29	128	....	0.011 3
	28	159	....	0.012 6
	27	202	....	0.014 2
	26	252	....	0.015 9
	25	320	....	0.017 9
	24	404	....	0.020 1
	23	511	....	0.022 6
	22	642	....	0.025 3
	21	812	....	0.028 5
	20	1,022	....	0.032 0
	18	1,624	....	0.040 3
	16	2,583	....	0.050 8
	14	4,107	....	0.064 1
	12	6,530	....	0.080 8
	10	10,380	....	0.101 9
	8	16,510	....	0.128 5
STRANDED CABLE	20	1,022	7—0.012 1	0.036 3
	18	1,624	7—0.015 2	0.045 6
	16	2,583	7—0.019 2	0.057 6
	14	4,100	7—0.024 2	0.073 0
	12	6,530	7—0.030 5	0.092 0
	10	10,400	7—0.038 5	0.116
	8	16,500	7—0.048 6	0.146
	6	26,300	7—0.061 2	0.184
	4	41,700	7—0.077 2	0.232
	2	66,400	7—0.097 4	0.292
	1	83,700	19—0.066 4	0.332
	1/0	106,000	19—0.074 5	0.373
	2/0	133,000	19—0.083 7	0.419
	3/0	168,000	19—0.094 0	0.470
	4/0	212,000	19—0.105 5	0.528
	..	250,000	37—0.082 2	0.575
	..	300,000	37—0.090 0	0.630
	..	350,000	37—0.097 3	0.681
	..	400,000	37—0.104 0	0.728
	..	450,000	37—0.110 3	0.772
	..	500,000	37—0.116 2	0.813
	..	550,000	61—0.095 0	0.855
	..	600,000	61—0.099 2	0.893
	..	650,000	61—0.103 2	0.929
	..	700,000	61—0.107 1	0.964
	..	750,000	61—0.110 9	0.998
	..	800,000	61—0.114 5	1.031
	..	850,000	61—0.118 0	1.062
	..	900,000	61—0.121 5	1.094
	..	950,000	61—0.124 8	1.123
	..	1,000,000	61—0.128 0	1.152
	..	1,250,000	91—0.117 2	1.289
	..	1,500,000	91—0.128 4	1.412
	..	1,750,000	127—0.117 3	1.526
	..	2,000,000	127—0.125 5	1.632

NOTE:—Number in ( ) indicates number of strands.
 * Indicates bunch stranded conductor.
** Indicates rope stranded conductor.

TABLE 57. NAVY, COMMERCIAL, AND AIRCRAFT CABLE DATA. *(Continued)*

AIRCRAFT CABLE

SIZE DESIGNATION	NOMINAL CONDUCTOR AREA (CIR. MILS.)	NO. OF STRANDS (MIN.)	DIA. OVER STRANDED CONDUCTOR ——— INCHES
AN 22	704	7	.032
20	1,119	7	.040
18	1,779	7	.050
16	2,409	19	.061
14	3,830	19	.076
12	6,088	19	.096
10	10,443	37	.132
8	16,864	133	.176
6	26,813	133	.218
4	42,613	133	.272
2	66,832	663	.345
1	81,807	812	.384
1/0	104,118	1,033	.432
2/0	133,665	1,327	.490
3/0	167,332	1,661	.548
4/0	211,954	2,104	.615

TABLE 58.   COPPER RODS

(Data from Delta Star Electric Company)

Diameter in inches	Area in C. M.	Pounds per foot	Ampere capacity at			Ohms per foot
			1,000 C. M. per ampere	1,200 C. M. per ampere	1,600 C. M. per ampere	
¼	62,500	0.189	63	52	39	0.000176
⁵⁄₁₆	97,700	0.295	98	82	61	0.000113
⅜	140,600	0.426	141	117	88	0.0000782
½	250,000	0.757	250	208	156	0.0000440
⅝	390,600	1.18	391	326	244	0.0000282
¾	562,500	1.70	563	470	350	0.0000196
⅞	765,600	2.32	766	640	480	0.0000144
1	1,000,000	3.03	1,000	835	630	0.0000110
1⅛	1,265,600	3.83	1,266	1,050	790	0.0000087
1¼	1,560,000	4.72	1,560	1,300	975	0.00000705
1⅜	1,890,600	5.72	1,891	1,580	1,180	0.00000582
1½	2,250,000	6.81	2,250	1,875	1,410	0.00000489
1⅝	2,640,600	7.99	2,641	2,200	1,650	0.00000417
1¾	3,062,500	9.27	3,063	2,550	1,810	0.00000359
1⅞	3,515,600	10.64	3,516	2,920	2,200	0.00000313
2	4,000,000	12.11	4,000	3,330	2,500	0.00000275

The column of ohms per foot is calculated from

$$R = \frac{KL}{A}$$

where K = resistance of mil foot of copper

= 11 ohms approximate, which is used for obtaining this column.

TABLE 59.   COPPER BARS

(*Data from Delta Star Electric Company*)

| Size in inches | Area in C. M. | Pounds per foot | Amperes at | | | Ohms per foot |
			1,000 C. M. per ampere	1,200 C. M. per ampere	1,600 C. M. per ampere	
⅛ × 1	159,154	0.482	160	133	100	0.0000691
⅛ × 1½	238,731	0.723	239	200	180	0.00004608
⅛ × 2	318,309	0.964	318	265	200	0.00003456
⅛ × 2½	397,886	1.21	398	330	250	0.00002764
⅛ × 3	477,463	1.45	477	400	300	0.00002307
⅛ × 3½	557,040	1.69	557	464	350	0.00001975
⅛ × 4	636,618	1.93	637	531	395	0.00001728
⅛ × 5	795,772	2.42	796	663	497	0.00001382
⅛ × 6	954,927	2.89	955	800	597	0.00001152
¼ × 1	318,309	0.964	318	265	200	0.00003456
¼ × 1½	477,463	1.45	477	400	298	0.00002307
¼ × 2	636,618	1.93	637	530	398	0.00001728
¼ × 2½	795,772	2.41	796	660	495	0.00001382
¼ × 3	954,927	2.89	955	800	597	0.00001152
¼ × 3½	1,114,081	3.38	1,114	928	696	0.00000987
¼ × 4	1,273,236	3.86	1,273	1,060	796	0.00000864
¼ × 5	1,591,545	4.82	1,592	1,325	995	0.00000691
¼ × 6	1,909,854	5.79	1,910	1,590	1,190	0.00000576
⅜ × 1	477,463	1.45	478	400	300	0.00002304
⅜ × 1½	716,194	2.17	716	597	448	0.00001536
⅜ × 2	954,927	2.89	955	796	597	0.00001152
⅜ × 2½	1,193,658	3.62	1,195	995	746	0.00000921
⅜ × 3	1,432,390	4.34	1,432	1,195	895	0.00000706
⅜ × 3½	1,671,122	5.06	1,671	1,390	1,045	0.00000658
⅜ × 4	1,909,854	5.79	1,910	1,590	1,194	0.00000576
⅜ × 5	2,387,317	7.24	2,387	1,990	1,490	0.00000461
⅜ × 6	2,864,781	8.68	2,865	2,387	1,790	0.00000388
½ × 1	636,618	1.93	638	530	400	0.00001728
½ × 1½	954,927	2.81	955	796	598	0.00001152
½ × 2	1,273,236	3.86	1,273	1,060	796	0.00000864
½ × 2½	1,591,545	4.82	1,592	1,326	995	0.00000691
½ × 3	1,909,854	5.79	1,910	1,592	1,194	0.00000576
½ × 3½	2,228,163	6.75	2,228	1,860	1,393	0.00000494
½ × 4	2,546,472	7.72	2,546	2,120	1,592	0.00000432
½ × 5	3,183,090	9.65	3,183	2,653	1,989	0.00000345
½ × 6	3,819,708	11.58	3,820	3,183	2,380	0.00000288

NOTES ON THE RESISTANCE AND REACTANCE OF CONDUCTORS

When the wires of a circuit are a considerable distance apart, some of the lines of force set up by the current in one conductor do not reach the other conductor, with the result that more counter electromotive force is induced by transformer action in one wire than the other. The net result is that there is a counter electromotive force tending to oppose the current in addition to the opposition offered by the ohmic resistance of the metal itself. When the frequency is known, the opposing effect can be expressed in *ohms reactance*. If these reactance ohms are combined with the true ohmic resistance of the conductors on the legs of a right triangle, with the resistance laid off on the horizontal leg and the reactance laid off on the vertical leg, the hypotenuse will represent the total opposing force, or *impedance*, of the circuit. If, then, the voltage of the circuit is divided by this impedance, the quotient will be the current that will flow, and the angle between the resistance leg of the triangle and the hypotenuse will be the angle by which the current will lag the voltage.

Examination of Table 60 will show that for circuits in air this opposing effect is not large. For example, the reactance of one solid No. 8 wire of a three-phase circuit and the neutral, at 60 cycles and when the wires are located at the vertices of an equilateral triangle and spaced 12 in. apart, is 0.1256 ohm per 1,000 ft. The ohmic resistance, from Table 56, is approximately 0.628 ohm, so that the impedance is $\sqrt{0.628^2 + 0.1256^2} = 0.644$ ohm and the current lags by an angle whose tangent is $0.1256/0.628 = 0.2$, or about $11\frac{1}{2}$ deg.

However, if the conductors are in separate iron conduits and carry large currents, the inductive effect is large, and there is a considerable drop in voltage and also heating of the conduit. The usual method of preventing this loss is to arrange the circuits so that each conduit will have at least two wires carrying the same amount of current, but in opposite directions (see Article 300, Section 3018, of the 1951 edition of the National Electrical Code and also Fig. 128 of this book).

TABLE 60.   REACTANCE* OF CONDUCTORS AT 60 CYCLES

(General Electric Company)

Ohms per 1000 Ft of One Conductor of Single-phase or Three-phase Circuit

Size AWG, MCM	Equiv. Distance D†, in. between Conductors				
	12	18	36	60	72
Solid					
8	0.1256	0.1349	0.1508	0.1625	0.1667
7	0.1230	0.1323	0.1481	0.1599	0.1641
6	0.1203	0.1296	0.1455	0.1572	0.1614
5	0.1176	0.1270	0.1428	0.1546	0.1587
4	0.1150	0.1243	0.1402	0.1519	0.1561
3	0.1123	0.1216	0.1375	0.1492	0.1534
2	0.1096	0.1190	0.1348	0.1466	0.1507
1	0.1070	0.1163	0.1322	0.1439	0.1481
Stranded					
0	0.1033	0.1126	0.1285	0.1403	0.1445
00	0.1006	0.1099	0.1258	0.1376	0.1418
000	0.0980	0.1073	0.1232	0.1350	0.1392
0000	0.0953	0.1046	0.1205	0.1323	0.1365
250	0.0922	0.1015	0.1174	0.1292	0.1333
300	0.0902	0.0994	0.1153	0.1271	0.1313

* Reactance is directly proportional to frequency.

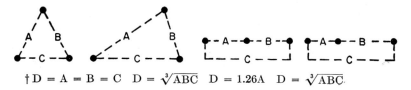

† $D = A = B = C$ $D = \sqrt[3]{ABC}$ $D = 1.26A$ $D = \sqrt[3]{ABC}$

TABLE 61. CONDUCTORS ALLOWED IN CONDUIT—1951 NEC
Rubber-covered, Types RF-32, R, RH, RW, and RU; thermoplastic,
Types TF, T, and TW.   One to nine conductors.

Size AWG, MCM	Number of conductors in one conduit or tubing*								
	1	2	3	4	5	6	7	8	9
18	½	½	½	½	½	½	½	¾	¾
16	½	½	½	½	½	½	¾	¾	¾
14	½	½	½	½	¾	¾	1	1	1
12	½	½	½	¾	¾	1	1	1	1¼
10	½	¾	¾	¾	1	1	1	1¼	1¼
8	½	¾	¾	1	1¼	1¼	1¼	1½	1½
6	½	1	1	1¼	1½	1½	2	2	2
4	½	1¼	1¼	1½	1½	2	2	2	2½
3	¾	1¼	1¼	1½	2	2	2½	2½	2½
2	¾	1¼	1¼	2	2	2	2½	2½	2½
1	¾	1½	1½	2	2½	2½	2½	3	3
0	1	1½	2	2	2½	2½	3	3	3
00	1	2	2	2½	2½	3	3	3	3½
000	1	2	2	2½	3	3	3	3½	3½
0000	1¼	2	2½	3	3	3	3½	3½	4
250	1¼	2½	2½	3	3	3½	4	4	4½
300	1¼	2½	2½	3	3½	4	4	4½	4½
350	1¼	3	3	3½	3½	4	4½	4½	5
400	1½	3	3	3½	4	4	4½	5	5
500	1½	3	3	3½	4	4½	5	5	6
600	2	3½	3½	4	4½	5	6	6	6
700	2	3½	3½	4½	5	5	6	6	
750	2	3½	3½	4½	5	6	6	6	
800	2	3½	4	4½	5	6	6		
900	2	4	4	5	6	6	6		
1,000	2	4	4	5	6	6			
1,250	2½	4½	4½	6	6				
1,500	3	5	5	6					
1,750	3	5	6	6					
2,000	3	6	6						

* Where a service run of conduit or electric metallic tubing does not exceed 50 ft in length
and does not contain more than the equivalent of two quarter bends from end to end, two
No. 4 insulated and one No. 4 bare conductor may be installed in 1-in. conduit or tubing.

TABLE 62. NUMBER OF LEAD-COVERED CONDUCTORS ALLOWED IN CONDUIT—1951 NEC

Lead-covered, Types RL and RHL—600 volt. The sizes apply to straight runs or to runs with nominal offsets equivalent to not more than two quarter bends.

Size AWG, MCM	Number of conductors in one conduit or tubing											
	Single-conductor cable				2-conductor cable				3-conductor cable			
	1	2	3	4	1	2	3	4	1	2	3	4
14	½	¾	¾	1	¾	1	1	1¼	¾	1¼	1½	1½
12	½	¾	¾	1	¾	1	1¼	1¼	1	1¼	1½	2
10	½	¾	1	1	¾	1¼	1¼	1½	1	1½	2	2
8	½	1	1¼	1½	1	1¼	1½	2	1	2	2	2½
6	¾	1¼	1½	1½	1¼	1½	2	2½	1¼	2½	3	3
4	¾	1¼	1½	1½	1¼	2	2½	2½	1½	3	3	3½
3	¾	1¼	1½	2	1¼	2	2½	3	1½	3	3	3½
2	1	1¼	1½	2	1¼	2	2½	3	1½	3	3½	4
1	1	1½	2	2	1½	2½	3	3½	2	3½	4	4½
0	1	2	2	2½	2	2½	3	3½	2	4	4½	5
00	1	2	2	2½	2	3	3½	4	2½	4	4½	5
000	1¼	2	2½	2½	2	3	3½	4	2½	4½	4½	6
0000	1¼	2½	2½	3	2½	3	3½	4½	3	5	6	6
250	1¼	2½	3	3	...	...	...	...	3	6	6	
300	1½	3	3	3½	...	...	...	...	3½	6	6	
350	1½	3	3	3½	...	...	...	...	3½	6	6	
400	1½	3	3	3½	...	...	...	...	3½	6	6	
500	1½	3	3½	4	...	...	...	...	4	6		
600	2	3½	4	4½								
700	2	4	4	5								
750	2	4	4	5								
800	2	4	4½	5								
900	2½	4	4½	5								
1,000	2½	4½	4½	6								
1,250	3	5	5	6								
1,500	3	5	6	6								
1,750	...	6	6									
2,000	3½	6	6									

TABLE 63. CARTRIDGE FUSES

N. E. C. Standard

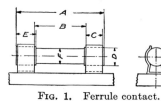
FIG. 1. Ferrule contact.

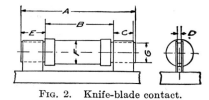
FIG. 2. Knife-blade contact.

Dimensions in Inches

Voltage	Rated capacity, amperes		A Length over terminals	B Distance between contact clips	C Width of contact clips	D Diameter of ferrules or thickness of terminal blades	E Minimum length of ferrules or of terminal blades outside of tube	F Diameter of tube	G Width of terminal blades
Not over 250	0–30	Fig. 1	2	1	½	9⁄16	½	½	
	31–60		3	1¾	⅝	13⁄16	⅝	¾	
	61–100	Fig. 2	5⅞	4	⅞	⅛	1	1	¾
	101–200		7⅛	4½	1¼	3⁄16	1⅜	1½	1⅛
	201–400		8⅝	5	1¾	¼	1⅞	2	1⅝
	401–600		10⅜	6	2⅛	¼	2¼	2½	2
Not over 600	0–30	Fig. 1	5	4	½	13⁄16	½	¾	
	31–60		5½	4¼	⅝	1 1⁄16	⅝	1	
	61–100	Fig. 2	7⅞	6	⅞	⅛	1	1¼	¾
	101–200		9⅝	7	1¼	3⁄16	1⅜	1¾	1⅛
	201–400		11⅝	8	1¾	¼	1⅞	2½	1⅝
	401–600		13⅜	9	2¼	¼	2¼	3	2

TABLE 64. COMMERCIAL FUSE SIZES IN AMPERES

125-volt plug fuses	250-volt cartridge fuses			
	Ferrule contact		Knife-blade contact	
	Switch size		Switch size	
	30 Amp.	60 Amp.	100 Amp.	200 Amp.
3	3	35	65	110
4	4	40	70	120
5	5	45	75	125
6	6	50	80	150
8	8	55	85	175
10	10	60	90	200
12	12	..	95	
15	15	..	100	
18				
20	20			
25	25			
30	30			

TABLE 65. TYPE A SAFETY SWITCHES

(Square D Company)

Fusible, 230 volts AC, 250 volts DC, visible blade 2-pole

Amp	Hp, a-c	Hp, d-c	Box No.	Cat. No.	Dimensions, in. A	B	C	D	E	F	G	H	Left side	Right side	Back	Top	Bottom
30	2	5	480A	A85251	9 7/8	5 5/8	3 3/4	5 1/2	7 3/8	1 1/8	7 3/4	3 1/8	2—AB	1—AB	2—AB	2—ABC	2—ABC
60	5	10	635	A86252	13 3/8	8 1/2	4	6 1/4	6 1/4	1 1/4	11 1/4	5 7/8	2—ABCD	2—ABCD	2—ABCD	3—ABCD	3—ABCD
100	10	15	650	A86253	19 3/8	11 5/8	4 5/8	7 1/4	7 1/4	1 3/8	17	9	2—CDEF	2—CDEF	2—CDEF	3—CDEF, A	3—CDEF, A
200	15	30	488	A86254	21 7/8	13 3/8	5 1/8	7 13/16	...	1 1/2	19 1/2	11	2—FG	2—FG	2—FG	2—DF, DG	2—DF, DG
400	30	50	459-D	88255	40 5/8	16 3/4	6 3/8	12	...	2 3/8	38	14	2—GH	2—GH	2—GH	2—DF, DGH	2—DF, DGH
									3-pole								
30	3	....	481-A	A85351	9 7/8	5 5/8	3 3/4	5 1/2	7 3/8	1 1/8	7 3/4	3 1/8	2—AB	1—AB	2—AB	2—ABC	2—ABC
60	7 1/2	....	635	A86352	13 3/8	8 1/2	4	6 1/4	6 1/4	1 1/2	11 1/4	5 7/8	2—ABCD	2—ABCD	2—ABCD	3—ABCD	3—ABCD
100	15	....	649	A86353	17 1/8	11 5/8	4 5/8	7 1/4	7 1/4	1 3/8	14 3/4	9	2—CDEF	2—CDEF	2—CDEF	3—CDEF, A	3—CDEF, A
200	30	....	488	A86354	21 7/8	13 3/8	5 1/8	7 13/16	...	1 1/2	19 1/2	11	2—FG	2—FG	2—FG	2—DF, DG	2—DF, DG
400	50	....	456-C	88355	40 5/8	21 7/8	6 3/8	12 1/4	...	2 3/8	38	19	2—GH	2—GH	2—GH	2—DF, DGH	2—DF, GDH
						Fusible, 575 volts AC, 600 volts DC, visible blade With arc suppressors, 2-pole											
30	....	7 1/2	483-A	A86261	12 7/8	7 3/8	3 3/4	5 1/2	9 3/8	1 1/8	10 3/4	4 7/8	2—AB	2—AB	2—AB	3—ABC	3—ABC
60	....	15	636	A86262	15 7/8	8 1/2	4	6 1/4	6 1/4	1 1/4	13 3/4	5 7/8	2—ABCD	2—ABCD	2—ABCD	3—ABCD	3—ABCD
100	...	25	650	A86263	19 3/8	11 5/8	4 5/8	7 1/4	7 1/4	1 3/8	17	9	2—CDEF	2—CDEF	2—CDEF	3—CDEF, 1A	3—CDEF, 1A
200	....	50	489	A86264	24 3/8	13 3/8	5 1/8	7 13/16	...	1 1/2	22	11	2—FG	2—FG	2—FG	2—DF, DG	2—DF, DG
400	....	....	462-D	88265	43 5/8	21 7/8	6 3/8	12 3/8	...	2 3/8	41	19	2—GH	2—GH	2—GH	4—DF, DGH	4—DF, DGH

TABLE 65. TYPE A SAFETY SWITCHES. *(Continued)*

575 volts AC 3-pole

Amp	Hp, a-c	Hp, d-c	Box No.	Cat. No.	Dimensions, in.								Left side	Right side	Back	Top	Bottom
					A	B	C	D	E	F	G	H					
30	7½	....	483-A	A85341	12⅞	7⅜	3¾	5½	7⅜	1⅛	10¾	4⅞	2—AB	2—AB	2—AB	3—ABC	3—ABC
60	20	....	636	A86342	15⅞	8½	4	6¼	6¼	1¼	13¾	5⅞	2—ABCD	2—ABCD	2—ABCD	3—ABCD	3—ABCD
100	30	....	650	A86343	19⅞	11⅝	4⅝	7¼	7¼	1⅜	17	9	2—CDEF	2—CDEF	2—CDEF	3—CDEF, A	3—CDEF, A
200	50	....	489	A86344	24⅜	13⅜	5⅛	7 13/16	...	1½	22	11	2—FG	2—FG	2—FG	2—DF, DG	2—DF, DGH
400	....	....	462-D	88345	43⅝	21⅞	6⅜	12⅜	...	2⅜	41	19	2—GH	2—GH	2—GH	4—DF, DGH	4—DF, DGH

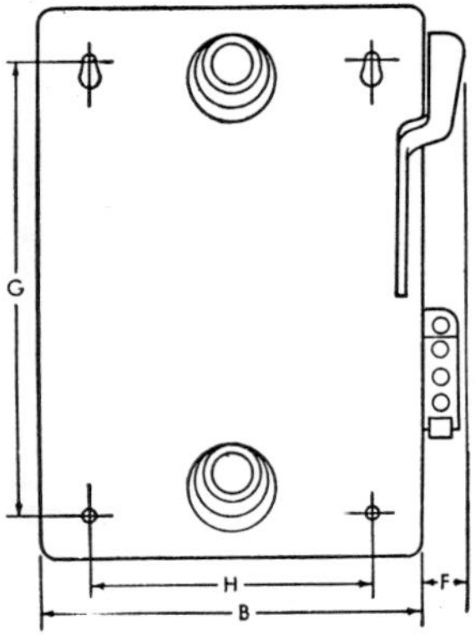

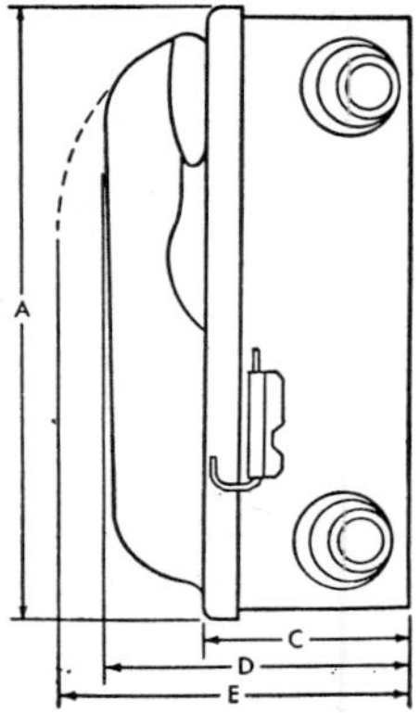

Knockout Code:

A—KO for ½″ Conduit
B—KO for ¾″ Conduit
C—KO for 1″ Conduit
D—KO for 1¼″ Conduit
E—KO for 1½″ Conduit
F—KO for 2″ Conduit
G—KO for 2½″ Conduit
H—KO for 3″ Conduit
J—KO for 3½″ Conduit

Example: 4-AB, ABCD means 4(½″, ¾″) 1(½″, ¾″, 1″, 1¼″) concentric or tangential KO's.

TABLE 66. INDUSTRIAL CIRCUIT BREAKERS

(Square D Company)

2-pole 250 volts AC 125/250 volts DC

Type	Amp.	Box No.	Dimensions, in.									Knockouts				
			A	B	C	D	E	F	G	H	J	Left side	Right side	Back	Top	Bottom
ML	15–50	704-C	12 1/4	6 3/4	3 5/16	10 3/16	4 9/16	4 9/16	1 3/8	1/4 × 5/16	4 11/16	2—ABCD	2—ABCD	2—ABCD	2—ABCD	2—ABCD
ML1	70–100	694-A	13 1/4	7 15/16	3 1/2	11	5 1/2	5 1/2	1 3/8	1/4	4 13/16	2—ABCD	2—ABCD	2—ABCD	2—ABCD	2—ABCD
															1—CDF	1—CDF
ML3	125–225	522-B	22 3/8	12 3/4	4 11/16	18 3/4	10	10	1 3/8	9/32 × 3/8	6 7/16	2—DEF	2—DEF	2—DEF	3—DEFG	3—DEFG
WL	225–600	613	38 9/16	17 11/16	7 1/8	35	15	15	1 3/8	9/32 × 3/8	10 7/16	2—GH	2—GH	2—GH	2—FGHJ	2—FGHJ
3-pole 250 Volts AC																
ML	15–50	704-C	12 1/4	6 3/4	3 5/16	10 3/16	4 9/16	4 9/16	1 3/8	1/4 × 5/16	4 11/16	2—ABCD	2—ABCD	2—ABCD	2—ABCD	2—ABCD
ML1	70–100	694-A	13 1/4	7 15/16	3 1/2	11	5 1/2	5 1/2	1 3/8	1/4	4 13/16	2—ABCD	2—ABCD	2—ABCD	2—ABCD	2—ABCD
															1—CDE	1—CDE
M13	125–225	522-B	22 3/8	12 3/4	4 11/16	18 3/4	10	10	1 3/8	9/32 × 3/8	6 7/16	2—DEF	2—DEF	2—DEF	3—DEFG	3—DEFG
WL	225–600	613	38 9/16	17 11/16	7 1/8	35	15	15	1 3/8	9/32 × 3/8	10 7/16	2—GH	2—GH	2—GH	2—FGHJ	2—FGHJ
2-pole 600 Volts A-C 250 Volts D-C																
ML1	15–50	694	13 1/4	7 5/16	3 1/2	11	5 1/2	5 1/2	1 3/8	1/4	4 13/16	2—ABCD	2—ABCD	2—ABCD	3—ABCD	3—ABCD
ML2	70–100	522	17 3/8	7 15/16	4 31/32	15	5 1/2	5 1/2	1 3/8	9/32 × 3/8	5 7/8	2—CDEF	2—CDEF	2—CDEF	2—ABCD	2—ABCD
															CDEF	CDEF
ML3	125–225	522-B	22 3/8	12 3/4	4 11/16	18 3/4	10	10	1 3/8	9/32 × 3/8	6 7/16	2—DEF	2—DEF	2—DEF	3—DEFG	3—DEFG
WL	225–600	613	38 9/16	17 11/16	7 1/8	35	15	15	1 3/8	9/32 × 3/8	10 7/16	2—GH	2—GH	2—GH	2—FGHJ	2—FGHJ
3-pole 600 Volts A-C																
ML1	15–50	694	13 1/4	7 15/16	3 1/2	11	5 1/2	5 1/2	1 3/8	1/4	4 13/16	2—ABCD	2—ABCD	2—ABCD	3—ABCD	3—ABCD
ML2	70–100	522	17 3/8	7 15/16	4 31/32	15	5 1/2	5 1/2	1 3/8	9/32 × 3/8	5 7/8	2—CDEF	2—CDEF	2—CDEF	2—ABCD	2—ABCD
															CDEF	CDEF
ML3	125–225	522-B	22 3/8	12 3/4	4 11/16	18 3/4	10	10	1 3/8	9/32 × 3/8	6 7/16	2—DEF	2—DEF	2—DEF	3—DEFG	3—DEFG
WL	225–600	613	38 9/16	17 11/16	7 1/8	35	15	15	1 3/8	9/32 × 3/8	10 7/16	2—GH	2—GH	2—GH	2—FGHJ	2—FGHJ

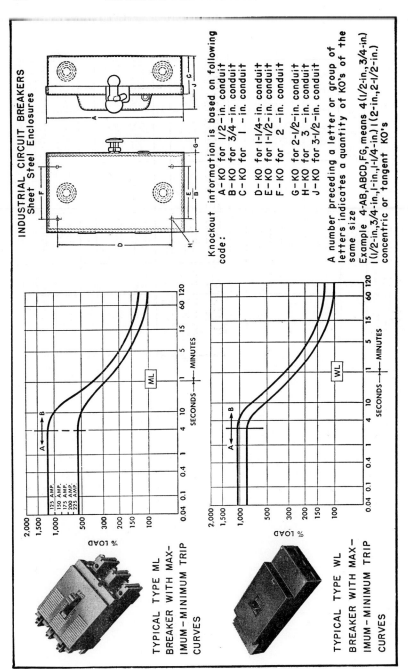

INDUSTRIAL CIRCUIT BREAKERS
Sheet Steel Enclosures

Knockout information is based on following code:

A—KO for 1/2-in. conduit
B—KO for 3/4-in. conduit
C—KO for 1 - in. conduit

D—KO for 1-1/4-in. conduit
E—KO for 1-1/2-in. conduit
F—KO for 2 -in. conduit

G—KO for 2-1/2-in. conduit
H—KO for 3 -in. conduit
J—KO for 3-1/2-in. conduit

A number preceding a letter or group of letters indicates a quantity of KO's of the same size
Example 4-AB, ABCD, FG, means 4(1/2-in., 3/4-in.) 1(1/2-in., 3/4-in., 1-in., 1-1/4-in.) 1(2-in., 2-1/2-in.) concentric or tangent KO's

TYPICAL TYPE ML BREAKER WITH MAX-IMUM–MINIMUM TRIP CURVES

TYPICAL TYPE WL BREAKER WITH MAX-IMUM–MINIMUM TRIP CURVES

TABLE 67. FULL-VOLTAGE, 110 VOLTS TO 600 VOLTS MAGNETIC STARTERS FOR SQUIRREL-CAGE MOTORS TO 50 HP AT 600 VOLTS
(*General Electric Company*)

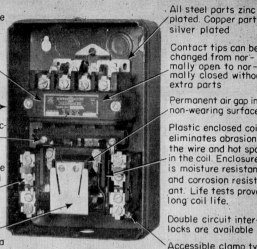

Variety of knockouts make starter adaptable to any conduit design

Contact tips can be easily removed without loss of springs

Modern enclosure finished in machine grey

Entire magnetic structure can be removed easily

Overload relays can be changed from manual to automatic without removal from case

Silicon steel magnet spreads pounding wear over a large area

All steel parts zinc plated. Copper parts silver plated

Contact tips can be changed from normally open to normally closed without extra parts

Permanent air gap in a non-wearing surface

Plastic enclosed coil eliminates abrasion of the wire and hot spots in the coil. Enclosure is moisture resistant and corrosion resistant. Life tests prove long coil life.

Double circuit interlocks are available

Accessible clamp type terminals and screws

Ratings and Dimensions—CR7006

NEMA size	Horsepower rating, 60-cycle, 3-phase			Approximate Dimensions of enclosure, in. (general purpose)		
	110 volts	220 volts	400–600 volts	Height, in.	Width, in.	Depth, in.
0	$1\frac{1}{2}$	2	2	$9\frac{3}{32}$	$6\frac{3}{32}$	$4\frac{21}{32}$
1	3	5	$7\frac{1}{2}$	$9\frac{3}{32}$	$6\frac{3}{32}$	$4\frac{21}{32}$
2	$7\frac{1}{2}$	15	25	$14\frac{1}{8}$	$8\frac{1}{8}$	$5\frac{11}{16}$
3	15	30	50	$17\frac{3}{4}$	$11\frac{1}{8}$	$7\frac{1}{4}$

TABLE 68. AUTOTRANSFORMER MOTOR STARTER
(*Allis-Chalmers Manufacturing Company*)

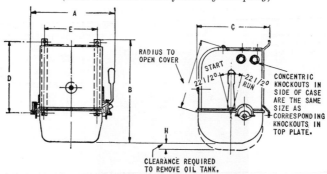

Outline dimensions are of the low voltage type *RMC* Starters and high voltage starter case only. Dimensions are approximate.

	MAX. H. P. RATING										
VOLTS	110	220		440-550							
CYCLES	25-50 60	25	50 60	25	50 60	A	B	C	D	E	H
	5-10	20	30	20	40	$18\frac{5}{8}$	$22\frac{1}{16}$	$17\frac{1}{8}$	16	12	$5\frac{1}{2}$
	15	40	40	40	60	$20\frac{5}{16}$	$25\frac{3}{16}$	$18\frac{5}{16}$	19	$13\frac{3}{4}$	6
		60	60	60	100	$22\frac{1}{16}$	$30\frac{5}{16}$	$19\frac{1}{8}$	24	$14\frac{1}{2}$	6
		125	125	150	150	$26\frac{13}{16}$	$33\frac{5}{16}$	$22\frac{11}{16}$	27	$19\frac{5}{8}$	6

Approximately two feet should be allowed above the top of the starter for cover clearance.

TABLE 68. AUTOTRANSFORMER MOTOR STARTER. (*Continued*)

Method of starting	Starting Current drawn from the line as a percentage of full load current	Inrush current to the motor as a percentage of full load current.	Starting torque as a percentage of full load torque
Across-the-line 100% line voltage	600	600	120
Auto-transformer 80% tap	409	480	77
Auto-transformer 65% tap	278	390	51
Auto-transformer 50% tap	175	300	30

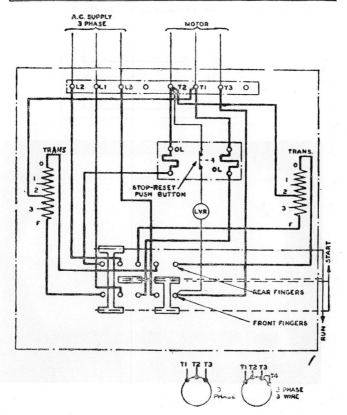

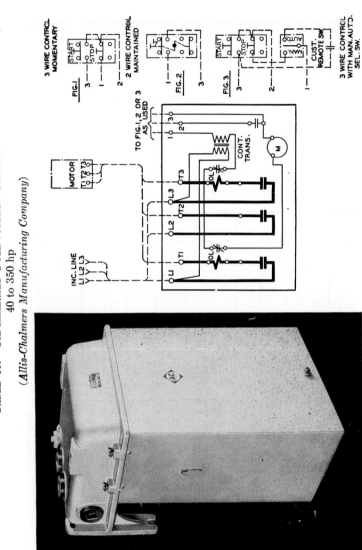

TABLE 69. OIL-IMMERSED FULL-VOLTAGE STARTER
40 to 350 hp
(Allis-Chalmers Manufacturing Company)

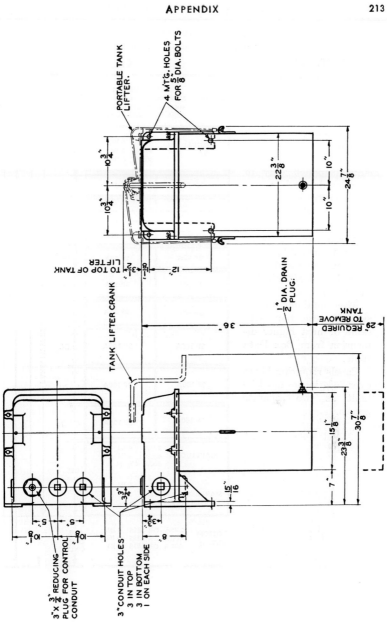

TABLE 70. HOW TO LAY OUT A PANELBOARD
(*Westinghouse Electric Corporation*)

INSTRUCTIONS

Use proper top and bottom gutter sections.

Add for neutral bar, if required.

Add proper "mains" section.

Add for branch circuits (supplied only in pairs as detailed in layout sketch).

Panel heights must be in multiples of 2 inches. For example, if panel height figures $23\frac{1}{2}''$, add a $\frac{1}{2}$-inch filler and use a panel height of 24". (See example.)

After obtaining dimension H, use box with same or next higher dimension from Box Data table.

Panels requiring boxes over $76\frac{3}{4}$ inches must be built as two separate panels.

SKETCH

TABLE 70. HOW TO LAY OUT A PANELBOARD. *(Continued)*

PANELBOARDS
RATINGS AND DIMENSIONS
Type MH Multibreaker Distribution Panelboards

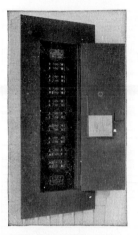

BRANCH CIRCUITS
1 and 2-pole; 15, 20, 25, 35 and 50-amp, Type M Breakers.

2 and 3-pole; 15, 20, 25, 35 and 50-amp, Type M1 breakers.

2 and 3-pole; 70, 90 and 100-amp, Type M2 breakers.

MAINS CAPACITY
Lugs only, 50 amp, 100 amp, 225 amp, 400 amp or 600 amp.

Main breakers, 50 amp, 100 amp, 225 amp.

SERVICE VOLTAGES
Single-phase, 3-wire, solid neutral. 125/250-volt, 3-phase, 4-wire, solid neutral. 120/208-volt, 3-phase, 230-volt.

STANDARD BOX HEIGHTS

Height Inches (I.D.)	Box Gauge Number	Trim Gauge Number
16¼	14	12
19	14	12
21¾	14	12
24½	14	12
27¼	14	12
30	14	12
32¾	14	12
35½	14	12
38¼	14	12
41	12	12
43¾	12	12
46½	12	12
49¼	12	12
52	12	12
54¾	12	12
57½	12	12
60¼	10	10
63	10	10
65¾	10	10
68½	10	10

EXAMPLE

		Inches
TOP GUTTER		4
SOLID NEUTRAL BAR		4
FILLER		½
20-Amp 2-Pole	25-Amp 2-Pole	2
3-Pole Space	3-Pole Space	3
35-Amp 2-Pole	50-Amp 3-Pole	3
70-Amp 2-Pole	70-Amp 2-Pole·	3
Filler Space	100-Amp 3-Pole	4½
225-Amp Main Lugs		4
Bottom Gutter		4
Total		32

Nearest cabinet size—
32¾″ H, 20″ W, 5¾″ D

TABLE 71. ELECTRICAL CLEARANCES FOR SWITCHGEAR ASSEMBLIES
(*Westinghouse Electric Corporation*)

ELECTRICAL CLEARANCES FOR SWITCHGEAR ASSEMBLIES

INDOOR

SURFACE CREEPING DISTANCE		VOLT. CLASS	STRIKING DISTANCE THRU. AIR *	
BETWEEN LIVE PARTS OF OPPOSITE POLARITY	BETWEEN LIVE PARTS AND GROUND INSULATING MATERIAL		BETWEEN NEAREST LIVE PARTS OF OPPOSITE POLARITY	BETWEEN LIVE PARTS AND GROUND
CONTROL CIRCUITS – SUPERVISORY CONTROL– BATTERY CHARGING CONN. ETC.				
3/8	1/4	UP TO 50	1/4	1/8
1/2	3/8	125	3/8	1/4
5/8	1/2	250	3/8	1/4
1	3/4	600	1/2	3/8
1 1/4	1 1/4	750	3/4	3/4
1 3/4	1 3/4	1500	1 1/4	1 1/4
ALL POWER CIRCUITS CONNECTED TO SYSTEMS ABOVE 150 KVA CAPACITY				
1	1/2	125 ⊕	1/2	1/2
1 1/4	5/8	250 ⊕	3/4	1/2
2	1	600 ⊕	1	1
2 1/8	1 1/4	750	1 1/4	1
2 1/2	1 3/4	1500	1 3/4	1 1/4
3	2 1/2	2500	2 1/2	2
3 1/2	3	3500	3	2 1/2
—	—	4500	3 1/2	2 1/2
—	—	7500	4	3 1/4
—	—	15000	7	5 1/2
—	—	23000	11	8 1/2
—	—	34500	16	12

OUTDOOR *

		VOLT. CLASS	PHASE TO PHASE	TO GROUND
		UP TO 3500	6	6
		5000	6	6
		7500	6	6
		15000	12	9
		23000	17	13
		34500	24	18
		46000	32	23
		69000	44	32
		115000	64	47
		138000	77	56
		161000	89	65
		230000	124	90

NOTE * FOR RIGID CONDUCTORS ONLY
WHEN SUPPORTED CLEAR OF SURFACE
FOR FLEXIBLE CONDUCTORS INCREASE CLEARANCE GIVEN
BY TWICE THE MAXIMUM SAG.
FOR VOLTAGES ABOVE 3500 ALL LIVE PARTS SHOULD BE
SUPPORTED ON INSULATING PILLARS.
VOLTAGE LIMITS FOR PANEL MATERIALS
SLATE UP TO 750 VOLTS
MARBLE UP TO 2500 VOLTS
MICARTA & EBONY ASBESTOS LUMBER UP TO 3500 VOLTS FOR PANELS
⊕ COMPLIES WITH UNDERWRITERS STANDARDS.

TABLE 72. ELECTRICAL CLEARANCES FOR INDUSTRIAL CONTROL
(*Westinghouse Electric Corporation*)

ELECTRICAL CLEARANCES FOR INDUSTRIAL CONTROL

SURFACE CREEPING DISTANCE				VOLTAGE	STRIKING DISTANCE THRU. AIR*			
BETWEEN LIVE PARTS OF OPPOSITE POLARITY		BETWEEN LIVE PARTS AND GROUND INSULATING MATERIAL			BETWEEN NEAREST LIVE PARTS OF OPPOSITE POLARITY		BETWEEN LIVE PARTS AND GROUND	
INSULATING MATERIAL / BARE CONDUCTOR		GROUNDED ANGLE / LIVE PART			LIVE INSULATOR CAPS		GROUNDED STRUCTURE / BARE CONDUCTOR	
AIR	OIL	AIR	OIL		AIR	OIL	AIR	OIL
1/4	1/4	1/4	1/4	150	1/4	1/4	1/4	1/4
3/8	3/8	1/4	1/4	300	1/4	1/4	1/4	1/4
3/4	3/4	3/8	3/8	600	3/8	3/8	1/4	1/4
2	1	1	1/2	2500	1	3/4	1/2	3/8
3 1/2	2	1 3/4	1	7000	2	1 1/2	1	3/4

THESE CLEARANCE DISTANCES SHOULD BE INCREASED FOR DIRTY OR MOIST CONDITIONS.

A LINING OR INSULATING MATERIAL EMPLOYED TO INSURE THE REQUIRED SPACING MUST NOT BE LESS THAN 1/32" IN THICKNESS.

* FOR RIGID CONDUCTORS ONLY

TABLE 73. BUS SPACINGS

(Data from Electrical Engineers' Equipment Company)

The distances given in the *A* columns are for minimum spacing, and distances given in *B* columns are good practice for large plants.

Dimensions in Inches

Voltage	Distance between centers of buses		Minimum distance between opposite live parts		Minimum distance between live parts and ground	
	A	B	A	B	A	B
250	$1\frac{1}{2}$ to	$2\frac{1}{2}$	1 to	2	$\frac{3}{4}$ to	$1\frac{1}{2}$
600	2 to	3	$1\frac{1}{2}$ to	$2\frac{1}{2}$	1 to	2
1,100	4 to	5	$2\frac{1}{2}$ to	$3\frac{1}{2}$	$1\frac{1}{2}$ to	$2\frac{1}{2}$
2,300	5 to	$6\frac{1}{2}$	$2\frac{3}{4}$ to	4	2 to	$2\frac{3}{4}$
4,000	6 to	$7\frac{1}{2}$	3 to	$4\frac{1}{2}$	$2\frac{1}{4}$ to	3
6,600	7 to	8	$3\frac{1}{2}$ to	$4\frac{1}{2}$	$2\frac{1}{2}$ to	3
7,500	8 to	9	4 to	$4\frac{1}{2}$	$2\frac{3}{4}$ to	$3\frac{1}{4}$
9,000	9 to	10	$4\frac{1}{4}$ to	$4\frac{1}{2}$	3 to	$3\frac{1}{2}$
11,000	9 to	11	$4\frac{1}{2}$ to	$4\frac{3}{4}$	$3\frac{1}{4}$ to	$3\frac{3}{4}$
13,200	9 to	12	$4\frac{3}{4}$ to	5	$3\frac{1}{2}$ to	$4\frac{1}{4}$
15,000	9 to	14	5 to	$5\frac{1}{2}$	$3\frac{3}{4}$ to	$4\frac{1}{2}$
16,500	10 to	14	$5\frac{1}{2}$ to	6	$4\frac{1}{2}$ to	5
18,000	11 to	14	6 to	7	5 to	6
22,000	12 to	15	$7\frac{1}{2}$ to	9	6 to	7
26,000	14 to	16	10 to	12	8 to	9
35,000	18 to	22	12 to	15	10 to	12
45,000	22 to	27	16 to	18	$13\frac{1}{2}$ to	15
56,000	28 to	31	$17\frac{1}{2}$ to	19	16 to	$17\frac{1}{2}$
66,000	34 to	38	22 to	24	$18\frac{1}{2}$ to	23
75,000	36 to	42	26 to	30	25 to	$27\frac{1}{2}$
90,000	46 to	54	32 to	35	27 to	29
104,000	54 to	60	$34\frac{1}{2}$ to	39	$28\frac{1}{2}$ to	32
110,000	60 to	72	38 to	41	33 to	36
122,000	66 to	78	42 to	47	$35\frac{1}{2}$ to	39
134,000	74 to	84	$48\frac{1}{2}$ to	56	39 to	41
148,000	82 to	96	59 to	67	45 to	50
160,000	88 to	104	70 to	84	53 to	62

TABLE 74. AMPERE RATINGS OF A-C AND D-C MOTORS AT FULL LOAD

(General Electric Company)

The following tables give average current values for motors of different types, frequencies and speeds. Variations of 10 per cent above or below the values given may be expected.

Hp.	110 volts				220 volts				440 volts		550 volts		
	D.C.	A.C.			D.C.	A.C.			A.C.		D.C.	A.C	
		3-phase	2-phase	Single-phase		3-phase	2-phase	Single-phase	3-phase	2-phase		3-phase	2-phase
¼	2.4	2	1.8	5	1.2	1	0.9	2.5	0.5	0.4	0.5	0.4	0.3
½	4.5	3.6	3.1	6.8	2.3	1.8	1.6	3.4	0.9	0.8	0.9	0.7	0.6
¾	6.8	5.3	4.6	10	3.4	2.7	2.3	5	1.3	1.2	1.3	1	0.9
1	8.8	7	6	13.3	4.4	3.5	3	6.6	1.8	1.5	1.8	1.3	1.1
2	16.8	13	11.2	25	8.4	6.5	5.6	12.4	3.3	2.8	3.4	2.6	2.2
3	24.5	19	14.7	36	12.3	9.5	7.4	18	4.8	3.7	4.9	3.8	3.3
5	40	31	29	58	20	15.4	14.3	29	7.7	7.2	8	6.2	5.4
7½	59	45	39	85	29	22.4	19.4	43	11.2	9.7	11.8	9	7.8
10	78	58	50	110	39	29	25	55	14.5	12.5	15.6	11.8	10.8
15	116	85	73	162	53	42	37	81	21.3	18.4	23	17.4	15
20	156	110	95	208	78	55	48	104	28	23.8	31	22.5	19.5
25	192	136	118	258	96	68	59	129	34	30	38	27	23
30	230	160	138	304	115	80	69	152	40	35	46	32	28
35	267	188	163	356	133	94	81	178	47	41	53	37	32
40	304	210	182	400	152	105	91	200	53	46	61	42	36
50	378	260	224	492	185	130	112	246	65	56	76	52	45
60	452	310	268	.....	226	155	134	.....	78	67	90	62	54
75	562	384	332	.....	281	192	166	.....	96	83	112	77	67
85	636	430	371	.....	318	214	185	.....	107	93	127	86	75
100	748	504	436	.....	374	252	218	.....	126	109	150	101	88
125	930	620	536	.....	465	310	268	.....	155	134	186	125	108
150	1,122	736	640	.....	561	368	320	.....	184	160	223	148	128
175	1,300	850	734	.....	650	425	367	.....	213	184	260	172	149
200	....	968	836	.....	742	484	418	.....	242	209	297	195	169
225	....	1,080	934	.....	835	540	467	.....	270	234	335	215	189
250	....	1,190	1,030	.....	925	595	515	.....	288	258	370	240	207
275	....	1,300	1,124	.....	1,020	650	562	.....	325	281	407	263	227
300	....	1,420	1,230	.....	1,120	710	615	.....	355	308	444	285	246
350	....	1,660	1,440	.....	1,285	830	720	.....	440	360	518	354	288
400	....	1,900	1,640	.....	1,480	950	820	.....	475	410	593	382	328
450	....	2,130	1,850	.....	1,665	1,065	925	.....	538	462	668	430	370
500	....	2,370	2,500	.....	1,845	1,185	1,025	.....	593	512	740	475	410

TABLE 75. DATA ON FRACTIONAL HORSEPOWER FOR 115-VOLT 60-CYCLE MOTORS

(*The Redmond Company, Inc.*)

From $\frac{1}{500}$ to $\frac{1}{10}$ hp

Hp	Watts output	Amp	Watts input	Rpm	Hp	Watts output	Amp	Watts input	Rpm
$\frac{1}{500}$	1.5	0.25	14	3,600	$\frac{1}{50}$	15	0.8	60	3,000
$\frac{1}{500}$	1.5	0.28	20	1,450	$\frac{1}{40}$	19	1.0	70	1,525
$\frac{1}{175}$	4.3	0.44	23	3,000	$\frac{1}{40}$	19	1.1	75	1,500
$\frac{1}{150}$	5	0.50	35	1,550	$\frac{1}{30}$	25	1.5	105	1,550
$\frac{1}{125}$	6	0.48	27	3,000	$\frac{1}{25}$	30	1.5	110	1,500
$\frac{1}{125}$	6	0.56	38	1,550	$\frac{1}{20}$	37	2	130	1,500
$\frac{1}{100}$	7.5	0.68	40	3,000	$\frac{1}{20}$	..	2.2	140	1,050
$\frac{1}{100}$	7.5	0.52	37	1,550	$\frac{1}{15}$	50	2.5	170	1,500
$\frac{1}{80}$	9.3	0.70	50	2,800	$\frac{1}{15}$	..	2.6	170	1,000
$\frac{1}{80}$	9	0.65	44	1,550	$\frac{1}{12}$	62	2.7	205	1,550
$\frac{1}{75}$	10	0.65	44	1,550	$\frac{1}{10}$	75	3.	220	1,550
$\frac{1}{70}$	11	0.70	48	1,550					

TABLE 75. DATA ON FRACTIONAL HORSEPOWER FOR 115-VOLT 60-CYCLE
MOTORS. (*Continued*)
From ⅛ hp to ¾ hp
(Prepared from NEMA standards)

Hp output	Watts output	Amp	Watts input	Syn. speed, rpm	Min eff × min pf to be not less than apparent eff		Apparent eff, per cent
					Min eff, per cent	Min pf, per cent	
⅛	93	2.9	207	3,600	45	57	28
	93	2.69	176	1,800	53	52	30
	93	3.85	207	1,200	45	43	21
	93	5.45	245	900	38	36	15
⅙	124	3.18	254	3,600	49	62	34
	124	3.00	215	1,800	58	56	36
	124	4.32	254	1,200	49	46	25
	124	6.00	296	900	42	38	18
¼	186	4.16	352	3,600	53	66	39
	186	3.86	301	1,800	62	60	42
	186	5.59	352	1,200	53	49	29
	186	8.10	414	900	45	40	20
⅓	249	5.27	460	3,600	54	67	41
	249	4.92	395	1,800	63	61	44
	249	6.98	460	1,200	54	50	31
	249	9.86	540	900	46	41	22
½	373	7.36	678	3,600	55	69	44
	373	6.90	574	1,800	65	63	47
	373	9.86	678	1,200	55	52	33
	373	14.10	794	900	47	43	23
¾	559	10.60	980	3,600	57	72	46
	559	9.95	835	1,800	67	65	49
	559	14.30	980	1,200	57	53	34
	559	20.20	1,140	900	49	44	24

TABLE 76. CIRCUIT CAPACITY FOR HOUSEHOLD APPLIANCES*
(*Edison Electrical Institute*)

Item	Capacity		
	Amperes	Wire	Volts
Air cooling unit...............	25	2	230
Automatic washer...................	20	2	115
Bathroom heater...................	20	2	115 or 230
Clothes dryer.....................	25	3	115/230
Dishwater-waste disposer (if necessary plumbing is installed)........	20	2	115
Fuel-fired heating equipment (if installed)........................	15 or 20		115
Home freeze unit..................	20	2	115 or 230
Range (up to 12 kw)......	35	3	115/230
Range (above 12 kw)..............	50	3	115/230
Summer cooling fan................	20	2	115 (switched)
Water heater.....................	†	†	†
Water pump......................	20	2	115 or 230
Workshop or bench................	20	2	115

* In some instances one of the circuits recommended may serve two devices which are not liable to be used at the same time, such as a summer cooling fan and a bathroom heater. The majority of appliances for residential use are made for 110 to 120 volt circuits. There is, however, a growing tendency to make fixed appliances for use on 208–220–240-volt circuits. It is recommended that the higher voltage be preferred in those cases where a choice exists.

† Consult a local utility company.

TABLE 77.   AMPERES FOR 1 KW. AT VARIOUS VOLTAGES AND POWER FACTORS
(Allis-Chalmers Manufacturing Company)

Three-phase Circuits

Volts	100 per cent	90 per cent	80 per cent	70 per cent
110	5.256	5.84	6.57	7.51
220	2.628	2.92	3.28	3.75
370	1.562	1.735	1.952	2.231
380	1.521	1.690	1.900	2.170
390	1.482	1.646	1.852	2.117
440	1.314	1.460	1.640	1.877
550	1.050	1.166	1.312	1.500
1,100	0.5256	0.584	0.657	0.751
2,200	0.2628	0.292	0.328	0.375
2,400	0.2400	0.266	0.3000	0.342
3,300	0.1750	0.1944	0.2187	0.250
6,600	0.0875	0.0972	0.1093	0.125
10,000	0.0578	0.0640	0.0722	0.0825
13,200	0.0438	0.0486	0.0546	0.0625
16,500	0.0350	0.0388	0.0437	0.0500
22,000	0.0263	0.0292	0.0328	0.0375
33,000	0.0175	0.0194	0.0219	0.0250
44,000	0.01314	0.0146	0.0164	0.01875
60,000	0.00963	0.0107	0.01203	0.0137
66,000	0.00875	0.0097	0.01095	0.0125
88,000	0.006575	0.0073	0.0082	0.00938
110,000	0.00526	0.00584	0.00657	0.00751

Two-phase Circuits

Volts	100 per cent	90 per cent	80 per cent	70 per cent
110	4.54	5.04	5.67	6.48
220	2.27	2.52	2.83	3.24
440	1.13	1.26	1.41	1.62
1,100	0.454	0.504	0.567	0.648
2,200	0.227	0.252	0.283	0.324

Single-phase Circuits

Volts	100 per cent	90 per cent	80 per cent	70 per cent
110	9.09	10.01	11.36	12.98
220	4.54	5.05	5.68	6.49
440	2.27	2.52	2.84	3.24
1,100	0.909	1.01	1.136	1.298
2,200	0.454	0.505	0.568	0.649

TABLE 78. AVERAGE VOLTAGE FOR VARIOUS LINE LENGTHS
(Allis-Chalmers Manufacturing Company)

The economical voltage to transmit power over a given distance depends on many factors such as the kilovolt-amperes transmitted, losses, cost of line and construction materials, regulation, etc. The following tables, therefore, give only approximate values for *estimating or preliminary design purposes only.*

Length of line, miles	Voltage
1–6	2,400
3–10	4,800
4–15	7,200
5–20	13,200
6–30	23,000
10–40	34,500
20–80	69,000
30–100	115,000
40–160	138,000
60–200	161,000
80–320	220,000

TABLE 79. APPROXIMATE CONDUCTOR SPACING FOR AVERAGE SYSTEM
CONDITIONS

Volts	Interaxial line spacing
2,400–7,200	2 ft 10 in.
13,200	3 ft 0 in.
23,000	3 ft 0 in.
34,500	4 ft 0 in.
69,000	8 ft 0 in
115,000	14 ft 0 in.
138,000	16 ft 0 in.
220,000	24 ft 0 in.

TABLE 80.　LENGTH OF COPPER WIRE FOR A DROP OF 1 VOLT
(Direct Current)

(Simplex Wire and Cable Company)

Dimensions in Feet

Size A. W. G.	10 amperes	50 amperes	100 amperes	125 amperes	150 amperes	175 amperes	225 amperes	250 amperes	275 amperes	325 amperes	400 amperes	450 amperes	500 amperes	550 amperes	600 amperes	650 amperes
1,000,000	9,650	1,930	965	773	643	550	430	386	353	296	241	214	193	176	161	148
900,000	8,650	1,735	865	692	576	495	385	346	315	266	216	192	173	157	144	
800,000	7,725	1,545	772	617	515	440	343	303	280	236	193	171	154	140		
700,000	6,750	1,350	675	540	450	385	300	270	245	207	168	150	135			
600,000	5,800	1,160	580	464	386	330	256	232	210	178	145	128				
500,000	4,825	965	482	386	322	275	214	193	175	148	120					
400,000	3,860	772	386	309	257	220	171	154	140	118						
300,000	2,900	580	290	232	193	165	128	116	105							
250,000	2,420	482	242	193	161	138	107	96								
4/0	2,030	416	208	166	138	118	92									
3/0	1,650	330	165	132	110	94										
2/0	1,310	262	131	105	87											
1/0	1,040	208	104	83												

Size A. W. G.	3 amperes	5 amperes	10 amperes	15 amperes	20 amperes	25 amperes	35 amperes	50 amperes	55 amperes	70 amperes	80 amperes	90 amperes	100 amperes	125 amperes	150 amperes	175 amperes	225 amperes
4/0	6,935	4,155	2,080	1,388	1,040	832	595	416	378	296	260	231	208	166	138	118	92
3/0	5,500	3,300	1,650	1,100	825	660	471	330	300	236	206	183	165	132	110	94	
2/0	4,360	2,620	1,310	875	655	525	374	262	238	187	164	146	131	105	87		
1/0	3,215	1,925	1,040	694	520	415	296	208	189	148	129	115	104	83			
1	2,740	1,650	823	550	411	329	235	165	149	117	103	91	82				
2	2,175	1,305	650	435	326	261	186	130	118	93	81	72					
3	1,725	1,035	518	344	258	206	147	103	94	74	64						
4	1,365	820	410	274	205	164	117	82	74	58							
5	1,035	650	325	216	163	130	93	65	59								
6	860	515	258	172	129	103	73	51									
8	540	324	162	108	81	65	46										
10	340	204	102	68	51	41											
12	210	128	64	42	32												
14	135	81	40	26													

Computed on a basis of standard annealed copper at 15°C. = 59°F.

TABLE 81. VOLTAGE DROP TABLE
(National Electrical Contractors Association, Inc.)

The first part of this table gives the drop on direct current and on alternating current at 100 per cent power factor. For exact calculations on alternating current at power factors below 100 per cent, see Charts 9 and 10.

Volts	Per cent drop										
550	4	2	1.6	1.4	1.2	1	0.8	0.5	0.4		
440	5	2.5	2	1.75	1.5	1.25	1	0.75	0.5		
220	10	5	4	3.5	3	2.5	2	1.5	1.0	0.75	0.5
110	20	10	8	7	6	5	4	3.0	2	1.5	1

Size of wire	Ampere-feet (amperes × single distance in ft)										
14	......	......	1,670	1,460	1,250	1,050	840	630	420	310	210
12	......	......	2,660	2,320	1,990	1,660	1,330	1,000	670	500	330
10	10,600	5,300	4,200	3,700	3,170	2,650	2,120	1,590	1,060	790	530
8	16,800	8,400	6,700	5,900	5,000	4,200	3,400	2,520	1,680	1,260	840
6	26,700	13,400	10,700	9,400	8,000	6,700	5,300	4,000	2,670	2,010	1,340
5	33,700	16,900	13,500	11,800	10,100	8,400	6,700	5,100	3,370	2,530	1,690
4	42,500	21,300	17,000	14,900	12,800	10,600	8,500	6,400	4,300	3,200	2,130
3	53,600	26,800	21,400	18,800	16,100	13,400	10,700	8,000	5,400	4,000	2,680
2	67,600	33,800	27,000	23,700	20,300	16,900	13,500	10,100	6,800	5,100	3,400
1	85,200	42,600	34,100	29,800	25,600	21,300	17,000	12,800	8,500	6,400	4,300
0	107,500	53,800	43,100	37,600	32,300	26,900	21,500	16,100	10,800	8,100	5,400
00	135,500	67,800	54,200	47,400	40,700	33,900	27,100	20,300	13,600	10,200	6,800
000	170,900	85,500	68,400	59,800	51,300	42,700	34,200	25,600	17,100	12,800	8,500
0000	215,000	107,800	86,200	75,400	64,700	53,900	43,100	32,300	21,600	16,200	10,800
250,000	254,600	127,300	101,900	89,100	76,400	63,700	50,900	38,200	25,500	19,100	12,700
300,000	305,600	152,800	122,200	106,900	91,700	76,400	61,100	45,800	30,600	22,900	15,300
350,000	356,500	178,200	142,600	124,800	106,900	89,100	71,300	53,500	35,600	26,700	17,800
400,000	407,400	203,700	163,000	142,600	122,200	101,900	81,500	61,100	40,700	30,600	20,400
450,000	458,300	229,200	183,300	160,400	137,500	114,600	91,700	68,700	45,800	34,400	22,900
500,000	509,300	254,600	203,700	178,200	152,800	127,300	101,900	76,400	50,900	38,200	25,500

Example. No. 1/0 wire, 125 amp, 440 volts, 200 ft from switchboard to panelboard. What is the per cent drop? *Solution.* Ampere-feet equal 125 × 200 = 25,000. Read along the horizontal line for 1/0 wire to the nearest ampere-feet value, which is 26,900. Read up to 440 volts, where it is found that the per cent drop is 1.25 per cent.

Example. It is desired to carry 70 amp 150 ft on Type R conductor, at 220 volts with a 2 per cent drop. What size conductor should be used? Try first No. 4, which has a carrying capacity of 70 amp. The ampere-feet are 70 × 150, or 10,500. Follow the horizontal line for No. 4 wire to the nearest number in the table, which is 10,600. Reading up to 220 volts, we find the drop is 2.5 per cent, or No. 4 is not large enough. Trying No. 3, we find that we can have as high as 10,700 amp-ft with a 2 per cent drop, so we use No. 3.

TABLE 82. FOOTCANDLES MAINTAINED IN SERVICE

(*Westinghouse Electric Corporation*)

COMMERCIAL INTERIORS

Installation	Foot Candles Maintained in Service (Not initial values)
AUDITORIUMS	10
BANKS	30-50
BARBER SHOPS AND BEAUTY PARLORS	50
DRAFTING ROOMS	*50
HOSPITALS	
Laboratories	30
Lobby and Reception room	20
Operating room (General)	50
Private rooms and Wards (supplementary)	30

Installation	Foot Candles Maintained in Service (Not initial values)
LIBRARY	
Reading room	30
Stack room	10
OFFICE BUILDINGS	
Intermittent Reading and Writing	30
Prolonged Close Work, Computing, Typing, Accounting, Designing	50
Conference Room, Filing	30
Mail Sorting	
PROFESSIONAL OFFICES	
Waiting rooms	20
Consultation	30
Examination	100

Installation	Foot Candles Maintained in Service (Not initial values)
SCHOOLS	
Classrooms, Laboratories, Manual training	30
Drawing rooms, Sight-saving	50
TRANSPORTATION	
Railroad cars	30
Platforms, Storage, Concourse	5
Ticket offices, Waiting room, Baggage checking	20
Washrooms	10

MERCHANDISING, AND DISPLAY

Installation	Foot Candles Maintained in Service (Not initial values)
BULLETIN AND POSTER BOARDS	
(Bright Surroundings)—Light Surfaces	50
(Bright Surroundings)—Dark surfaces	100
(Dark Surroundings)—Light surfaces	20
(Dark Surroundings)—Dark surfaces	50
GASOLINE SERVICE STATIONS	
Yard and Lavatories	10
Pump island and Sales room	30
Work areas (repair and washing)	50
STORE INTERIORS	
General merchandise area	50
Show cases, Wall cases, Counter displays	100
Feature displays	200
Stock rooms	10
SHOW WINDOWS	
Secondary Business Districts—General	100
—Feature displays	200
Main Business Districts—General	300
—Feature displays	500

INDOOR RECREATIONAL FACILITIES

Installation	Foot Candles Maintained in Service (Not initial values)
BILLIARDS AND BOWLING	
General	10
On tables and pins	50
GYMNASIUM	
Locker and Shower Rooms	10
Recreation Areas	
Badminton, Basketball, Boxing, Fencing, Handball, Squash, Tennis, Wrestling and Volley Ball	
Recreation	20
Exhibition Games and Matches	30
HOCKEY	30
SWIMMING POOLS	10

INDUSTRIAL INTERIORS

Foot Candles Maintained in Service (Not initial values)

AIRPLANE HANGARS
Engine and instrument repair...... 50
Frame repair and General maintenance 30
Recovering area................... 30
Storage (live).................... 10

AUTOMOBILE MANUFACTURING
Assembly line.................. *100
Frame assembly and
Body manufacturing............ 20
Finishing and Inspection........ *200

BAKERIES........................ 20

BREWERIES
Brew house...................... 5
Boiling, Keg washing and filling.. 10
Bottling........................ 20

CANNING AND PRESERVING....... 20

CLOTH PRODUCTS
Cutting, Inspection, Sewing—
Light goods................... 30
Dark goods.................. *200
Pressing, Cloth treating—
Light goods................... 30
Dark goods.................. 100

COAL TIPPLES AND CLEANING PLANTS
Breaking, Screening and Cleaning... 10
Picking......................... 200

ELECTRICAL EQUIPMENT MFG.
Impregnating.................... 30
Insulating and Coil Winding...... 100
Testing......................... 50

FOUNDRIES
Charging floor, Tumbling, Cleaning,
Pouring and Shaking out....... 5
Rough molding and Core making.... 10
Fine molding and Core making..... 20
Cleaning and Grinding castings.... 30

INSPECTION (General)
Rough........................... 20
Medium.......................... 50
Fine............................ *100
Extra fine...................... *200

LAUNDRIES........................ 30

LOCKER ROOMS.................... 10

MACHINE SHOPS
Rough bench and Machine work.... 20
Medium bench and Machine work,
Ordinary automatic machines,
Rough grinding, Medium buffing
and Polishing................ **30
Fine bench and Machine work, Fine
automatic machines, Medium grind-
ing, Fine buffing and Polishing.. **100
Extra fine Bench and Machine work,
Grinding and fine work....... *200

PACKING AND BOXING............. 10

PAINT SHOPS
Dipping, simple Spraying, Firing,
Rubbing, Ordinary Hand Painting
and Finishing Art, Stencil and
Special Spraying.............. 20
Fine Hand Painting and Finishing.. 50
Extra fine Hand Painting and
Finishing.................... 100

PLATING......................... 10

POWER PLANTS, ENGINE ROOMS, BOILERS
Boilers, Coal and Ash handling,
Storage battery rooms,........ 5
Auxiliary equipment, Oil switches
and Transformers, Engines, Gener-
ators, Blowers, Compressors... 20
Switchboards and Meters........ 30

PRINTING PLANTS
Presses......................... 30
Imposing stones............... **100
Proofreading.................... 100

RUBBER GOODS, MECHANICAL
Calendering, Stock cutting,
Hose looms................... 30
Molded products................ 50
Extruded products.............. 30
Inspection..................... 100

STAIRWAYS, PASSAGEWAYS, CORRIDORS....................... 5

STRUCTURAL STEEL FABRICATION 10

TEXTILE MILLS (Cotton)
Opening, Mixing, Picking, Carding
and Drawing,
Slubbing, Roving, Spinning,..... 20
Spooling, Warping,.............. 40
(Beaming and slashing on comb)—
Grey goods..................... 40
Denims........................ **200
(Inspection)—grey goods—hand
turning..................... **100
Denims—rapidly moving.......... **200
(Automatic Tying-in, Weaving).. **100
(Drawing-in by hand).......... **200
(Weaving)....................... 50

TEXTILE MILLS (Silk and Rayon)
Soaking, Fugitive tinting and condi-
tioning or setting of twist,... 10
Winding, Twisting, Rewinding and
Coning, Quilling, Slashing,.... 30
Warping on Creel, on Running ends
Reel, on Beam, or on Warp at Beaming 50
Drawing-in (on Heddles and Reed). 100
Weaving (on Heddles and Reeds).. 10
Weaving (on Warp Back of Harness) 20
Weaving (on Woven cloth)........ 30

TEXTILE MILLS (Woolen)
Carding, Picking, Washing, Combing,
Twisting, Dyeing,............. 15
Drawing-in, Warping............ 100
Weaving light goods........... *100
Weaving dark goods............. 25
Knitting machines.............. 30

TOILETS AND WASHROOMS........ 10

WELDING......................... 30

WOODWORKING
Rough sawing and Bench work.... 20
Medium machine and Bench work.. 30
Fine bench and Machine work.... 50

---

* Many present-day values are much lower than those required to give the same visibility as for reading under 10 footcandles. Those marked with a single asterisk are especially low in this respect.

** Large area sources of low surface brightness are necessary for the inspection of shiny or polished work surfaces or parts.

TABLE 83. LAMP DATA AND REFLECTION FACTORS
(*Westinghouse Electric Corporation*)

MERCURY

Watts	Bulb	Base	Finish	Burning Hours Per Start	Rated Av. Life (Hours)	Initial Lumens
250	T-9	Med.	Clear	5	2000	7000
400	T-16	Mogul	Clear	5	3000	16,000
400	T-16	Mogul	Clear	10	5000	16,000
3000	T-9½	S.C. Term.	Clear	5	2000	120,000

Approximate Ballast Loss Per Lamp—Watts

Lamp	110-125 Volt Single Lamp Low PF	110-125 Volt Single Lamp High PF	110-125 Volt Two Lamp High PF	220-250 Volt Single Lamp Low PF	220-250 Volt Single Lamp High PF	220-250 Volt Two Lamp High PF
Fluorescent						
40 W 48"T12	13	15	8.75	12	13	7.25
40 W 48"T12 (Instant Start)	......	......	14	......	......	12.5
100 W 60"T17	......	24	17.5	......	24	17.5
Slimline						
15 W 42"T6 (.1 Amp)	11	10	5.75	......	......	......
25 W 42"T6 (.2 Amp)	15.5	17	9	......	......	......
23 W 64"T6 (.1 Amp)	12.5	10	7.5	......	......	......
38 W 64"T6 (.2 Amp)	22	17	12	......	......	......
22 W 72"T8 (.1 Amp)	12.5	10	7.5	......	......	......
38 W 72"T8 (.2 Amp)	22	17	12	......	......	......
30 W 96"T8 (.1 Amp)	......	11.5	8	......	......	......
52 W 96"T8 (.2 Amp)	......	19.5	14	......	......	......
Mercury						
250 W AH2	......	40	......	......	40	......
400 W AH1	......	40	27.5	......	40	25
			230 Volts			460 Volts
3000 W AH9	......	165	140	......	135	125

DIFFUSE REFLECTION FACTORS

Color	Average Reflection Factor	Color	Average Reflection Factor
White	.88	Medium	
		Blue-Green	.54
		Yellow	.65
Very Light		Buff	.63
Blue-Green	.76	Grey	.61
Cream	.81		
Blue	.65	Dark	
Buff	.76	Blue	.08
Grey	.83	Yellow	.50
		Brown	.10
		Grey	.25
Light		Green	.07
Blue-Green	.72	Black	.03
Cream	.79		
Blue	.55	Wood Finishes	
Buff	.70	Maple	.42
Grey	.73	Walnut	.16
		Mahogany	.12

TABLE 83. LAMP DATA AND REFLECTION FACTORS. (*Continued*)

INCANDESCENT   LAMP DATA

Watts	Bulb	Base	Finish	Rated Av. Life (Hours)	Initial Lumens
General Service Lamps					
100	A-21	Med.	I.F.	750	1620
150	PS-25	Med.	I.F.	750	2600
200	PS-30	Med.	I.F.	750	3650
300	PS-35	Med.	I.F.-C.L.	750	5850
300	PS-35	Mogul	I.F.-C.L.	1000	5650
500	PS-40	Mogul	I.F.-C.L.	1000	9850
750	PS-52	Mogul	I.F.-C.L.	1000	14,900
1000	PS-52	Mogul	I.F.-C.L.	1000	21,000
1000	T-24	Bipost	I.F.	1000	19,500
1500	PS-52	Mogul	I.F.-C.L.	1000	33,500
Projector and Reflector Lamps					
150	PAR-38	Med. Skt.	Projector Spot	1000	990 (0-15°)
150	PAR-38	Med. Skt.	Projector Flood	1000	1150 (0-30°)
150	R-40	Med.	Light Inside Frosted	1000	700 (0-15°)
300	R-40	Med.	Reflector Spot	1000	1460 (0-15°)
150	R-40	Med.	Inside Frosted	1000	700 (0-30°)
300	R-40	Med.	Reflector Flood	1000	1620 (0-30°)

FLUORESCENT

Watts	Bulb	Base	Finish	Burning Hours Per Start	Rated Av. Life (Hours)	Initial Lumens
Standard Lamps						
40	T-12	Med.Bipin	White†	3	2500	2320
40	T-12	Med.Bipin	White†	6	4000	2320
40	T-12	Med.Bipin	White†	12	6000	2320
40	T-12	Med.Bipin	Daylight	3	2500	1920
40	T-12	Med.Bipin	Daylight	6	4000	1920
40	T-12	Med.Bipin	Daylight	12	6000	1920
100	T-17	Mog.Bipin	White†	3	3000	4200
100	T-17	Mog.Bipin	White†	6	4500	4200
100	T-17	Mog.Bipin	White†	12	6500	4200
100	T-17	Mog.Bipin	Daylight	3	3000	3800
100	T-17	Mog.Bipin	Daylight	6	4500	3800
100	T-17	Mog.Bipin	Daylight	12	6500	3800
Slimline Lamps				Current		
15	42″T6	Single Pin	White	0.1	2500*	900
25	42″T6	Single Pin	White	0.2	2500*	1400
23	64″T6	Single Pin	White	0.1	2500*	1400
38	64″T6	Single Pin	White	0.2	2500*	2150
22	72″T8	Single Pin	White	0.1	2500*	1400
38	72″T8	Single Pin	White	0.2	2500*	2350
30	96″T8	Single Pin	White	0.1	2500*	1950
52	96″T8	Single Pin	White	0.2	2500*	3300

†The 4500° white lamp is about halfway between white and daylight in both color and lumen output. The soft white lamp produces about 25% less light than the standard white.
*Life under specified test conditions at 3 burning hours per start. At 0.2 amperes will be 4000 hours at 6 and 6000 hours at 12 burning hours per start.

TABLE 84. PERFORMANCE DATA ON STANDARD INCANDESCENT LAMPS‡

WATTS	BULB AND OTHER DESCRIPTION	BASE	FILAMENT	RATED AVERAGE LIFE (hours)	MAX. OVER-ALL LENGTH (inches)	AVERAGE LIGHT CENTER LENGTH (inches)	APPROX. FILAMENT TEMP. (K)	MAX. BARE BULB TEMPERATURE (F)*	BASE TEMPERATURE (F)†	APPROX. INITIAL LUMENS	RATED INITIAL LUMENS PER WATT	APPROX. MEAN LUMENS DURING LIFE
10	S-14 inside frosted or clear	Med.	C-9	1500	$3\frac{1}{2}$	$2\frac{1}{2}$	2422	106	106	78	7.8	70
15	A-15 inside frosted	Med.	C-9	1200	$3\frac{1}{2}$	$2\frac{3}{8}$	—	—	—	141	9.4	121
25	A-19 inside frosted	Med.	C-9	1000	$3\frac{15}{16}$	$2\frac{1}{2}$	2583	110	108	260	10.5	220
40	A-19 inside frosted	Med.	C-9	1000	$4\frac{1}{4}$	$2\frac{7}{8}$	2750	260	221	465	11.6	425
50	A-19 inside frosted	Med.	CC-6	1000	$4\frac{7}{16}$	$3\frac{1}{8}$	—	—	—	660	13.2	620
60	A-19 inside frosted	Med.	CC-6	1000	$4\frac{7}{16}$	$3\frac{1}{8}$	2772	252	195	835	13 9	785
75	A-19 inside frosted	Med.	CC-6	750	$4\frac{7}{16}$	$3\frac{1}{8}$	2816	272	202	1150	15 3	1080
100	A-21 inside frosted	Med.	CC-6	750	$5\frac{5}{16}$	$3\frac{7}{8}$	2849	261	201	1620	16.2	1520
150	PS-25 inside frosted or clear	Med.	C-9	750	$6\frac{15}{16}$	$5\frac{1}{4}$	2872	290	209	2600	17.2	2400
200	PS-30 inside frosted or clear	Med.	C-9	750	$8\frac{1}{16}$	6	2894	307	212	3700	18 5	3300
300	PS-30 inside frosted or clear	Med.	C-9	750	$8\frac{1}{16}$	6	2936	374	173	5900	19.7	5250
300	PS-35 inside frosted or clear	Mog.	C-9	1000	$9\frac{3}{8}$	7	—	—	—	5050	18.8	5000
500	PS-40 inside frosted or clear	Mog.	C-9	1000	$9\frac{3}{4}$	7	2944	389	213	9900	19.8	8700
750	PS-52 inside frosted or clear	Mog.	C-7A	1000	$13\frac{1}{16}$	$9\frac{1}{2}$	—	—	—	15600	20.8	13400
1000	PS-52 inside frosted or clear	Mog.	C-7A	1000	$13\frac{1}{16}$	$9\frac{1}{2}$	2994	480	235	21500	21 6	18000
1500	PS-52 inside frosted or clear	Mog.	C-7A	1000	$13\frac{1}{16}$	$9\frac{1}{2}$	3037	510	265	33000	22.0	25500

* Lamp burning base up. Ambient temperature 77 F.
† At junction of base and bulb.

‡ Tables 84–90 inclusive are published by permission from the Illuminating Engineering Society and with exception of Table 88 are taken from the 1951 edition of the IES Handbook.

TABLE 84. *(Continued)*

The following equations enable the lamp user and designer to predetermine the performance under varying conditions of either gas-filled or vacuum lamps (capital letters represent normal rated values):

$$\frac{life}{LIFE} = \left(\frac{LUMENS}{lumens}\right)^{a} = \left(\frac{LUMENS/WATT}{lumens/watt}\right)^{b} = \left(\frac{VOLTS}{volts}\right)^{d} = \left(\frac{AMPS}{amps}\right)^{u}$$

$$\frac{lumens}{LUMENS} = \left(\frac{volts}{VOLTS}\right)^{k} = \left(\frac{lumens/watt}{LUMENS/WATT}\right)^{h} = \left(\frac{watts}{WATTS}\right)^{s} = \left(\frac{amps}{AMPS}\right)^{y} = \left(\frac{ohms}{OHMS}\right)^{z}$$

$$\frac{LUMENS/WATT}{lumens/watt} = \left(\frac{LUMENS}{lumens}\right)^{f} = \left(\frac{VOLTS}{volts}\right)^{c} = \left(\frac{AMPS}{amps}\right)^{j}$$

$$\frac{amps}{AMPS} = \left(\frac{volts}{VOLTS}\right)^{t} \text{ and } \frac{watts}{WATTS} = \left(\frac{volts}{VOLTS}\right)^{n}$$

The exponents are as follows:

	a	b	d	u	h	k	s	y
Gas-filled lamps..	3.86	7.1	13.1	24.1	1.84	3.38	2.19	6.25
Vacuum lamps..	3.85	7.0	13.5	23.3	1.82	3.51	2.22	6.05

	z	t	n	f	c	j
Gas-filled lamps..	7.36	0.541	1.54	0.544	1.84	3.40
Vacuum lamps..	8.36	0.580	1.58	0.550	1.93	3.33

Exponents d, k, and t are taken as fundamental. The other exponents are derived from them. Values given apply to lamps operated at efficiencies near normal and are accurate enough for calculations in the voltage range normally encountered.

TABLE 85. PERFORMANCE DATA ON TYPICAL FILAMENT- (HOT-)CATHODE PREHEAT-STARTING FLUORESCENT LAMPS
(IES Lighting Handbook)

Approx. lamp watts[b]	4	6	8	13	13	14	15	15[e]	18[f]	20[n]	25	30	32[g]	40[n]	85[d]	90[d]	100[d]
Nominal length (inches)[e]	6	9	12	21	12	15	18	18	18	24	33	36		48	60	60	60
Bulb[h]	T5	T5	T5	T5	T8	T12	T8	T12	T8	T12	T12	T8	T10	T12	T17	T17	T17
Base (bipin)	Min	Min	Min	Min	Med	Med	Med	Med	Med	Med	Med	Med	4 pin	Med	Mog	Mog	Mog
Approx. lamp amperes	0.125	0.147	0.170	0.160	0.420	0.385	0.300	0.330	0.395	0.370	0.520	0.355	0.435	0.425	1.62	1.55	1.52
Approx. lamp volts	35	46.5	56	95	36	39	55	46	51	57	53	98	83	102.5	55	65	70.5
Preheat amperes—Max	0.18	0.25	0.27	0.27	0.75	0.65	0.65	0.65	0.65	0.65	0.85	0.65	0.75	0.75	2.20	2.20	2.20
—Min	0.13	0.16	0.18	0.18	0.45	0.44	0.44	0.44	0.44	0.44	0.65	0.40	0.55	0.55	1.40	1.40	1.40
Starting volts[i]	118	118	118	200	118	118	118	118	118	118	118	200	150	200	150	150	150
Rated Life[j] (hours)	7500	7500	7500	7500	7500	7500	7500	7500	7500	7500	7500	7500	7500	7500	7500	7500	7500
Lumen maintenance at 3000 hours[k]						76%	72%	79%		80%		74%		82%		82%	78%
Initial lumens:																	
White	73	210	330	582		490	650	600	710	980	1430	1560	1600	2400	4500	4860	4600
Cool White[l]		200	310	547		475	615	570		900	1370	1500		2250	4300	4600	4350
Daylight	68	185	295	505		430	570	525		820	1210	1400		2000	3900	4250	4000
Warm White[m]										1020				2480			
Candelite								540		840				2040			
Soft White						380	525	480		760		1260		1840	3400	3700	3500
Deluxe Cool White														1400			
Deluxe Warm White														1500			
Vis-A-Ray										980				2320			
Blue White														2140			
Blue							315	300		460		780					
Green							900	855		1300		2250					
Pink							300	285		440		750					
Gold							375	355		540		930					
Red							45	42		60		120					

TABLE 85. PERFORMANCE DATA ON TYPICAL FILAMENT- (HOT-)CATHODE PREHEAT-STARTING FLUORESCENT LAMPS. (Continued)

Footlamberts:

White..........[l]	2615	2870	2690	1410	2200	1360	1550	1630	2400	2040	1830	1980	2020
Cool White.....[l]	2490	2700	2520	1360	2080	1295	1420	1560	2310		1715	1890	1915
Daylight..........	2310	2560	2330	1235	1915	1190	1300	1380	2160		1525	1715	1760
Warm White.....[m]							1610				1890		
Candelite........						1225	1330				1555		
Soft White.......				1090	1775	1009	1200		1940		1400	1500	
Deluxe Cool White..											1068		
Deluxe Warm White..											1143		
Vis-A-Ray........							1550				1775		1540
Blue White.......											1615		
Blue.............				1065	680		730		1200				
Green............				3040	1940		2050		3470				
Pink.............				1015	645		695		1150				
Gold.............				1270	805		855		1430				
Red..............				152	95		95		185				

[a] Industry averages. A.S.A. proposed dimensions and electrical characteristics used when available. Individual lumen ratings vary at present time.
[b] Wattage consumed by auxiliary must be added to obtain total. See Table 8-46 for wattage loss of typical ballasts.
[c] Actually rated at 14.4 watts.
[d] 85, 90 and 100 watt lamps interchangeable on same ballast.
[e] Includes lamp plus two sockets.
[f] Semicircular lamp 12 inches nominal outside diameter.
[g] Circular lamp 12 inches nominal outside diameter.
[h] Figures indicate nominal outside diameter in eighths of an inch.
[i] Open circuit voltage at 118 volts line. 110 to 125 volt circuit ballasts available for all types, higher voltage ballasts for some.
[j] Average life under specific test conditions with 3 hours burning per start.
[k] Also designated as 4500K White.
[l] Averages of White, Cool White and Daylight lamps.
[m] Also designated as Warm Tint and Warmtone.
[n] Fluorescent sunlamps are available in lamps of these dimensions and electrical characteristics.

TABLE 86. PERFORMANCE DATA ON TYPICAL FILAMENT- (HOT-)CATHODE INSTANT-STARTING FLUORESCENT LAMPS

(IES Lighting Handbook)

Nominal length (inches) [b]	42	64	72	96	48	48	72	96	60
Bulb [c]	T6	T6	T8	T8	T12	T12	T12	T12	T17
Base	Single pin	Single pin	Single pin	Single pin	Bipin	Single pin	Single pin	Single pin	Bipin
Starting volts [d]	450	600	600	750	450	450	550	650	450
Lamp current (milliamperes)	120, 200, 300	120, 200, 300	120, 200, 300	120, 200, 300	425	427	425	425	420
Approx. lamp volts	175, 145, 130	270, 225, 200	240, 220, 200	320, 285, 265	105	99	150	194	107
Lamp watts [e]	18, 25, 33	27½, 37, 51	26, 37.5, 51	34, 49, 69	41	38.5	57	73	40
Rated life (hours) [f]	4000	4000	4000	4000	4000	4000	4000	4000	4000
Initial lumens [g] — White	1050, 1400, 1800	1650, 2250, 2850	1675, 2375, 3100	2225, 3250, 4300	2350	3020	3660	5800	2350
Initial lumens — 4500K White	1000, 1340, 1700	1560, 2150, 2700	1600, 2275, 3000	2125, 3100, 4100	2200	2870	3500	5540	2200
Initial lumens — Daylight	900, 1200, 1530	1400, 1900, 2400	1400, 2000, 2650	1900, 2750, 3650	1950	2570	3100	4925	1950
Footlamberts — White	1910, 2550, 3280	1900, 2590, 3280	1250, 1770, 2310	1250, 1800, 2380	1790	1830	1845	2160	1035
Footlamberts — 4500K White	1820, 2440, 3100	1800, 2470, 3110	1195, 1700, 2240	1175, 1720, 2270	1675	1715	1765	2070	970
Footlamberts — Daylight	1640, 2180, 2790	1610, 2190, 2760	1045, 1495, 1980	1050, 1520, 2020	1485	1520	1560	1840	860

a Industry averages. A.S.A. proposed dimensions and electrical characteristics used when available.
b Includes lamp plus two sockets.
c Figures indicate nominal outside diameter in eighths of an inch.
d Open circuit voltage at 118 volts line. 110 to 125 volt circuit ballasts available for all types.
e Wattage consumed by auxiliary must be added to obtain total.
f Average life under specific test conditions with three hours burning per start.
g Three standard colors shown, but other colors are available.

TABLE 87. CHARACTERISTICS OF SEVERAL MERCURY-VAPOR DISCHARGE LAMPS USED IN GENERAL LIGHTING
(IES Lighting Handbook)

Designation[b]	A-H4*†	A-H5*	C-H5†	A-H1*†‡ B-H1*†	J-H1†	EH-1*†‡	A-H12†	A-H9*†
Lamp watts, rated	100	250	250	400	400	400	1000	3000
Approx. watts with ballast	123–127	290	285	440–452	440	440–452	1085	3165–3220
Lumens at 100 (hours)	3300	11,000	11,000	15,000	18,000[a]	20,000	55,000	120,000
Lamp LPW at 100 (hours)	33	44	44	37.5	45	50	57	37.3–40
Rated life, hours[c]	1000	2500	4000	4000	4000	3000–5000§	4000	5000
Bulb	T-10	T-18	T-14	T-16	BT-37	T-20 or BT-37§	T-28	T-9, 9½
Burning position	Any	Any	Any	[d]	Any	Any	Any	Any
Base	Admed. Sc.	Mogul Sc.	Mogul Sc.	Mogul Sc.	Mogul Sc.	Mogul Sc.	Mogul Sc.	S. C. Term
Max. over-all length, inches	5⅝	8	8	13	11½	11–11½§	14	55
Light center length, inches	3⁷⁄₁₆	5	5	7¾	7	7	9	9
Arc length, inches	1		1⅝	6	2¾	2¾	5	48
Arc tube material	Quartz	Quartz	Quartz	Glass	Quartz	Quartz	Quartz	Glass
Lamp operating volts	130	135	135	135	135	135	135	535
Lamp starting current, amps	1.3	2.9	2.9	4.7–5.0	4.7	4.7–5.0	12	9.3
Lamp operating current, amps	0.9	2.1	2.1	3.2	3.2	3.2	8.2	6.1
Supply voltage (primary volts)	115, 230	115, 230 or 118, 236	115, 230	115, 230	115, 230	115, 230	115, 230, 460	230, 460, 575
Transformer secondary open circuit voltage[e]	245–250	250	250	220	220	220	220	850
Overall power factor, per cent[f]	50, 90	50, 90, 95	90, 95	60, 90, 95	90, 95	60, 90, 95	90	90
Starting time to full output, minutes	3	10	4	7–14§	4	4–8§	4	7
Re-starting time, minutes	3	4	4	7–14§	4	4–5§	6	8

* General Electric; † Westinghouse; ‡ Sylvania; § Varies among manufacturers.
[a] Color corrected by addition of fluorescent coating on inner surface of outer bulb.
[b] For complete designations and application data consult manufacturer's catalogs.
[c] *Life Rating.* Rated lives of lamps listed above are based or specified test conditions with the lamps turned off and re-started no oftener than once every five burning hours. The life rating of the A-H1 and B-H1 lamps is ℓ000 hours for 10 hours per start. The A-H9 life rating is 5000, 6000, and 10,000 hours for 5, 10 and 144 hours per start respectively.
[d] *Burning Position.* A-H1 designed for base-up burning; B-H1 for base-down; both types must be operated within 10 degrees of vertical.
[e] *Starting Voltage.* The listed transformer secondary open circuit voltages provide for satisfactory lamp starting in normal indoor use. Higher open circuit voltages are desirable for dependable starting at lower temperatures.
[f] *Power Factor.* The higher power factor is obtained with transformers incorporating integral correction. Two-lamp transformers for 250 and 400 watt lamps have an overall power factor of 95 per cent.

TABLE 88. AVERAGE MAINTAINED ILLUMINATION PRODUCED ON THE HORIZONTAL WORKING PLANE PER 1,000 LAMP LUMENS* FOR VARIOUS SPACING,† MAINTENANCE, AND UTILIZATION CONDITIONS
(*IES Lighting Handbook*)

Area† per lamp (sq ft)	Maintenance factor	Coefficient of utilization																	
		0.36	0.38	0.40	0.42	0.44	0.46	0.48	0.50	0.52	0.54	0.56	0.58	0.60	0.62	0.64	0.66	0.68	0.70
10	70	25.2	26.6	28.0	29.4	30.8	32.2	33.6	35.0	36.4	37.8	39.2	40.6	42.0	43.4	44.8	46.2	47.6	49.0
	60	21.6	22.8	24.0	25.2	26.4	27.6	28.8	30.0	31.2	32.4	33.6	34.8	36.0	37.2	38.4	39.6	40.8	42.0
	50	18.0	19.0	20.0	21.0	22.0	23.0	24.0	25.0	26.0	27.0	28.0	29.0	30.0	31.0	32.0	33.0	34.0	35.0
12	70	21.0	22.1	23.3	24.5	25.6	26.8	28.0	29.1	30.3	31.5	32.6	33.8	35.0	36.1	37.3	38.5	39.6	40.8
	60	18.0	19.0	20.0	21.0	22.0	23.0	24.0	25.0	26.0	27.0	28.0	29.0	30.0	31.0	32.0	33.0	34.0	35.0
	50	15.0	15.8	16.6	17.5	18.3	19.2	20.0	20.8	21.6	22.5	23.3	24.1	25.0	25.8	26.6	27.5	28.3	29.1
14	70	18.0	19.0	20.0	21.0	22.0	23.0	24.0	25.0	26.0	27.0	28.0	29.0	30.0	31.0	32.0	33.0	34.0	35.0
	60	15.4	16.2	17.1	18.0	18.8	19.7	20.5	21.4	22.2	23.1	24.0	24.8	25.7	26.5	27.4	28.2	29.1	30.0
	50	12.8	13.5	14.2	15.0	15.7	16.4	17.1	17.8	18.5	19.2	20.0	20.7	21.4	22.1	22.8	23.5	24.2	25.0
16	70	15.7	16.6	17.5	18.3	19.2	20.1	21.0	21.8	22.7	23.6	24.5	25.3	26.2	27.1	28.0	28.8	29.7	30.6
	60	13.5	14.2	15.0	15.7	16.5	17.2	18.0	18.7	19.5	20.2	21.0	21.7	22.5	23.2	24.0	24.7	25.5	26.2
	50	11.2	11.8	12.5	13.1	13.7	14.3	15.0	15.6	16.2	16.8	17.5	18.1	18.7	19.3	20.0	20.6	21.2	21.8
18	70	14.0	14.7	15.5	16.3	17.1	17.8	18.6	19.4	20.2	21.0	21.7	22.5	23.3	24.1	24.8	25.6	26.4	27.2
	60	12.0	12.6	13.3	14.0	14.6	15.3	16.0	16.6	17.3	18.0	18.6	19.3	20.0	20.6	21.3	22.0	22.6	23.3
	50	10.0	10.5	11.1	11.6	12.2	12.7	13.3	13.8	14.4	15.0	15.5	16.1	16.6	17.2	17.7	18.3	18.8	19.4
20	70	12.6	13.3	14.0	14.7	15.4	16.1	16.8	17.5	18.2	18.9	19.6	20.3	21.0	21.7	22.4	23.1	23.8	24.5
	60	10.8	11.4	12.0	12.6	13.2	13.8	14.4	15.0	15.6	16.2	16.8	17.4	18.0	18.6	19.2	19.8	20.4	21.0
	50	9.00	9.50	10.0	10.5	11.0	11.5	12.0	12.5	13.0	13.5	14.0	14.5	15.0	15.5	16.0	16.5	17.0	17.5
30	70	8.40	8.86	9.32	9.80	10.0	10.7	11.2	11.6	12.1	12.6	13.0	13.5	14.0	14.4	14.9	15.4	15.8	16.3
	60	7.20	7.60	8.00	8.40	8.80	9.20	9.60	10.0	10.4	10.8	11.2	11.6	12.0	12.4	12.8	13.2	13.6	14.0
	50	6.00	6.33	6.66	7.00	7.33	7.66	8.00	8.33	8.66	9.00	9.33	9.66	10.0	10.3	10.6	11.0	11.3	11.6
40	70	6.30	6.65	7.00	7.30	7.70	8.05	8.40	8.75	9.10	9.45	9.80	10.1	10.5	10.8	11.2	11.5	11.9	12.2
	60	5.40	5.70	6.00	6.30	6.60	6.90	7.20	7.50	7.80	8.10	8.40	8.70	9.00	9.30	9.60	9.90	10.2	10.5
	50	4.50	4.75	5.00	5.25	5.50	5.75	6.00	6.25	6.50	6.75	7.00	7.25	7.50	7.75	8.00	8.25	8.50	8.75
50	70	5.02	5.32	5.60	5.88	6.16	6.44	6.72	7.00	7.28	7.56	7.84	8.12	8.40	8.68	8.96	9.24	9.52	9.80
	60	4.32	4.56	4.80	5.04	5.28	5.52	5.76	6.00	6.24	6.48	6.72	6.96	7.20	7.44	7.68	7.92	8.16	8.40
	50	3.60	3.80	4.00	4.20	4.40	4.60	4.80	5.00	5.20	5.40	5.60	5.80	6.00	6.20	6.40	6.60	6.80	7.00
60	70	4.20	4.43	4.66	4.90	5.13	5.36	5.60	5.83	6.06	6.30	6.53	6.76	7.00	7.23	7.46	7.70	7.93	8.16
	60	3.60	3.80	4.00	4.20	4.40	4.60	4.80	5.00	5.20	5.40	5.60	5.80	6.00	6.20	6.40	6.60	6.80	7.00
	50	3.00	3.16	3.33	3.50	3.66	3.83	4.00	4.16	4.33	4.50	4.66	4.83	5.00	5.16	5.33	5.50	5.66	5.83
70	70	3.60	3.80	4.00	4.20	4.40	4.60	4.80	5.00	5.20	5.40	5.60	5.80	6.00	6.20	6.40	6.60	6.80	7.00
	60	3.08	3.25	3.43	3.60	3.77	3.94	4.11	4.28	4.45	4.63	4.80	4.97	5.14	5.31	5.48	5.65	5.83	6.00
	50	2.57	2.71	2.85	3.00	3.14	3.28	3.43	3.57	3.71	3.85	4.00	4.14	4.28	4.43	4.57	4.71	4.85	5.00
80	70	3.15	3.34	3.50	3.67	3.85	4.02	4.20	4.37	4.55	4.72	4.90	5.07	5.25	5.42	5.60	5.77	5.95	6.12
	60	2.70	2.85	3.00	3.15	3.30	3.45	3.60	3.75	3.90	4.05	4.20	4.35	4.50	4.65	4.80	4.95	5.10	5.25
	50	2.25	2.37	2.50	2.62	2.75	2.87	3.00	3.12	3.25	3.37	3.50	3.62	3.75	3.87	4.00	4.12	4.25	4.37
90	70	2.80	2.95	3.12	3.26	3.42	3.57	3.73	3.88	4.04	4.20	4.35	4.51	4.66	4.82	4.97	5.13	5.28	5.44
	60	2.40	2.53	2.66	2.80	2.93	3.06	3.20	3.33	3.46	3.60	3.73	3.86	4.00	4.13	4.26	4.40	4.53	4.66
	50	2.00	2.11	2.22	2.33	2.44	2.55	2.66	2.77	2.88	3.00	3.11	3.22	3.33	3.44	3.55	3.66	3.77	3.88
100	70	2.52	2.66	2.80	2.94	3.08	3.22	3.36	3.50	3.64	3.78	3.92	4.06	4.20	4.34	4.48	4.62	4.76	4.90
	60	2.16	2.28	2.40	2.52	2.64	2.76	2.88	3.00	3.12	3.24	3.36	3.48	3.60	3.72	3.84	3.96	4.08	4.20
	50	1.80	1.90	2.00	2.10	2.20	2.30	2.40	2.50	2.60	2.70	2.80	2.90	3.00	3.10	3.20	3.30	3.40	3.50
150	70	1.68	1.77	1.86	1.96	2.05	2.14	2.24	2.33	2.42	2.52	2.61	2.70	2.80	2.89	2.98	3.08	3.17	3.26
	60	1.44	1.52	1.60	1.68	1.76	1.84	1.90	1.98	2.06	2.14	2.22	2.30	2.38	2.46	2.54	2.62	2.70	2.78
	50	1.20	1.26	1.33	1.40	1.46	1.53	1.60	1.66	1.73	1.80	1.86	1.93	2.00	2.06	2.13	2.20	2.26	2.33
200	70	1.26	1.33	1.40	1.47	1.54	1.61	1.68	1.75	1.82	1.89	1.96	2.03	2.10	2.17	2.24	2.31	2.38	2.45
	60	1.08	1.14	1.20	1.26	1.32	1.38	1.44	1.50	1.56	1.62	1.68	1.74	1.80	1.86	1.92	1.98	2.04	2.10
	50	.900	.950	1.00	1.05	1.10	1.15	1.20	1.25	1.30	1.35	1.40	1.45	1.50	1.55	1.60	1.65	1.70	1.75

* If lamp output is 2,000 lumens, multiply tabulated values by 2,000/1,000.
If lamp output is 500 lumens, multiply tabulated values by 500/1,000. Table applies to all types of lamps.
† If area per luminaire or per room rather than area per lamp is used, divide tabulated values by number of lamps per luminaire or number of lamps per room, respectively.

TABLE 89. ROOM INDEXES FOR A WIDE RANGE OF ROOM SIZES
(IES Lighting Handbook)

Classify the room according to the proportions and the mounting height above the floor. Use upper column headings for direct, semi-direct and general diffusing luminaires. For semi-indirect and totally indirect units choose column at bottom of page. Wherever the circumstances are such that the room index falls between two given figures, use the letter applying to the smaller dimensions, or interpolate in the utilization table. A horizontal work plane 30—36 inches above the floor is assumed.

ROOM WIDTH Feet	ROOM LENGTH Feet	DIRECT, SEMI-DIRECT AND GENERAL DIFFUSING LIGHTING — Mounting Height Above Floor, feet													
		7	8	9	10	11	12	13	15	17	19	23	27	33	43
8	10	H	I	I	J	J	J								
	12	G	I	I	J	J	J	J							
	14	G	H	I	J	J	J	J							
	16	G	H	I	J	J	J	J							
	18	G	H	I	I	J	J	J	J						
	20	F	H	H	I	J	J	J	J	J					
	24	F	G	H	I	J	J	J	J	J					
	30	F	H	H	I	J	J	J	J	J					
	35	F	G	G	H	I	I	J	J	J	J				
	40	E	F	G	H	H	I	J	J	J	J				
	50	E	F	G	H	H	I	I	J	J	J				
10	10	G	H	I	J	J	J	J							
	12	G	H	I	I	J	J	J	J						
	14	F	H	H	I	J	J	J	J	J					
	16	F	G	H	I	I	J	J	J	J					
	18	F	G	H	I	I	J	J	J	J					
	20	F	G	H	I	I	J	J	J	J	J				
	24	F	G	G	H	I	I	J	J	J	J				
	30	E	F	G	G	H	I	I	J	J	J	J			
	35	E	F	G	G	H	H	I	I	J	J	J			
	40	E	F	F	G	H	H	I	J	J	J	J			
	50	E	F	F	G	G	H	H	I	J	J	J	J		
	60	E	F	F	G	G	H	H	I	J	J	J	J		
	70	E	F	F	G	G	H	H	I	I	J	J	J		
12	12	G	G	H	I	I	J	J	J						
	14	F	G	H	I	I	J	J	J						
	16	F	G	H	I	I	I	J	J	J					
	18	F	F	G	H	H	I	J	J	J					
	20	F	F	G	G	H	I	I	J	J	J				
	24	E	F	G	G	H	H	I	J	J	J				
	30	E	F	F	G	H	H	I	I	J	J	J			
	35	E	E	F	G	G	H	I	I	J	J	J			
	40	E	E	F	F	G	H	I	I	J	J	J	J		
	50	E	E	F	F	G	G	H	I	I	J	J	J		
	60	E	E	F	F	G	G	H	I	J	J	J	J		
	70	E	E	F	F	F	G	H	I	I	J	J	J		
	80	E	E	F	F	F	G	G	H	I	I	J	J		
	100	E	E	F	F	F	G	G	H	I	I	J	J		
14	14	F	F	G	H	I	I	I	J	J	J				
	16	E	F	G	H	H	I	I	J	J	J				
	18	E	F	G	H	H	I	I	J	J	J				
	20	E	F	F	H	H	I	I	J	J	J	J			
	24	E	E	F	G	G	H	I	I	J	J	J			
	30	E	E	F	F	G	H	H	I	J	J	J			
	35	D	E	F	F	F	G	H	H	I	J	J	J		
	40	D	E	E	F	F	G	G	H	H	I	J	J		
	50	D	E	E	F	F	F	G	G	H	I	J	J	J	
	60	D	E	E	F	F	F	G	G	H	I	J	J	J	
	70	D	E	E	F	F	F	G	G	H	I	I	J	J	
	80	D	E	E	F	F	F	G	G	F	I	I	J	J	
	100	D		E	E	F	F	F	G	G	I	I	J	J	
16	16	E	F	G	G	H	I	I	J	J	J				
	18	E	F	G	G	H	H	I	J	J	J				
	20	E	E	F	G	G	H	I	I	J	J				
	24	D	E	F	F	G	H	H	I	J	J	J			
	30	D	E	E	F	F	G	H	I	J	J	J			
	35	D	D	E	F	F	G	G	H	I	J	J	J		
	40	D	D	E	E	F	F	G	H	I	J	J	J		
	50	D	D	E	E	F	F	G	G	H	I	J	J	J	
	60	D	D	E	E	F	F	G	G	H	I	I	J	J	
	70	D	D	E	E	E	F	F	G	G	H	I	I	J	J
	80	D	D	E	E	E	F	F	G	G	H	H	I	J	J
	100	D		E	E	E	F	F	G	G	H	H	I	J	
		9	10½	12	13½	15	16½	18	21	24	27	33	39	48	63

SEMI-INDIRECT AND INDIRECT LIGHTING. Ceiling Height Above Floor, feet

TABLE 89. ROOM INDEXES FOR A WIDE RANGE OF ROOM SIZES
(Continued)

ROOM WIDTH	ROOM LENGTH	DIRECT, SEMI-DIRECT AND GENERAL DIFFUSING LIGHTING Mounting Height Above Floor, feet															
Feet	Feet	7	8	9	10	11	12	13	15	17	19	23	27	33	43	53	63
18	18	E	E	F	G	H	H	I	I	J	J						
	20	D	E	F	G	G	H	H	I	J	J						
	24	D	E	F	F	G	H	H	I	J	J	J					
	30	D	E	F	F	G	H	H	I	J	J	J					
	35	C	D	E	F	F	G	H	H	I	J	J	J				
	40	C	E	E	F	F	G	G	H	I	J	J	J				
	50	C	D	E	E	F	G	G	H	I	J	J	J	J			
	60	C	D	E	E	F	G	G	H	H	I	J	J	J			
	70	C	D	E	E	E	F	F	G	H	I	I	J	J			
	80	C	D	E	E	E	F	F	G	H	I	I	J	J			
	100	C	D	E	E	E	F	F	G	H	H	I	I	J			
	120	C	D	E	E	E	F	F	F	G	H	H	I	I	J		
20	20	D	E	F	F	G	H	H	I	J	J						
	24	D	E	F	F	G	G	H	I	J	J						
	30	C	D	E	F	F	G	G	H	I	J	J					
	35	C	D	E	F	F	G	G	H	I	J	J					
	40	C	D	E	E	E	F	F	H	I	I	J	J				
	50	C	D	E	E	E	F	F	G	H	I	J	J	J			
	60	C	D	D	E	E	F	F	G	H	H	I	J	J			
	70	C	D	D	E	E	F	F	G	H	H	I	J	J			
	80	C	D	D	E	E	E	F	F	G	H	I	J	J	J		
	100	C	D	D	E	E	E	F	F	G	G	H	I	J	J		
	120	C	D	D	E	E	E	F	F	G	H	H	I	J	J		
	140	C	D	D	E	E	E	F	F	G	G	H	H	I	J		
24	24	C	D	E	F	F	G	G	H	I	I	J	J				
	30	C	D	E	E	F	G	G	H	I	I	J	J				
	35	C	D	E	E	F	F	G	G	H	I	J	J				
	40	C	C	D	D	E	F	F	G	H	I	I	J				
	50	C	C	D	E	E	F	F	G	H	H	I	J				
	60	C	C	D	D	D	E	E	F	G	H	I	J				
	70	C	C	D	D	E	E	E	F	G	H	I	J	J			
	80	C	C	D	D	E	E	E	F	G	G	I	J	J			
	100	C	C	D	D	E	E	E	F	G	G	H	I	J			
	120	C	C	D	D	E	E	E	F	F	G	H	I	J	J		
	140	C	C	D	D	E	E	E	F	F	G	H	I	J	J		
30	30	B	C	D	E	E	F	F	G	H	H	I	J				
	35	B	C	D	E	E	F	F	G	H	H	I	J				
	40	B	C	D	D	D	E	F	F	G	H	I	J				
	50	B	C	C	D	D	E	E	F	G	H	I	J				
	60	B	C	C	D	D	E	E	F	G	H	I	J	J			
	70	B	C	C	C	D	D	E	E	F	G	H	I	J			
	80	B	C	C	C	D	D	E	F	F	G	H	I	J			
	100	B	C	C	C	D	D	E	F	F	G	H	I	J	J		
	120	B	C	C	C	C	D	E	E	F	F	G	H	I	J		
	140	B	C	C	C	D	D	E	E	F	F	G	H	I	J		
35	35	B	C	C	D	E	E	F	F	G	H	I	I	J			
	40	A	B	C	C	D	E	E	G	G	G	H	I	J			
	50	A	B	C	C	D	E	E	F	F	G	H	I	J	J		
	60	A	B	C	C	D	D	E	?	F	G	H	I	J	J		
	70	A	B	C	C	C	D	E	E	F	F	H	I	J	J		
	80	A	B	C	C	C	D	D	E	F	F	G	H	I	J		
	100	A	B	C	C	C	D	D	E	E	F	G	H	I	J		
	120	A	B	C	C	C	D	D	E	E	F	F	G	I	J		
	140	A	B	C	C	C	D	D	E	E	F	G	I				
40	40	A	B	C	C	D	E	E	F	F	G	H	I	J	J		
	50	A	B	B	C	C	D	E	F	F	G	H	I	J	J		
	60	A	B	B	C	C	D	D	E	F	G	H	I	J	J		
	70	A	B	B	C	C	D	D	E	E	F	G	H	I	J	J	
	80	A	B	B	C	C	D	D	E	E	F	G	H	I	J	J	
	100	A	B	B	C	C	D	D	E	E	F	F	G	H	J	J	J
	120	A	B	B	C	C	C	C	D	E	E	F	G	H	J	J	J
	140	A	B	B	C	C	C	C	D	E	F	G	H	I	J	J	J
		9	10½	12	13½	15	16½	18	21	24	27	33	39	48	63	78	93

SEMI-INDIRECT AND INDIRECT LIGHTING. Ceiling Height Above Floor, feet

TABLE 89. ROOM INDEXES FOR A WIDE RANGE OF ROOM SIZES
(Continued)

ROOM WIDTH	ROOM LENGTH	DIRECT, SEMI- DIRECT AND GENERAL DIFFUSING LIGHTING Mounting Height Above Floor, feet															
Feet	Feet	7	8	9	10	11	12	13	15	17	19	23	27	33	43	53	63
50	50	A	A	B	B	C	C	D	E	E	F	G	H	I	J	J	
	60	A	A	B	B	C	C	D	E	E	F	G	H	I	J	J	
	70	A	A	B	B	C	C	D	D	E	F	F	G	H	I	J	
	80	A	A	B	B	C	C	C	D	E	E	F	G	H	I	J	J
	100	A	A	B	B	C	C	C	D	D	E	F	F	G	I	J	J
	120	A	A	B	B	C	C	C	D	D	E	F	F	G	I	J	J
	140	A	A	B	B	C	C	C	D	D	E	E	F	G	I	J	J
	170	A	A	B	B	C	C	C	D	D	E	E	F	G	H	I	J
	200	A	A	B	B	C	C	C	D	D	E	E	F	G	H	I	J
60	60	A	A	A	B	B	C	C	D	E	E	F	G	H	I	J	J
	70	A	A	A	A	B	C	C	D	E	E	F	G	H	I	J	J
	80	A	A	A	A	B	B	C	D	D	E	F	F	G	I	J	J
	100	A	A	A	A	B	B	C	C	D	E	F	F	G	H	I	J
	120	A	A	A	A	B	B	C	C	D	D	E	F	G	H	I	J
	140	A	A	A	A	B	B	C	C	C	D	E	F	G	H	I	J
	170	A	A	A	A	B	B	C	C	C	D	E	F	F	H	I	J
	200	A	A	A	A	B	B	C	C	C	D	D	E	F	H	I	J
80	80	A	A	A	A	A	B	B	C	C	D	E	F	G	H	I	J
	140	A	A	A	A	A	A	B	B	C	C	D	E	F	G	H	I
	200	A	A	A	A	A	A	A	B	B	C	C	D	E	F	G	H
100	100	A	A	A	A	A	A	A	B	B	C	D	E	F	G	H	I
	150	A	A	A	A	A	A	A	B	B	C	C	D	E	F	G	H
	200	A	A	A	A	A	A	A	B	B	C	D	D	E	F	G	H
120	120	A	A	A	A	A	A	A	A	B	B	C	D	E	F	G	H
	160	A	A	A	A	A	A	A	A	A	B	C	D	E	F	G	H
	200	A	A	A	A	A	A	A	A	A	B	B	C	D	E	F	G
		9	10½	12	13½	15	16½	18	21	24	27	33	39	48	63	78	93
		SEMI-INDIRECT AND INDIRECT LIGHTING. Ceiling Height Above Floor, feet															

For dimensions greater than those shown in the table, the room index may be calculated with the formulas on page 9-2, or the following procedure can be used:

  1. Divide length and width by some common factor which reduces dimensions to values within limits of table.

  2. Subtract 3 feet from mounting height (or ceiling height) and divide this dimension by the same factor employed in step 1.

  3. Add 3 feet to the scaled-down height dimension. Use this value and the reduced length and width obtained in step 1 to select the room index from the table.

  To determine room index for areas with work planes other than 30–36 inches above the floor, use the formulas on page 9-2, or select a mounting height in Table 9-1 which represents the distance between light source (or ceiling) and work plane plus 30–36 inches.

The relationships between numerical room ratios and the letter room indices used in Tables 90-1 through 90-9 are:

ROOM INDEX	TABLE 9-1 BASED ON THIS ROOM RATIO	RANGE OF ROOM RATIOS
J	0.6	Less than 0.7
I	0.8	0.7 –0.9
H	1.0	0.9 –1.12
G	1.25	1.12–1.38
F	1.5	1.38–1.75
E	2.0	1.75–2.25
D	2.5	2.25–2.75
C	3.0	2.75–3.5
B	4.0	3.5 –4.5
A	5.0	4.5 up

TABLE 90-1.   COEFFICIENTS OF UTILIZATION, EFFICIENCIES,* DISTRIBUTION CHARACTERISTICS,† AND MAINTENANCE FACTORS‡ FOR TYPICAL LUMINAIRES COMPUTED FOR A WIDE RANGE OF INSTALLATION CONDITIONS§
(*IES Lighting Handbook*)

DISTRI-BUTION AND MAX. SPACING§	ROOM IN-DEX	Ceiling 75% Walls 50%	30%	10%	Ceiling 50% Walls 50%	30%	10%	Ceiling 30% Walls 30%	10%	TYPICAL LUMINAIRE†	ESTIMATED MAINTE-NANCE FACTORS*
1. Direct 0% 80% MS = 1.0 MH	J	.38	.32	.28	.37	.32	.28	.31	.28	Open or Louvered	G .65 M .55 P .45
	I	.46	.42	.38	.46	.40	.38	.41	.38	Enclosed dust-tight	G .70 M .65 P .55
	H	.50	.46	.43	.50	.46	.43	.46	.43		
	G	.54	.50	.48	.53	.50	.47	.49	.47		
	F	.58	.54	.51	.56	.53	.50	.52	.50		
	E	.62	.59	.56	.60	.58	.55	.58	.56		
	D	.67	.64	.60	.65	.63	.61	.62	.61		
	C	.69	.66	.63	.67	.65	.63	.64	.62		
	B	.72	.70	.67	.70	.68	.66	.67	.66		
	A	.74	.71	.69	.72	.70	.68	.69	.67		
2. Direct 0% 75% MS = 0.9 MH	J	.43	.40	.39	.42	.40	.39	.40	.38	Industrial fluorescent	See Distribution
	I	.51	.50	.49	.50	.49	.48	.49	.46	2-lamp, open or closed end 80% ...... (1)	
	H	.55	.54	.54	.54	.53	.52	.53	.52	2-lamp, louvered 65% ...... (5)	
	G	.59	.57	.57	.58	.56	.56	.56	.55	2-lamp, dust and vapor tight 65% ...... (5)	
	F	.62	.60	.59	.59	.58	.58	.58	.57	2-lamp, longitudinal shield 70% ...... (3)	
	E	.64	.63	.62	.63	.62	.61	.62	.60	2-lamp, open or closed end 70% ...... (3)	
	D	.68	.65	.64	.66	.64	.64	.64	.63	3-lamp, open or closed end 70% ...... (3)	
	C	.69	.67	.65	.67	.66	.65	.65	.64	2-lamp, 85–100 w, open or closed end 70% ...... (3)	
	B	.70	.68	.67	.68	.67	.66	.66	.65		
	A	.71	.70	.69	.69	.68	.67	.67	.66		
3. Direct 0% 70% MS = 1.0 MH	J	.33	.28	.25	.32	.28	.25	.27	.25	Mercury (H9) type	G .70 M .60 P .50
	I	.41	.36	.34	.40	.36	.33	.36	.33		See Distribution
	H	.45	.41	.38	.43	.41	.38	.40	.38	Porcelain enamelled 80% ...... (1)	
	G	.48	.45	.42	.47	.44	.41	.43	.41	Aluminum (45° shielding) 65% ...... (6)	
	F	.50	.48	.45	.49	.46	.44	.46	.44		
	E	.55	.52	.49	.54	.51	.49	.50	.49		
	D	.59	.56	.53	.57	.55	.53	.55	.53		
	C	.60	.58	.55	.59	.57	.55	.56	.55		
	B	.63	.61	.59	.62	.60	.58	.59	.57		
	A	.64	.62	.60	.63	.61	.60	.60	.59		
4. Direct 0% 70% MS = 0.6 MH	J	.40	.38	.36	.39	.38	.36	.38	.36	Porcelain enamelled 80% ...... (1)	
	I	.48	.46	.45	.47	.46	.45	.45	.44	Aluminum (45° shielding) 65% ...... (6)	
	H	.51	.51	.50	.51	.50	.49	.50	.49		
	G	.55	.54	.54	.54	.53	.52	.52	.51		
	F	.58	.56	.55	.55	.55	.54	.55	.53		
	E	.60	.59	.58	.59	.58	.57	.57	.56		G M P
	D	.64	.61	.60	.62	.60	.60	.60	.59	Enclosed dust-tight	.80 .72 .65
	C	.65	.63	.61	.63	.62	.60	.60	.60	Glassteel or S.B. diffuser	.65 .55 .45
	B	.65	.64	.63	.64	.62	.62	.62	.61	Others	.75 .65 .55
	A	.66	.65	.64	.64	.63	.62	.62	.62		
5. Direct 0% 65% MS = 1.0 MH	J	.31	.26	.23	.30	.26	.23	.25	.23		See Distribution
	I	.37	.34	.31	.37	.33	.31	.33	.31	Low-bay incandescent filament units	
	H	.41	.38	.35	.40	.38	.35	.37	.35	Dome reflector with I.F. lamp 80% ...... (1)	
	G	.45	.41	.39	.44	.41	.38	.40	.38	Dome reflector with white bowl lamp 65% ...... (3)	
	F	.47	.44	.41	.45	.43	.41	.42	.41	Dust and vapor-tight dome reflector 65% ...... (5)	
	E	.51	.48	.46	.50	.47	.45	.47	.45	Prismatic glass 70% ...... (3)	
	D	.55	.52	.49	.53	.51	.49	.51	.49	S.B. diffuser with aluminum insert 65% ...... (6)	
	C	.56	.54	.51	.55	.53	.51	.52	.51	Glassteel diffuser (multiply C.U. of no. 1 by .75)	
	B	.59	.57	.55	.57	.55	.54	.55	.53	Deep bowl porcelain enamelled 65% ...... (5)	
	A	.60	.58	.56	.59	.58	.55	.56	.55		
6. Direct 0% 65% MS = 0.8 MH	J	.36	.33	.32	.35	.33	.32	.34	.31		G M P
	I	.43	.41	.40	.42	.40	.40	.40	.38	Enclosed dust-tight	.80 .72 .65
	H	.46	.45	.45	.45	.44	.44	.44	.43	Others	.75 .65 .55
	G	.50	.48	.48	.49	.47	.46	.47	.46		See Distribution
	F	.52	.51	.49	.50	.49	.48	.49	.48	High and medium bay units	
	E	.55	.54	.52	.54	.53	.51	.52	.50	Mirrored or Prismatic Glass, or Aluminum	
	D	.58	.56	.55	.57	.55	.54	.55	.54	Spread 75% ...... (2)	
	C	.59	.58	.55	.58	.56	.55	.55	.55	Concentrating 70% ...... (4)	
	B	.60	.59	.58	.59	.58	.57	.57	.56	Deep bowl porcelain enamelled reflector 70% ...... (3)	
	A	.61	.60	.59	.60	.59	.58	.58	.57		

* Maintenance conditions: G—good; M—medium; P—poor.
§ MS—Maximum spacing between units. MH—Mounting height above floor, CH—Ceiling height above floor.
† S.B.—Silvered bowl lamp, I. F.—inside-frosted.

TABLE 90-2. COEFFICIENTS OF UTILIZATION, EFFICIENCIES,* DISTRIBUTION CHARACTERISTICS,† AND MAINTENANCE FACTORS‡ FOR TYPICAL LUMINAIRES COMPUTED FOR A WIDE RANGE OF INSTALLATION CONDITIONS.§ (Continued)

DISTRIBUTION AND MAX. SPACING‡	ROOM INDEX	Ceiling 75% Walls			Ceiling 50% Walls			Ceiling 30% Walls		TYPICAL LUMINAIRE / ESTIMATED MAINTENANCE FACTORS*
		50%	30%	10%	50%	30%	10%	30%	10%	
7. Direct 0% 50% MS=0.7 MH	J	.29	.27	.26	.28	.27	.26	.27	.26	Prismatic / Louvered / See Distribution. G .70 M .65 P .55
	I	.34	.33	.32	.33	.32	.32	.32	.32	
	H	.37	.36	.36	.36	.35	.35	.35	.34	
	G	.39	.39	.38	.38	.37	.37	.37	.36	
	F	.41	.40	.39	.40	.39	.38	.39	.38	
	E	.43	.42	.42	.42	.41	.40	.41	.40	
	D	.45	.44	.43	.44	.43	.42	.42	.42	
	C	.46	.45	.44	.45	.44	.43	.43	.42	
	B	.47	.45	.45	.46	.44	.44	.44	.43	
	A	.47	.46	.46	.46	.45	.44	.44	.44	
8. Direct 0% 55% MS=0.9 MH	J	.26	.22	.19	.25	.22	.19	.21	.19	Recessed downlights. Concentrating.... (7) Spread (8). Note: Distribution and outputs of recessed downlights vary widely. Where possible, obtain or compute utilization of specific luminaires used.
	I	.32	.29	.26	.31	.28	.26	.28	.26	
	H	.35	.32	.30	.34	.32	.30	.31	.30	
	G	.38	.35	.33	.37	.35	.32	.34	.32	
	F	.40	.37	.35	.39	.37	.35	.36	.35	
	E	.43	.41	.39	.42	.40	.39	.40	.39	
	D	.46	.44	.42	.45	.43	.42	.43	.42	
	C	.48	.46	.44	.46	.45	.44	.44	.43	
	B	.50	.48	.46	.48	.47	.46	.46	.45	
	A	.51	.49	.48	.50	.48	.47	.47	.46	
9. Direct 0% 100% MS=0.6 MH	J	.71	.66	.63	.70	.65	.62	.64	.61	Bare / Flush shielding. PAR-38 floodlamp. Use 1850 as total lumens per lamp.‡ G .75 M .70 P .65
	I	.78	.73	.71	.76	.72	.70	.70	.69	
	H	.83	.78	.75	.80	.77	.74	.76	.74	
	G	.85	.81	.80	.83	.80	.77	.79	.77	
	F	.87	.84	.83	.85	.83	.81	.82	.80	
	E	.91	.89	.86	.90	.88	.85	.86	.84	
	D	.95	.93	.91	.93	.92	.90	.90	.89	
	C	.97	.96	.94	.95	.94	.92	.92	.91	
	B	1.00	.99	.97	.97	.96	.95	.95	.94	
	A	1.02	1.00	.99	1.00	.99	.97	.97	.96	
10. Direct 0% 60% MS=0.5 MH	J	.52	.49	.47	.51	.49	.47	.48	.47	PAR-38 floodlamp with 45° shielding. Use 1850 as total lumens per lamp.‡ G .75 M .70 P .65
	I	.55	.53	.51	.54	.52	.51	.51	.50	
	H	.57	.55	.53	.56	.54	.53	.53	.53	
	G	.58	.57	.55	.57	.56	.55	.55	.54	
	F	.59	.58	.57	.58	.57	.56	.56	.56	
	E	.61	.60	.59	.60	.59	.58	.58	.57	
	D	.63	.62	.61	.61	.61	.60	.60	.59	
	C	.64	.64	.63	.63	.63	.62	.62	.61	
	B	.65	.65	.64	.64	.64	.63	.63	.62	
	A	.66	.66	.65	.65	.65	.64	.64	.63	
11. Direct 0% 100% MS=0.8 MH	J	.59	.53	.49	.58	.52	.48	.52	.48	R-40 floodlamp (bare). Use 1500 lumens for 150-w and 3200 lumens for 300-w lamps.‡ 150-w 300-w / G .85 .90 / M .80 .85 / P .75 .80
	I	.68	.63	.59	.67	.62	.58	.61	.58	
	H	.72	.67	.64	.71	.67	.64	.67	.63	
	G	.77	.72	.69	.75	.71	.68	.70	.67	
	F	.80	.76	.72	.78	.74	.71	.73	.71	
	E	.85	.81	.78	.83	.80	.77	.79	.76	
	D	.90	.87	.83	.87	.85	.83	.85	.82	
	C	.93	.90	.87	.90	.88	.86	.87	.84	
	B	.97	.94	.92	.94	.92	.90	.91	.88	
	A	.99	.96	.94	.96	.94	.92	.93	.90	
12. Direct 0% 70% MS=0.7 MH	J	.50	.47	.45	.50	.47	.45	.46	.44	R-40 floodlamp with 13° shielding. Use 1500 lumens for 150-w and 3200 lumens for 300-w lamps.‡ 150-w 300-w / G .85 .90 / M .80 .85 / P .75 .80
	I	.55	.52	.50	.55	.52	.50	.51	.49	
	H	.59	.56	.54	.58	.55	.53	.55	.52	
	G	.61	.58	.57	.60	.57	.55	.57	.55	
	F	.63	.60	.59	.62	.59	.57	.59	.57	
	E	.65	.63	.62	.64	.62	.61	.61	.60	
	D	.67	.66	.65	.66	.65	.64	.64	.63	
	C	.69	.68	.67	.67	.66	.65	.65	.64	
	B	.71	.70	.69	.69	.68	.67	.67	.66	
	A	.73	.72	.71	.71	.70	.69	.69	.68	

* Maintenance conditions: G—good; M—medium; P—poor.
‡ For calculating illumination.
§ MS—Maximum spacing between units. MH—Mounting height above floor. CH—Ceiling height above floor.

TABLE 90-3. COEFFICIENTS OF UTILIZATION, EFFICIENCIES,* DISTRIBUTION CHARACTERISTICS,† AND MAINTENANCE FACTORS‡ FOR TYPICAL LUMINAIRES COMPUTED FOR A WIDE RANGE OF INSTALLATION CONDITIONS.§ (Continued)

DISTRIBUTION AND MAX. SPACING§	ROOM INDEX	Ceiling 75% Walls 50%	30%	10%	Ceiling 50% Walls 50%	30%	10%	Ceiling 30% Walls 30%	10%	TYPICAL LUMINAIRE / ESTIMATED MAINTENANCE FACTORS*
13. Direct 0% 75% MS = 0.9 MH	J	.36	.30	.26	.35	.30	.26	.29	.24	
	I	.43	.39	.36	.43	.37	.36	.38	.36	
	H	.47	.43	.40	.47	.43	.40	.43	.40	
	G	.51	.47	.45	.50	.47	.44	.46	.44	
	F	.54	.51	.48	.52	.50	.47	.49	.47	
	E	.58	.55	.52	.56	.54	.52	.54	.52	
	D	.63	.60	.56	.61	.59	.57	.58	.57	
	C	.65	.62	.59	.63	.61	.59	.60	.58	
	B	.67	.66	.63	.66	.64	.62	.63	.62	
	A	.69	.67	.65	.67	.66	.64	.65	.63	
14. Direct 0% 70% MS = 0.9 MH	J	.33	.28	.25	.32	.28	.25	.27	.25	G .70 M .60 P .55 #
	I	.41	.36	.34	.40	.36	.33	.36	.33	See Distribution
	H	.45	.41	.38	.43	.41	.38	.40	.38	**Single lamp deep troffer**
	G	.48	.45	.42	.47	.44	.41	.43	.41	
	F	.50	.48	.45	.49	.46	.44	.46	.44	White, no baffles, 70% .... (15)
	E	.55	.52	.49	.54	.51	.49	.50	.49	White with baffles 65% .... (16)
	D	.59	.56	.53	.57	.55	.53	.55	.53	White with prismatic cover plate 60% .... (17)
	C	.60	.58	.55	.59	.57	.55	.56	.55	Semi-specular or semi-diffused aluminum, open 65% ...... (16)
	B	.63	.61	.59	.62	.60	.58	.59	.57	Semi-specular or semi-diffused aluminum baffles
	A	.64	.62	.60	.63	.61	.60	.60	.59	60% ...... (17)
15. Direct 0% 70% MS = 0.8 MH	J	.37	.34	.32	.36	.34	.32	.34	.31	
	I	.45	.42	.41	.44	.41	.40	.41	.39	
	H	.49	.46	.45	.48	.45	.44	.45	.44	
	G	.52	.50	.48	.51	.49	.48	.48	.47	
	F	.55	.53	.50	.53	.51	.50	.51	.50	
	E	.58	.56	.54	.57	.55	.53	.55	.53	
	D	.61	.59	.57	.60	.58	.57	.57	.56	
	C	.63	.61	.58	.62	.60	.58	.59	.57	
	B	.65	.62	.61	.63	.61	.60	.60	.59	
	A	.66	.64	.63	.64	.62	.61	.62	.60	
16. Direct 0% 65% MS = 0.8 MH	J	.32	.29	.29	.31	.29	.27	.29	.26	G .70 M .60 P .55 #
	I	.38	.36	.35	.38	.35	.34	.35	.34	See Distribution
	H	.42	.40	.39	.41	.39	.38	.39	.38	**Two lamp shallow troffer**
	G	.45	.43	.42	.44	.42	.41	.41	.41	
	F	.47	.45	.43	.45	.44	.43	.44	.43	
	E	.49	.48	.46	.49	.47	.46	.47	.46	
	D	.53	.50	.49	.52	.50	.49	.49	.49	
	C	.54	.52	.50	.53	.51	.50	.50	.49	White, open 75% .... (13)
	B	.55	.54	.53	.54	.52	.52	.52	.51	White, with prismatic or ribbed cover 65% ...... (16)
	A	.57	.55	.54	.55	.53	.52	.53	.52	White, with louvers 60% .... (17)
17. Direct 0% 60% MS = 0.8 MH	J	.33	.31	.29	.32	.31	.29	.31	.29	Aluminum with louvers 55% .... (18)
	I	.40	.38	.37	.39	.37	.37	.37	.35	
	H	.43	.42	.41	.42	.41	.40	.41	.40	
	G	.46	.45	.44	.45	.44	.43	.43	.43	
	F	.48	.47	.46	.47	.46	.44	.45	.45	
	E	.51	.50	.48	.50	.48	.47	.48	.47	
	D	.54	.52	.50	.52	.51	.50	.50	.49	
	C	.55	.53	.51	.53	.52	.51	.51	.50	
	B	.56	.54	.53	.54	.53	.52	.52	.51	
	A	.57	.55	.54	.55	.54	.53	.53	.52	
18. Direct 0% 55% MS = 0.8 MH	J	.30	.28	.27	.30	.28	.27	.29	.26	G .70 M .60 P .55 #
	I	.37	.35	.34	.36	.34	.34	.34	.32	See Distribution
	H	.39	.38	.38	.39	.37	.37	.38	.36	**Three lamp shallow white troffer**
	G	.42	.41	.40	.41	.40	.39	.40	.39	
	F	.44	.43	.42	.42	.42	.41	.42	.41	
	E	.46	.46	.44	.46	.45	.43	.44	.43	
	D	.50	.47	.46	.48	.47	.46	.46	.46	Open 70% .... (14)
	C	.50	.49	.47	.49	.48	.47	.47	.46	With louvers 55% .... (18)
	B	.51	.50	.49	.50	.48	.48	.48	.47	With prismatic cover plate 60% .... (17)
	A	.52	.51	.50	.51	.49	.48	.49	.48	

* Maintenance conditions: G—good; M—medium; P—poor.
# Maintenance factor assumed to be .50 for poor conditions if troffer has glass cover.
§ MS—Maximum spacing between units. MH—Mounting height above floor. CH—Ceiling height above floor.

TABLE 90-4. COEFFICIENTS OF UTILIZATION, EFFICIENCIES,* DISTRIBUTION CHARACTERISTICS,† AND MAINTENANCE FACTORS‡ FOR TYPICAL LUMINAIRES COMPUTED FOR A WIDE RANGE OF INSTALLATION CONDITIONS.§ *(Continued)*

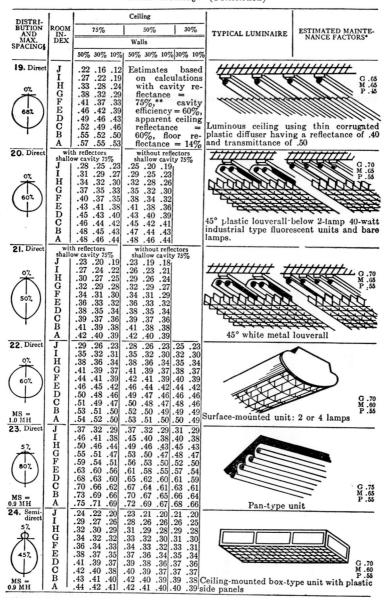

19. Direct — 0% — 68%

ROOM INDEX	Ceiling 75% / Walls 50%	30%	10%
J	.22	.16	.12
I	.27	.22	.19
H	.33	.28	.24
G	.38	.32	.29
F	.41	.37	.33
E	.46	.42	.39
D	.49	.46	.43
C	.52	.49	.46
B	.55	.52	.50
A	.57	.55	.53

Estimates based on calculations with cavity reflectance = 75%,** cavity efficiency = 60%, apparent ceiling reflectance = 60%, floor reflectance = 14%

Luminous ceiling using thin corrugated plastic diffuser having a reflectance of .40 and transmittance of .50
G .65 M .65 P .45

20. Direct — 0% — 60%

ROOM INDEX	with reflectors shallow cavity 75%			without reflectors shallow cavity 75%		
J	.28	.25	.23	.25	.20	.19
I	.31	.29	.27	.29	.25	.23
H	.34	.32	.30	.32	.28	.26
G	.37	.35	.33	.35	.32	.30
F	.40	.37	.35	.38	.34	.32
E	.43	.41	.38	.41	.38	.36
D	.45	.43	.40	.43	.40	.39
C	.46	.44	.42	.45	.42	.41
B	.48	.45	.43	.47	.44	.43
A	.48	.46	.44	.48	.46	.44

45° plastic louverall below 2-lamp 40-watt industrial type fluorescent units and bare lamps.
G .70 M .65 P .55

21. Direct — 0% — 50%

ROOM INDEX	with reflectors shallow cavity 75%			without reflectors shallow cavity 75%		
J	.23	.20	.19	.23	.19	.18
I	.27	.24	.22	.26	.23	.21
H	.30	.27	.25	.29	.26	.24
G	.32	.29	.28	.32	.29	.27
F	.34	.31	.30	.34	.31	.29
E	.36	.33	.32	.36	.33	.32
D	.38	.35	.34	.38	.35	.34
C	.39	.37	.36	.39	.37	.36
B	.41	.39	.38	.41	.38	.38
A	.42	.40	.39	.42	.40	.39

45° white metal louverall
G .70 M .65 P .55

22. Direct — 0% — 60% — MS = 1.0 MH

ROOM INDEX	C75 W50	W30	W10	C50 W50	W30	W10	C30 W30	W10
J	.29	.26	.23	.28	.26	.23	.25	.23
I	.35	.32	.31	.35	.32	.30	.32	.30
H	.38	.36	.34	.38	.36	.34	.35	.34
G	.41	.39	.37	.41	.39	.37	.38	.37
F	.44	.41	.39	.42	.41	.39	.40	.39
E	.46	.45	.42	.46	.44	.42	.44	.42
D	.50	.48	.46	.49	.47	.46	.46	.46
C	.51	.49	.47	.50	.48	.47	.48	.46
B	.53	.51	.50	.52	.50	.49	.49	.49
A	.54	.52	.50	.53	.51	.50	.50	.49

Surface-mounted unit: 2 or 4 lamps
G .70 M .60 P .55

23. Direct — 5% — 80% — MS = 0.9 MH

ROOM INDEX	C75 W50	W30	W10	C50 W50	W30	W10	C30 W30	W10
J	.37	.32	.29	.37	.32	.29	.31	.29
I	.46	.41	.38	.45	.40	.38	.40	.38
H	.50	.46	.44	.49	.46	.43	.45	.43
G	.55	.51	.47	.53	.50	.47	.48	.47
F	.59	.54	.51	.56	.53	.50	.52	.50
E	.63	.60	.56	.61	.58	.55	.57	.54
D	.68	.63	.60	.65	.62	.60	.61	.59
C	.70	.66	.62	.67	.64	.61	.63	.61
B	.73	.69	.66	.70	.67	.65	.66	.64
A	.75	.71	.69	.72	.69	.67	.68	.66

Pan-type unit
G .75 M .65 P .55

24. Semi-direct — 5% — 45% — MS = 0.9 MH

ROOM INDEX	C75 W50	W30	W10	C50 W50	W30	W10	C30 W30	W10
J	.24	.22	.20	.23	.21	.20	.21	.20
I	.29	.27	.26	.28	.26	.26	.26	.25
H	.32	.30	.29	.31	.29	.28	.29	.28
G	.34	.32	.32	.33	.32	.30	.31	.30
F	.36	.34	.33	.34	.33	.32	.33	.31
E	.38	.37	.35	.37	.36	.34	.35	.34
D	.41	.39	.37	.39	.38	.36	.37	.36
C	.42	.40	.38	.40	.39	.37	.37	.37
B	.43	.41	.40	.42	.40	.39	.39	.38
A	.44	.42	.41	.42	.41	.40	.40	.39

Ceiling-mounted box-type unit with plastic side panels
G .70 M .60 P .55

* Maintenance conditions: G—good; M—medium; P—poor.
§ MS—Maximum spacing between units. MH—Mounting height above floor. CH—Ceiling height above floor.
** Higher cavity reflectance is recommended.

TABLE 90-5. COEFFICIENTS OF UTILIZATION, EFFICIENCIES,* DISTRIBUTION CHARACTERISTICS,† AND MAINTENANCE FACTORS‡ FOR TYPICAL LUMINAIRES COMPUTED FOR A WIDE RANGE OF INSTALLATION CONDITIONS.§ (*Continued*)

DISTRIBUTION AND MAX. SPACING§	ROOM IN-DEX	Ceiling 75% Walls 50%	30%	10%	Ceiling 50% Walls 50%	30%	10%	Ceiling 30% Walls 30%	10%	TYPICAL LUMINAIRE	ESTIMATED MAINTENANCE FACTORS*
25. Semi-direct 10% 60% MS = 0.8 MH	J	.34	.30	.28	.32	.30	.28	.29	.27	Ceiling-mounted troffer	G .70 M .60 P .50
	I	.41	.38	.37	.39	.37	.35	.36	.34		
	H	.44	.42	.41	.43	.40	.39	.40	.38		
	G	.48	.46	.44	.46	.44	.42	.42	.42		
	F	.50	.49	.46	.48	.46	.44	.45	.44		
	E	.53	.52	.50	.51	.50	.47	.48	.47		
	D	.56	.54	.53	.55	.52	.51	.51	.50		
	C	.59	.57	.54	.56	.54	.52	.52	.51		
	B	.60	.58	.57	.57	.56	.55	.54	.53		
	A	.62	.60	.59	.59	.57	.56	.56	.54		
26. Semi-direct 10% 50% MS = 0.8 MH	J	.25	.22	.20	.24	.21	.20	.21	.19	Ceiling-mounted box type with ribbed glass panels or louver bottom / Ceiling-mounted wedge type	G .65 M .55 P .50
	I	.30	.28	.26	.28	.27	.25	.26	.25		
	H	.34	.31	.27	.32	.30	.28	.29	.28		
	G	.37	.34	.32	.35	.33	.31	.32	.30		
	F	.39	.37	.34	.37	.35	.33	.34	.32		
	E	.42	.40	.37	.40	.38	.36	.37	.35		
	D	.45	.42	.40	.43	.40	.39	.39	.38		
	C	.47	.44	.41	.44	.42	.40	.40	.39		
	B	.49	.46	.44	.46	.44	.42	.42	.41		
	A	.50	.48	.45	.48	.45	.43	.43	.42		
27. Semi-direct 15% 55% MS = 0.8 MH	J	.30	.26	.24	.28	.25	.23	.25	.22	Surface troffer with louvers	G .70 M .60 P .50
	I	.36	.33	.31	.35	.31	.30	.31	.29		
	H	.40	.37	.35	.38	.35	.33	.34	.32		
	G	.43	.40	.37	.43	.40	.38	.39	.37		
	F	.46	.43	.40	.43	.40	.38	.39	.37		
	E	.49	.47	.44	.46	.44	.42	.42	.40		
	D	.53	.49	.47	.50	.47	.45	.45	.44		
	C	.55	.52	.49	.51	.49	.47	.45	.45		
	B	.57	.54	.52	.53	.51	.49	.48	.47		
	A	.59	.56	.54	.55	.52	.50	.50	.48		
28. Semi-direct 15% 50% MS = 0.9 MH	J	.28	.25	.23	.27	.25	.23	.24	.22	Prismatic lens type (4 lamp)	G .70 M .60 P .50
	I	.35	.32	.30	.32	.30	.29	.28	.27		
	H	.37	.35	.35	.36	.34	.32	.31	.29		
	G	.40	.38	.37	.39	.36	.35	.33	.32		
	F	.43	.40	.39	.41	.39	.36	.35	.34		
	E	.46	.44	.42	.43	.41	.40	.38	.36		
	D	.49	.47	.44	.46	.44	.42	.40	.39		
	C	.50	.48	.46	.47	.45	.44	.41	.40		
	B	.52	.49	.48	.49	.47	.45	.43	.42		
	A	.53	.51	.49	.50	.48	.47	.45	.43		
29. Semi-direct 20% 50% MS = 0.9 MH	J	.25	.21	.18	.23	.19	.17	.19	.17	Ceiling-mounted box type, louvered-bottom / Suspended wedge type	G .70 M .60 P .50
	I	.31	.26	.24	.29	.25	.23	.24	.23		
	H	.34	.30	.28	.32	.29	.26	.28	.25		
	G	.38	.34	.31	.35	.32	.29	.30	.28		
	F	.40	.37	.33	.37	.34	.31	.32	.30		
	E	.44	.41	.37	.41	.38	.35	.36	.34		
	D	.47	.44	.40	.44	.41	.39	.39	.37		
	C	.50	.46	.43	.46	.43	.40	.40	.38		
	B	.53	.50	.47	.48	.45	.44	.43	.41		
	A	.55	.51	.48	.50	.47	.45	.44	.43		
30. Semi-direct 20% 45% MS = 0.9 MH	J	.23	.20	.18	.22	.19	.17	.18	.17	Suspended wedge type	G .70 M .60 P .50
	I	.29	.26	.24	.27	.24	.22	.23	.21		
	H	.32	.29	.27	.30	.27	.26	.26	.24		
	G	.36	.33	.30	.33	.30	.28	.28	.27		
	F	.38	.35	.32	.35	.32	.30	.30	.29		
	E	.41	.38	.35	.38	.36	.33	.33	.31		
	D	.43	.41	.38	.41	.38	.36	.36	.34		
	C	.47	.43	.40	.43	.39	.37	.37	.35		
	B	.49	.46	.44	.45	.42	.40	.39	.37		
	A	.51	.48	.45	.46	.43	.42	.40	.39		

* Maintenance conditions: G—good; M—medium; P—poor.
§ MS—Maximum spacing between units. MH—Mounting height above floor. CH—Ceiling height above floor.

TABLE 90-6. COEFFICIENTS OF UTILIZATION, EFFICIENCIES,* DISTRIBUTION CHARACTERISTICS,† AND MAINTENANCE FACTORS‡ FOR TYPICAL LUMINAIRES COMPUTED FOR A WIDE RANGE OF INSTALLATION CONDITIONS.§ *(Continued)*

DISTRIBUTION AND MAX. SPACING§	ROOM INDEX	Ceiling 75% Walls 50%	30%	10%	Ceiling 50% Walls 50%	30%	10%	Ceiling 30% Walls 30%	10%	TYPICAL LUMINAIRE	ESTIMATED MAINTENANCE FACTORS*
31. Semi-direct 25% 65% MS = 0.9 MH	J	.28	.22	.18	.26	.21	.18	.20	.17	Bare lamp channel	G .75 M .65 P .55
	I	.35	.29	.25	.33	.27	.24	.26	.24		
	H	.39	.33	.30	.37	.32	.28	.30	.27		
	G	.44	.38	.33	.40	.36	.32	.33	.30		
	F	.47	.42	.37	.43	.39	.34	.37	.33		
	E	.53	.47	.42	.49	.44	.40	.41	.38		
	D	.57	.51	.46	.53	.48	.44	.45	.42		
	C	.60	.55	.49	.55	.50	.46	.48	.44		
	B	.66	.60	.55	.59	.54	.51	.51	.49		
	A	.68	.63	.58	.62	.57	.54	.53	.51		
32. Semi-direct 25% 55% MS = 1.0 MH	J	.33	.32	.28	.31	.28	.26	.28	.25	Prismatic or open louvered glass or plastic	G .70 M .65 P .55
	I	.40	.37	.35	.38	.35	.33	.33	.31		
	H	.44	.41	.39	.41	.39	.37	.37	.35		
	G	.47	.45	.43	.44	.41	.40	.40	.38		
	F	.51	.48	.45	.46	.44	.42	.42	.40		
	E	.54	.51	.49	.50	.48	.45	.45	.43		
	D	.50	.54	.51	.53	.50	.48	.48	.46		
	C	.60	.57	.53	.55	.52	.49	.48	.47		
	B	.62	.59	.57	.57	.54	.53	.51	.49		
	A	.64	.61	.58	.59	.56	.54	.52	.51		
33. Semi-direct 25% 45% MS = 1.0 MH	J	.24	.20	.18	.22	.19	.17	.18	.16	Half cylinder shielded	G .65 M .55 P .45
	I	.29	.26	.23	.27	.24	.22	.23	.20		
	H	.33	.29	.26	.30	.27	.25	.25	.23		
	G	.36	.33	.29	.33	.30	.28	.28	.26		
	F	.39	.35	.32	.35	.32	.29	.30	.28		
	E	.42	.39	.36	.38	.36	.33	.33	.31		
	D	.46	.42	.39	.41	.38	.36	.35	.34		
	C	.48	.44	.42	.43	.40	.38	.37	.35		
	B	.51	.48	.45	.46	.42	.41	.39	.38		
	A	.53	.50	.47	.48	.44	.42	.41	.39		
34. Semi-direct 30% 60% MS = 1.0 MH	J	.29	.24	.21	.28	.23	.20	.21	.19	Half cylinder bare	G .75 M .65 P .55
	I	.37	.31	.28	.34	.29	.26	.28	.25		
	H	.41	.36	.33	.33	.34	.31	.32	.29		
	G	.46	.40	.36	.41	.37	.34	.34	.32		
	F	.49	.44	.39	.44	.40	.37	.38	.35		
	E	.54	.49	.45	.49	.45	.41	.42	.39		
	D	.59	.53	.49	.53	.49	.46	.46	.43		
	C	.61	.56	.52	.54	.51	.48	.48	.45		
	B	.66	.61	.57	.59	.55	.53	.51	.49		
	A	.68	.64	.60	.61	.57	.55	.53	.51		
35. Gen. Diffuse 30% 45% MS = 1.0 MH	J	.29	.26	.24	.26	.24	.23	.24	.21	"V" shaped aluminum with center louver Glass sides louvered bottom, top reflectors	G .70 M .60 P .50
	I	.35	.32	.30	.32	.30	.28	.28	.26		
	H	.39	.36	.34	.35	.33	.32	.31	.29		
	G	.42	.40	.37	.38	.36	.34	.33	.32		
	F	.45	.42	.39	.40	.38	.36	.35	.34		
	E	.48	.45	.43	.43	.41	.39	.38	.36		
	D	.52	.48	.46	.46	.44	.42	.40	.39		
	C	.53	.50	.48	.48	.45	.43	.41	.40		
	B	.56	.53	.51	.50	.47	.46	.43	.42		
	A	.57	.55	.53	.51	.49	.47	.44	.43		
36. Gen. Diffuse 35% 45% MS = 1.0 MH	J	.23	.19	.16	.21	.17	.15	.16	.14	Glass enclosing globes	G .70 M .65 P .55
	I	.29	.24	.22	.26	.22	.19	.21	.18		
	H	.33	.28	.25	.29	.26	.23	.23	.21		
	G	.37	.32	.28	.32	.28	.26	.26	.23		
	F	.40	.35	.32	.35	.31	.28	.28	.26		
	E	.44	.40	.36	.39	.35	.32	.32	.29		
	D	.48	.43	.39	.42	.38	.35	.35	.32		
	C	.51	.46	.42	.44	.40	.37	.37	.34		
	B	.55	.50	.46	.48	.44	.41	.39	.37		
	A	.57	.53	.49	.50	.46	.43	.41	.39		

* Maintenance conditions: G—good; M—medium; P—poor.
§ MS—Maximum spacing between units. MH—Mounting height above floor. CH—Ceiling height above floor.

TABLE 20-7. COEFFICIENTS OF UTILIZATION, EFFICIENCIES,* DISTRIBUTION CHARACTERISTICS,† AND MAINTENANCE FACTORS‡ FOR TYPICAL LUMINAIRES COMPUTED FOR A WIDE RANGE OF INSTALLATION CONDITIONS.§ *(Continued)*

DISTRIBUTION AND MAX. SPACING‡	ROOM INDEX	Ceiling 75% Walls 50%	30%	10%	Ceiling 50% Walls 50%	30%	10%	Ceiling 30% Walls 30%	10%	TYPICAL LUMINAIRE	ESTIMATED MAINTENANCE FACTORS*
37. Gen. Diffuse 35% / 45% MS = 1.0 MH	J	.31	.29	.26	.28	.26	.24	.24	.23	Open top, opaque sides, louvered bottom	G .70 M .65 P .60
	I	.38	.36	.34	.35	.33	.31	.31	.28		
	H	.42	.39	.38	.37	.36	.35	.34	.33		
	G	.45	.43	.41	.42	.39	.37	.36	.35		
	F	.48	.45	.43	.43	.41	.39	.38	.37		
	E	.54	.49	.48	.46	.44	.42	.41	.39		
	D	.55	.53	.50	.49	.47	.45	.42	.42		
	C	.58	.56	.53	.51	.49	.47	.44	.43		
	B	.61	.58	.56	.53	.51	.49	.45	.44		
	A	.62	.59	.58	.55	.53	.51	.47	.45		
38. Gen. Diffuse 40% / 40% MS = 1.1 MH	J	.28	.24	.22	.24	.22	.20	.20	.18	Open top, plastic sides, louvered bottom	G .70 M .60 P .50
	I	.34	.30	.29	.30	.27	.26	.25	.23		
	H	.38	.35	.32	.33	.30	.29	.28	.26		
	G	.41	.38	.36	.36	.34	.32	.30	.29		
	F	.44	.41	.38	.38	.36	.34	.32	.30		
	E	.48	.45	.42	.42	.39	.37	.34	.33		
	D	.52	.48	.45	.44	.42	.40	.37	.36		
	C	.54	.50	.47	.46	.44	.42	.38	.37		
	B	.57	.53	.51	.48	.46	.44	.40	.39		
	A	.58	.55	.53	.50	.48	.46	.41	.40		
39. Gen. Diffuse 45% / 50% MS = 1.1 MH	J	.29	.23	.19	.26	.21	.18	.19	.16	Unshielded grid, slimline	G .75 M .65 P .55
	I	.37	.31	.27	.33	.28	.24	.26	.22		
	H	.41	.36	.32	.36	.32	.29	.29	.26		
	G	.46	.41	.36	.40	.36	.32	.32	.29		
	F	.50	.44	.39	.43	.39	.35	.34	.32		
	E	.55	.49	.45	.48	.44	.40	.39	.36		
	D	.59	.54	.50	.52	.48	.45	.43	.41		
	C	.62	.58	.54	.54	.50	.48	.45	.43		
	B	.67	.63	.59	.58	.55	.52	.48	.47		
	A	.70	.65	.62	.61	.57	.54	.50	.48		
40. Gen. Diffuse 45% / 35% MS = 1.2 MH	J	.26	.23	.21	.23	.21	.19	.19	.17	Open top, plastic sides, louvered bottom	G .70 M .65 P .60
	I	.32	.29	.27	.28	.26	.24	.23	.21		
	H	.37	.33	.31	.31	.29	.27	.26	.24		
	G	.40	.36	.34	.34	.31	.30	.28	.26		
	F	.42	.39	.36	.36	.33	.32	.30	.28		
	E	.46	.43	.40	.40	.37	.35	.32	.30		
	D	.50	.46	.43	.42	.39	.38	.34	.33		
	C	.52	.48	.45	.44	.41	.39	.35	.34		
	B	.55	.52	.49	.46	.44	.42	.37	.36		
	A	.57	.54	.51	.48	.45	.43	.39	.37		
41. Gen. Diffuse 45% / 35% MS = 1.0 MH	J	.24	.20	.17	.21	.17	.15	.15	.14	Semi-indirect unit with louvered bottom	G .70 M .65 P .55
	I	.29	.25	.23	.26	.22	.20	.20	.18		
	H	.33	.29	.26	.28	.26	.23	.22	.20		
	G	.37	.33	.30	.32	.28	.26	.24	.23		
	F	.40	.35	.32	.34	.30	.28	.26	.23		
	E	.44	.40	.36	.37	.34	.31	.29	.27		
	D	.47	.43	.40	.40	.37	.34	.32	.30		
	C	.50	.46	.42	.42	.39	.36	.33	.31		
	B	.53	.50	.47	.44	.42	.40	.35	.34		
	A	.56	.51	.49	.47	.44	.41	.37	.35		
42. Gen. Diffuse 45% / 30% MS = 1.2 MH	J	.24	.21	.19	.21	.19	.17	.17	.15	Suspended box type with translucent sides and clear ribbed bottom	G .65 M .55 P .45
	I	.29	.26	.24	.26	.23	.22	.21	.19		
	H	.33	.30	.28	.28	.26	.24	.23	.21		
	G	.36	.33	.31	.31	.28	.27	.25	.23		
	F	.39	.36	.33	.33	.30	.29	.26	.25		
	E	.42	.39	.37	.36	.33	.31	.29	.27		
	D	.46	.42	.40	.38	.36	.34	.31	.29		
	C	.48	.44	.42	.40	.37	.35	.32	.30		
	B	.51	.48	.45	.42	.40	.38	.33	.32		
	A	.52	.50	.48	.43	.41	.40	.35	.33		

* Maintenance conditions: G—good; M—medium; P—poor.
§ MS—Maximum spacing between units. MH—Mounting height above floor. CH—Ceiling height above floor.

TABLE 90-8. Coefficients of Utilization, Efficiencies,* Distribution Characteristics,† and Maintenance Factors‡ for Typical Luminaires Computed for a Wide Range of Installation Conditions.§ (*Continued*)

DISTRIBUTION AND MAX. SPACING§	ROOM IN-DEX	Ceiling 75%			Ceiling 50%			Ceiling 30%		TYPICAL LUMINAIRE	ESTIMATED MAINTENANCE FACTORS*
		Walls									
		50%	30%	10%	50%	30%	10%	30%	10%		
43. Gen. Diffuse 50% / 35% MS = 1.2 MH	J	.26	.23	.20	.23	.20	.18	.18	.16	Open top, glass sides, louvered bottom	G .70 M .65 P .60
	I	.33	.29	.26	.28	.25	.23	.22	.20		
	H	.36	.33	.30	.29	.28	.26	.25	.23		
	G	.40	.36	.34	.34	.31	.29	.27	.26		
	F	.43	.39	.36	.36	.33	.31	.29	.27		
	E	.48	.44	.40	.40	.37	.35	.32	.30		
	D	.51	.47	.44	.43	.40	.38	.34	.33		
	C	.54	.50	.46	.45	.42	.40	.36	.34		
	B	.57	.53	.51	.47	.45	.43	.37	.36		
	A	.59	.56	.53	.49	.47	.44	.39	.38		
44. Semi-indirect 60% / 20% MS = 1.0 CH	J	.21	.17	.15	.15	.14	.12	.12	.09	Glass or plastic, clear top, diffusing bottom	G .70 M .65 P .55
	I	.26	.22	.20	.21	.18	.16	.15	.13		
	H	.29	.26	.23	.23	.20	.19	.17	.15		
	G	.33	.28	.26	.26	.23	.21	.18	.17		
	F	.36	.32	.28	.28	.25	.23	.20	.20		
	E	.39	.36	.32	.31	.28	.26	.22	.20		
	D	.43	.38	.36	.33	.30	.28	.24	.22		
	C	.45	.41	.38	.35	.32	.30	.25	.24		
	B	.48	.46	.42	.37	.35	.34	.27	.26		
	A	.51	.48	.45	.40	.37	.35	.28	.27		
45. Semi-indirect 65% / 20% MS = 1.0 CH	J	.24	.20	.19	.19	.17	.16	.14	.13	Semi-silvered bowl	G .70 M .60 P .55
	I	.30	.26	.24	.24	.22	.20	.18	.16		
	H	.33	.30	.28	.26	.24	.22	.20	.18		
	G	.37	.34	.31	.30	.27	.25	.22	.20		
	F	.40	.36	.33	.32	.29	.27	.23	.22		
	E	.44	.40	.38	.35	.32	.30	.25	.24		
	D	.48	.44	.41	.37	.34	.33	.27	.26		
	C	.50	.46	.44	.39	.36	.34	.28	.27		
	B	.54	.50	.48	.41	.39	.37	.30	.28		
	A	.56	.52	.50	.43	.41	.39	.31	.30		
46. Semi-indirect 55% / 20% MS = 1.2 CH	J	.18	.14	.13	.14	.12	.10	.09	.08	Translucent trough, semi-indirect	G .60 M .50 P .40
	I	.22	.19	.17	.18	.15	.14	.12	.11		
	H	.25	.22	.20	.20	.18	.16	.14	.13		
	G	.28	.25	.22	.22	.20	.18	.16	.15		
	F	.30	.27	.24	.24	.22	.20	.17	.16		
	E	.34	.30	.28	.27	.24	.22	.19	.18		
	D	.37	.33	.31	.29	.26	.25	.21	.20		
	C	.39	.36	.33	.30	.28	.26	.22	.21		
	B	.42	.39	.37	.32	.30	.28	.24	.23		
	A	.44	.41	.39	.34	.32	.30	.25	.24		
47. Semi-indirect 65% / 10% MS = 1.2 CH	J	.16	.13	.11	.12	.10	.08	.07	.06	Plastic trough	G .60 M .50 P .40
	I	.21	.17	.15	.16	.13	.11	.08	.08		
	H	.24	.20	.18	.17	.15	.13	.11	.09		
	G	.27	.23	.20	.20	.17	.15	.12	.11		
	F	.30	.26	.22	.22	.19	.17	.13	.12		
	E	.33	.30	.27	.24	.21	.20	.15	.14		
	D	.37	.33	.30	.26	.24	.22	.17	.16		
	C	.39	.35	.32	.28	.26	.24	.18	.17		
	B	.42	.39	.36	.30	.28	.27	.19	.18		
	A	.44	.41	.39	.33	.30	.28	.21	.19		
48. Semi-indirect 70% / 10% MS = 1.2 CH	J	.18	.14	.13	.13	.11	.09	.08	.07	Glass or plastic bowl	G .70 M .60 P .50
	I	.23	.19	.17	.17	.14	.12	.09	.07		
	H	.26	.22	.20	.19	.16	.14	.12	.10		
	G	.30	.25	.22	.21	.19	.17	.13	.12		
	F	.32	.28	.25	.24	.21	.19	.14	.13		
	E	.36	.32	.29	.27	.23	.21	.16	.15		
	D	.40	.35	.32	.29	.26	.24	.18	.17		
	C	.42	.38	.35	.30	.28	.26	.19	.18		
	B	.46	.42	.40	.33	.31	.29	.21	.20		
	A	.48	.44	.42	.35	.32	.31	.24	.21		

* Maintenance conditions: G—good; M—medium; P—poor.
§ MS—Maximum spacing between units. MH—Mounting height above floor. CH—Ceiling height above floor.

TABLE 90-9. COEFFICIENTS OF UTILIZATION, EFFICIENCIES,* DISTRIBUTION CHARACTERISTICS,† AND MAINTENANCE FACTORS‡ FOR TYPICAL LUMINAIRES COMPUTED FOR A WIDE RANGE OF INSTALLATION CONDITIONS.§ (*Continued*)

DISTRIBUTION AND MAX. SPACING§	ROOM INDEX	Ceiling** 75% Walls** 50%	30%	10%	Ceiling 50% 50%	30%	10%	Ceiling 30% 30%	10%	TYPICAL LUMINAIRE	ESTIMATED MAINTENANCE FACTORS*
49. Indirect 80% 5% MS = 1.2 CH	J	.18	.14	.12	.12	.10	.08	.06	.05		G .70 M .60 P .50
	I	.22	.18	.16	.16	.13	.11	.08	.07		
	H	.26	.22	.19	.18	.15	.13	.10	.08		
	G	.30	.25	.22	.21	.18	.16	.11	.10		
	F	.32	.28	.24	.23	.19	.18	.12	.11		
	E	.36	.32	.29	.26	.22	.20	.14	.13		
	D	.40	.36	.32	.27	.25	.23	.16	.15		
	C	.42	.38	.35	.29	.26	.25	.17	.16		
	B	.47	.43	.40	.32	.30	.28	.19	.18		
	A	.49	.45	.43	.34	.32	.30	.20	.19	Conical dense-glass indirect	
50. Indirect	J	.10	.08	.06	.07	.05	.04				G .60 M .50 P .40
	I	.14	.11	.09	.09	.07	.06				
	H	.17	.14	.11	.10	.09	.07				
	G	.21	.17	.15	.13	.11	.10				
	F	.23	.20	.18	.15	.13	.11				
	E	.27	.24	.21	.17	.15	.14				
	D	.33	.28	.26	.20	.19	.17				
	C	.33	.30	.28	.21	.20	.19				
	B	.34	.32	.30	.22	.21	.20				
	A	.37	.36	.34	.24	.23	.23			Open fluorescent cove (no reflector)	
51. Indirect	J	.12	.09	.07	.08	.06	.04				G .60 M .50 P .40
	I	.16	.13	.10	.10	.08	.06				
	H	.19	.16	.13	.12	.10	.08				
	G	.24	.19	.17	.15	.13	.11				
	F	.27	.24	.20	.17	.15	.14				
	E	.31	.28	.25	.20	.18	.16				
	D	.35	.33	.30	.22	.21	.20				
	C	.38	.35	.33	.25	.23	.21				
	B	.40	.38	.36	.26	.24	.22				
	A	.43	.41	.39	.28	.27	.26			Open fluorescent cove with reflector	
52. Indirect 75% 0% MS = 1.2 CH	J	.15	.12	.10	.10	.08	.07	.04	.04		G .65 M .55 P .45
	I	.19	.15	.14	.13	.10	.09	.06	.05		
	H	.22	.18	.16	.14	.12	.10	.08	.06		
	G	.25	.21	.18	.17	.14	.13	.08	.08		
	F	.27	.24	.21	.19	.16	.14	.09	.08		
	E	.31	.27	.25	.21	.18	.16	.10	.10		
	D	.34	.30	.28	.22	.20	.19	.12	.11		
	C	.36	.33	.30	.24	.22	.20	.13	.12		
	B	.40	.37	.34	.26	.25	.23	.14	.14		
	A	.42	.39	.37	.28	.26	.25	.16	.14	Open indirect bowl	
53. Indirect 80% 0% MS = 1.2 CH	J	.16	.12	.11	.10	.08	.07	.05	.04		Fluorescent G .60 M .50 P .40 Incandescent Filament G .65 M .55 P .45
	I	.20	.16	.14	.14	.11	.09	.06	.06		
	H	.23	.20	.17	.15	.13	.11	.08	.06		
	G	.27	.23	.20	.18	.15	.14	.09	.08		
	F	.29	.25	.22	.20	.17	.15	.10	.09		
	E	.33	.29	.26	.22	.19	.18	.11	.10		
	D	.36	.32	.30	.24	.22	.20	.13	.12		
	C	.39	.35	.32	.26	.23	.21	.14	.13		
	B	.43	.40	.37	.28	.26	.25	.15	.14		
	A	.45	.42	.39	.30	.28	.26*	.17	.15	Indirect	
54. Indirect 85% 0% MS = 1.2 CH	J	.17	.13	.11	.11	.09	.08	.05	.04		G .70 M .60 P .55
	I	.21	.17	.15	.14	.12	.10	.07	.06		
	H	.25	.21	.18	.16	.14	.12	.08	.07		
	G	.28	.24	.21	.20	.16	.14	.09	.08		
	F	.31	.27	.23	.21	.18	.16	.10	.09		
	E	.35	.31	.28	.24	.20	.19	.12	.11		
	D	.39	.34	.31	.26	.23	.21	.14	.13		
	C	.41	.37	.34	.27	.25	.23	.14	.14		
	B	.46	.42	.39	.30	.28	.26	.16	.15		
	A	.48	.44	.42	.32	.30	.28	.18	.16	Silvered bowl lamps	

* Maintenance conditions: G—good; M—medium; P—poor.
§ MS—Maximum spacing between units. MH—Mounting height above floor. CH—Ceiling height above floor.

CHART 1. AMERICAN STANDARD GRAPHICAL ELECTRICAL SYMBOLS FOR ELECTRIC POWER AND CONTROL

For a complete chart of symbols, see American Standard Z32.3—1946, approved by the American Standards Association, Inc.

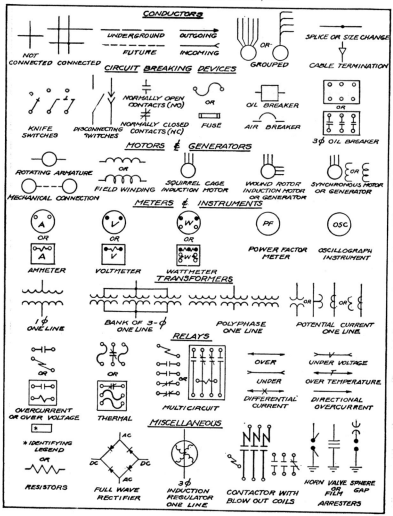

CHART 2. AMERICAN STANDARD GRAPHICAL ELECTRICAL SYMBOLS FOR TELEPHONE, TELEGRAPH, AND RADIO USE

For a complete chart of symbols, see American Standard Z32.5—1944, approved by the American Standards Association, Inc.

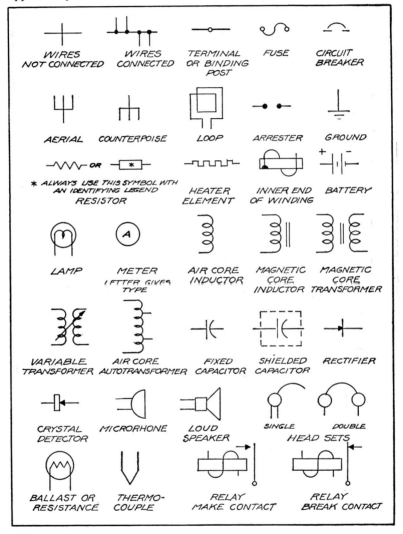

CHART 3.   AMERICAN STANDARD GRAPHICAL ELECTRICAL SYMBOLS FOR ARCHITECTURAL PLANS

American Standard Z32.9—1943, approved by the American Standards Association, Inc.

Ceiling Wall

GENERAL OUTLETS

Outlet.

Blanked Outlet.

Drop Cord.

Electrical Outlet; for use only when circle used alone might be confused with columns, plumbing symbols, etc.

Fan Outlet.

Junction Box.

Lamp Holder.

Lamp Holder with Pull Switch.

Pull Switch.

Outlet for Vapor Discharge Lamp.

Exit Light Outlet.

Clock Outlet. (Specify Voltage)

CONVENIENCE OUTLETS

Duplex Convenience Outlet.

Convenience Outlet other than Duplex. 1 = Single, 3 = Triplex, etc.

Weatherproof Convenience Outlet.

Range Outlet.

Switch and Convenience Outlet.

Radio and Convenience Outlet.

Special Purpose Outlet. (Des. in Spec.)

Floor Outlet.

SWITCH OUTLETS

S Single Pole Switch.

S_2 Double Pole Switch.

S_3 Three Way Switch.

S_4 Four Way Switch

S_D Automatic Door Switch.

S_E Electrolier Switch.

S_K Key Operated Switch.

S_P Switch and Pilot Lamp.

S_{CB} Circuit Breaker.

S_{WCB} Weatherproof Circuit Breaker.

S_{MC} Momentary Contact Switch.

S_{RC} Remote Control Switch.

S_{WP} Weatherproof Switch.

S_F Fused Switch.

S_{WF} Weatherproof Fused Switch.

SPECIAL OUTLETS

$a,b,c,$etc.
$a,b,c,$etc.
S $a,b,c,$etc.

Any Standard Symbol as given above with the addition of a lower case subscript letter may be used to designate some special variation of Standard Equipment of particular interest in a specific set of Architectural Plans.

When used they must be listed in the Key of Symbols on each drawing and if necessary further described in the specifications.

PANELS, CIRCUITS, AND MISCELLANEOUS

Lighting Panel

Power Panel.

Branch Circuit; Concealed in Ceiling or Wall.

Branch Circuit; Concealed in Floor.

Branch Circuit; Exposed.

Home Run to Panel Board. Indicate number of Circuits by number of arrows.
Note: Any circuit without further designation indicates a two-wire circuit.   For a greater number of wires indicate as follows: —///— (3 wires) —////— (4 wires), etc.

Feeders. Note: Use heavy lines and designate by number corresponding to listing in Feeder Schedule.

Underfloor Duct and Junction Box. Triple System. Note: For double or single systems eliminate one or two lines. This symbol is equally adaptable to auxiliary system layouts.

G   Generator.

M   Motor.

I.   Instrument.

T   Power Transformer. (or draw to scale.)

Controller.

Isolating Switch.

AUXILIARY SYSTEMS

Push Button.

Buzzer.

Bell.

Annunciator.

Outside Telephone.

Interconnecting Telephone.

Telephone Switchboard.

T   Bell Ringing Transformer.

D   Electric Door Opener.

F   Fire Alarm Bell.

F   Fire Alarm Station.

City Fire Alarm Station.

F A   Fire Alarm Central Station.

F S   Automatic Fire Alarm Device.

W   Watchman's Station.

W   Watchman's Central Station.

H   Horn.

N   Nurse's Signal Plug.

M   Maid's Signal Plug.

R   Radio Outlet.

CC   Signal Central Station.

Interconnection Box.

Battery.

Auxiliary System Circuits.
Note: Any line without further designation indicates a 2-Wire System. For a greater number of wires designate with numerals in manner similar to ——12-No. 18W-3/4" C., or designate by number corresponding to listing in Schedule.

a,b,c Special Auxiliary Outlets.
Subscript letters refer to notes on plans or detailed description in specifications.

CHART 4.   EXPLOSION-PROOF CONDULET DIAGRAM—LIGHTING
(*Crouse-Hinds Company*)

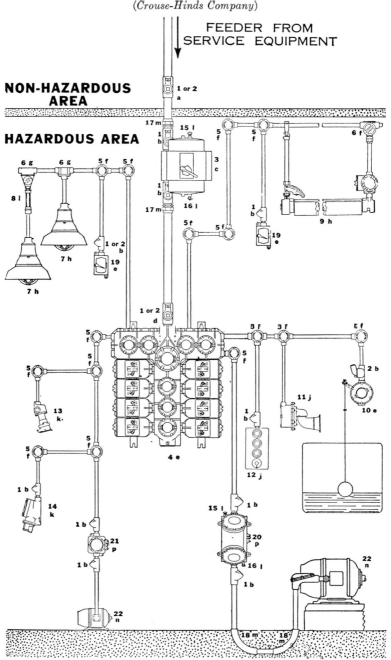

CHART 4. EXPLOSION-PROOF CONDULET DIAGRAM—LIGHTING
(Continued)

Key to Numerals

1. Sealing condulet. Type EYS for vertical conduits only.

2. Sealing condulet. Type EZS for vertical or horizontal conduits.

3. Circuit breaker condulet. Type EPC.

4. Panelboard. Type EDP. Branch circuits are factory-sealed. No seals required in mains or branches unless 2 in. or over in size.

5. Junction condulets. Series GUA, GUB and GUJ, have threaded covers. Series CPS has ground flat surface covers.

6. Fixture hanger condulets. Types EFHC, GUAC, or CPS.

7. Incandescent fixture condulet. Type EVA.

8. Flexible fixture support. Type ECGF.

9. Fluorescent fixture. Condulet Type EVF.

10. Float switch condulet. Type EMS.

11. Signal condulets. Type ETH horns and sirens. Type ESR Bells.

12. Visularm condulets Type EKP.

13. Plug receptacle condulet. Type CES-delayed action.

14. Plug receptacle condulet. Type FSQ. Interlocked with switch.

15. Breather. Type ECD.

16. Drain. Type ECD.

17. Union. Type UNY.

18. Elbow condulets. Type ELB.

19. Switch condulet. Series EFS.

20. Manual line starter. Type FLF.

21. Manual line starter. Type GUSC.

22. Motors. Explosion-proof.

1949 NEC References

a. Paragraph 5015a-3. Seal required where conduit passes from hazardous to nonhazardous location.

b. Paragraph 5015a-1. Seals required within 18 in. of all arcing devices.

c. Section 3882. Circuit breaker of rating not greater than rating of panelboard required if supply conductors have overcurrent protection over 200 amp.

d. Paragraph 5015a-2. Seal required if conduit is 2 in. or over.

e. Paragraph 5016a. All arcing devices must be explosion-proof.

f. Paragraph 5014a. All boxes must be explosion-proof and threaded for rigid conduit.

g. Paragraph 5019a-4. All boxes and fittings for support of lighting fixtures must be approved for the purpose.

h. Paragraph 5019a-1. a-2. All lighting fixtures, fixed or portable, must be explosion-proof.

i. Paragraph 5019a-3. Pendent fixture stems must be threaded for rigid conduit or approved flexible connector if over 12 in. Rigid stems must have flexible connector.

j. Section 5024. All signal circuits, irrespective of voltage, must be explosion-proof.

k. Section 5022. Receptacles and plugs must be explosion-proof and polarized and must provide ground connections for portables.

l. Section 5015. Breathers and drains are needed in all humid locations.

m. Paragraph 5014a-1. All joints and fittings must be explosion-proof.

n. Paragraph 5018a. Motors must be explosion-proof.

p. Section 4322

CHART 5. EXPLOSION-PROOF CONDULET DIAGRAM—POWER
(*Crouse-Hinds Company*)

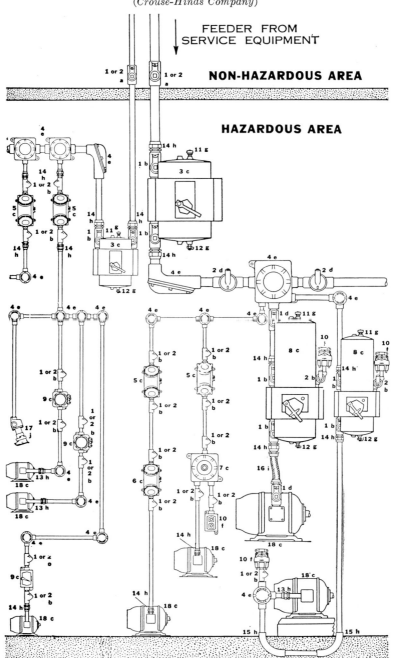

CHART 5. EXPLOSION-PROOF CONDULET DIAGRAM—POWER. (*Continued*)

| Key to Numerals | 1949 NEC References |

Key to Numerals

1. Sealing condulets. Type EYS is for vertical conduits only.
2. Sealing condulets. Type EZS is for vertical or horizontal conduits.
3. Circuit breaker condulet. Type EPC.
4. Junction condulets. Series GUA, GUB, and GUJ have threaded covers. Series CPS and Type LBH have ground flat surface covers.
5. Circuit breaker condulet. Type FLB.
6. Manual line starter condulet. Type FLF.
7. Magnetic line starter condulet. Types GUB or FLM.
8. Combination circuit breaker and line starter condulet. Type EPC.
9. Switch or motor starter condulet. Series EFS or Type GUSC.
10. Push-button station condulets. Series EFS or Type OFC.
11. Breather. Type ECD.
12. Drain. Type ECD.
13. Union. Type UNF.
14. Union. Type UNY.
15. Elbow condulet. Type ELB.
16. Flexible coupling. Type ECH.
17. Plug receptacle. Type CES. Factory sealed.
18. Explosion-proof motor.

1949 NEC References

a. Paragraph 5015a-3. Seals required where conduits pass from hazardous to nonhazardous locations.
b. Paragraph 5015a-1. Seals required within 18 in. of all arcing devices.
c. Article 430 should be studied for detailed requirements for conductors, motor feeders, motor feeder and motor branch circuit protection, motor over-current protection, motor controllers, and motor-disconnecting means.
d. Paragraph 5015a-2. Seals required if conduit is 2 in. or larger in size.
e. Section 5014. All boxes must be explosion-proof and threaded for rigid conduit.
f. Section 5016. Push-button stations must be explosion-proof.
g. Section 5015. Breathers and drains needed in all humid locations.
h. Paragraph 5014a-1. All joints and fittings must be explosion-proof.
i. Paragraph 5014a. Flexible connections must be explosion-proof.
j. Section 5022. Receptacles and plugs must be explosion-proof and polarized and must provide ground connections for portables.

CHART 6. TYPICAL LINE VOLTAGE MAGNETIC STARTERS
(Square D Company)

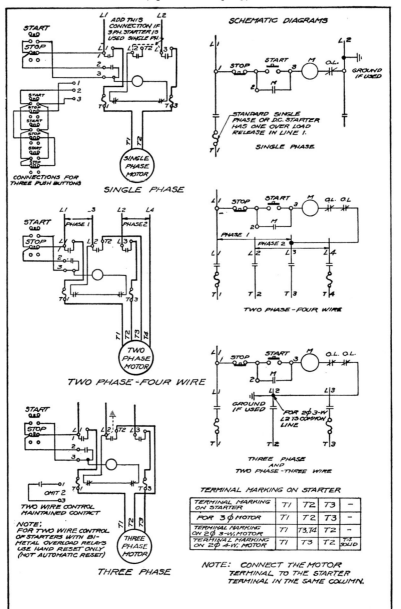

CHART 7. CURVES SHOWING DISTANCES DIFFERENT CURRENTS CAN
BE TRANSMITTED WITH ONE VOLT DROP
(Direct Current)

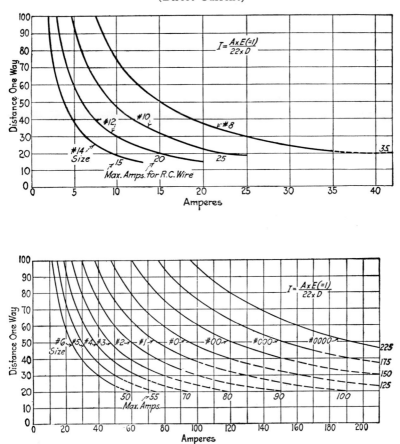

CHART 8. CURVES SHOWING VOLTS DROP WITH DIFFERENT WIRES WHEN
A GIVEN CURRENT IS TRANSMITTED A GIVEN DISTANCE
(Direct Current)

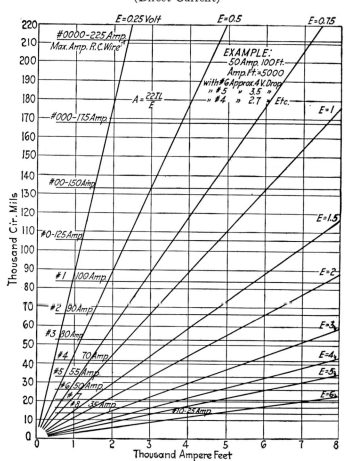

CHART 9. VOLTAGE-DROP CURVES FOR SINGLE-PHASE 60-CYCLE TWO- OR THREE-WIRE CIRCUITS

(*Westinghouse Electric Corporation*)

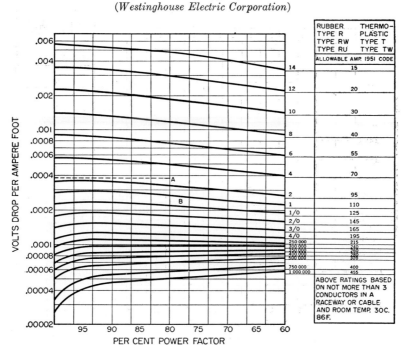

Use of chart

Since the curves are based on voltage drop per ampere-foot, any particular current, length of run, and voltage drop must be stated in terms of this unit. The following problem should explain this method. In preparing the graphs, it was assumed that the conductors were closely spaced (*i.e.*, contained in conduit) with a copper temperature of 49°C.

Problem. With a load of 21 kw, at 80 per cent power factor, on a three-wire 120–240 volt circuit, what wire size should be used to keep the voltage drop less than 3 per cent? The total run is 175 ft.

Solution. The current carried equals

$$\frac{21 \text{ kw} \times 1,000}{240 \text{ volts} \times .80 \text{ p.f.}} = 109 \text{ amp}$$

This is equivalent to 109 amp × 175 ft = 19,100 amp-ft. The permissible voltage drop is 3 per cent of 240 volts = 7.2 volts. Therefore, since 7.2 volts drop will be permitted for 19,100 amp-ft, the drop for 10,000 amp-ft should be limited to

$$\frac{7.2}{19,100} = 0.00038 \text{ volts}$$

The size of the wire may be found by noting where the line through 80 per cent power factor intersects the line through 0.00038 volts (point *A*). This would indicate that the use of No. 2 conductors would be satisfactory from a voltage-drop standpoint. However, the determining factor in this case would be the 1951 NEC which, for 109 amp, requires No. 1 with Type R insulation or No. 2 with Type RH insulation (see table page 190). With No. 1 conductors, the actual drop would be:

$$\frac{0.00022 \text{ (point } B)}{0.0003 \text{ (point } A)} \times 7.2 \text{ volts} = 5.3 \text{ or } 2.2 \text{ per cent.}$$

Chart 10. Voltage drop Curves for Three phase 60 cycle Circuits
(Westinghouse Electric Corporation)

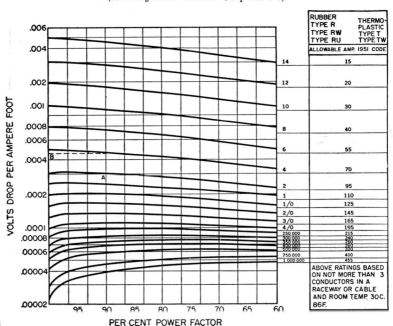

Use of chart

This chart is based on the same conditions as the chart on the preceding page and is used in the same manner. However, since this graph covers three-phase systems, and is based on phase-to-phase voltages, the calculations regarding voltage and current would be based on such considerations. An illustration of this is given below.

Problem. What load can be carried on a circuit of No. 4 conductors if connected to a three-phase four-wire 120–208 volt 60-cycle supply, without exceeding a 4-volt drop (minimum 204 volts) in a run of 150 ft? The average power factor is 90 per cent.

Solution. Follow the 90 per cent power-factor line vertically until it meets the line representing No. 4 conductors (point *A*). Follow this point horizontally to the left, and it will be seen that 4.6 volts drop (point *B*) will result from 10,000 amp-ft.

Since a drop of 4 volts is the desired maximum, the total allowable ampere-feet is

$$\frac{4}{0.00046} = 8{,}700$$

To determine the current, this figure must be divided by the run,

$$\frac{8{,}700 \text{ amp-ft}}{150 \text{ ft}} = 58 \text{ amp}$$

The total load would then be determined as follows:

$$\frac{58 \text{ amp} \times 208 \text{ volt} \times \sqrt{3} \times 0.90 \text{ p.f.}}{1{,}000 \text{ (watts to kw)}} = 18.8 \text{ kw}$$

INDEX

A

Air-break switch, 55
Air circuit breaker, 50
Aircraft cable, 194–196
Alternating-current switchboard, 43
American Institute of Steel Construction tables, 141–145
American Standards Association charts, 251–253
Ampere rating of motors, 219–221
Amperes per kilowatt, 223
Angle iron, 141
Angles, equal, table of, 141
  gauges for, 145
  specifications for, 15
Apparatus, for d-c switchboard, 40
  for outdoor substation, 55–57
  for three-phase 13,000-volt switchboard, 29–34
  for three-phase 2,300 switchboard, 44, 46, 48, 50, 51
Application of units in measuring illumination, 104
Arrangement of views, 11
Automatic starters, 209, 258
  Allis-Chalmers, 210, 212
  connection diagram, 258
  contactor for, 94
  details, 213
  General Electric, 94–97, 209
Autotransformer motor starter, 210–211

B

B & S gauge wire table, 192
Bars, copper, 198
  specifications for, 15
  "T," 144

Beams, "I," 142
  specifications for, 15
Bill of material, 34
  for d-c generator panel, 42
  example of, 125
  preparing, 34, 131
Bolts, nuts, and washers, 148–150
  specifications for, 16
Burndy connectors, 178–185
Bus spacings, 218
Bus supports, indoor, 176
Buses, arrangement of, 39, 45, 53, 54
Bushings, malleable iron, 155

C

Cabinet, details of, 215
Cabinet shop, 99–101
Cables, aircraft, 196
  commercial, 195
  Navy, 194
Calculations, original, 8–9
Candlepower, definition of, 104
Carpentry shop, 98–99
Carriage bolts, button-head, 149
Cartridge fuses, 202, 203
Channels, 16, 143
Charts, 251–262
Checking circuits, 35
Choice of reflecting equipment, 110
Circuit breakers, drawout General Electric, 45–46, 48, 50
  Square D, 207–208
  Westinghouse, 30, 32, 40
Circuit diagrams, apparatus, 17, 19–23
  motor starters, 94, 96, 97
  one-line, 19
  practical illustration of, 29–34
  schematic, 24
  structure, 39
Circuiting and scheduling, 73–75